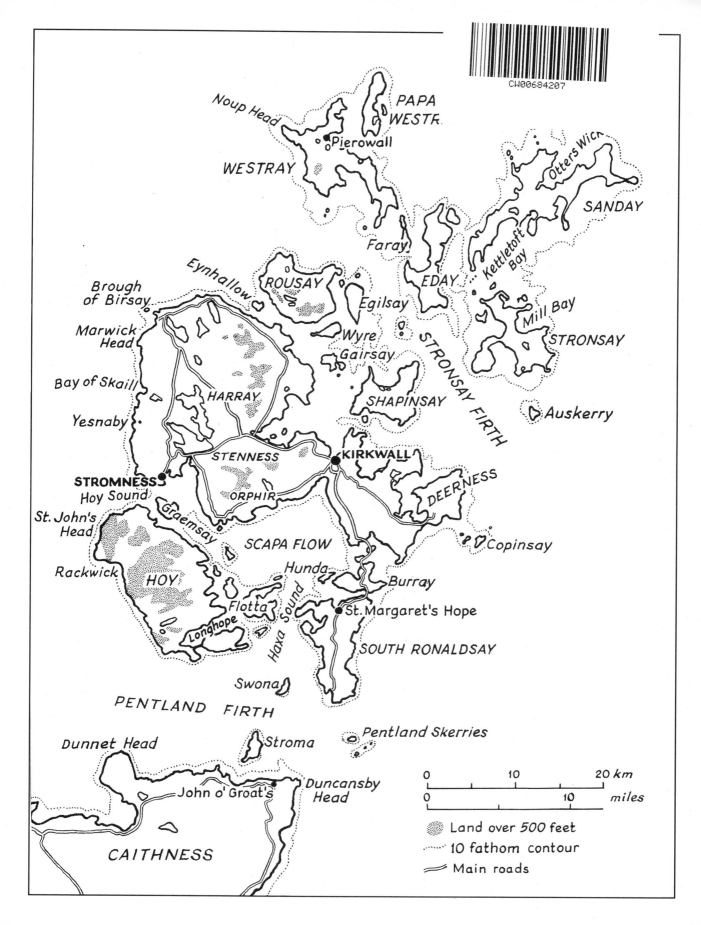

PAPA
WESTR.

Noup Head

Pierowall

WESTRAY

Otters Wick

SANDAY

Faray

EDAY

Kettletoft Bay

Brough of Birsay

Eynhallow

ROUSAY

Egilsay

Mill Bay

STRONSAY

Marwick Head

Wyre

Gairsay

Bay of Skaill

HARRAY

SHAPINSAY

STRONSAY FIRTH

Auskerry

Yesnaby

STENNESS

KIRKWALL

St. John's Head

ORPHIR

DEERNESS

STROMNESS

Hoy Sound

Graemsay

SCAPA FLOW

Copinsay

Rackwick

HOY

Hunda

Burray

Flotta

Haxa Sound

St. Margaret's Hope

Longhope

SOUTH RONALDSAY

Swona

PENTLAND FIRTH

Pentland Skerries

Dunnet Head

Stroma

John o' Groat's

Duncansby Head

CAITHNESS

| 0 | | 10 | | 20 km |
| 0 | | | 10 | miles |

🫧 Land over 500 feet

········· 10 fathom contour

〜 Main roads

ORKNEY NATURE

Marwick Head and rock platforms.
Photo: Richard Welsby

ORKNEY NATURE

R. J. Berry

Illustrations by John Holloway

T & A D
POYSER

NATURAL
HISTORY

Academic Press
Harcourt Place, 32 Jamestown Road, London NWI 7BY, UK
http://www.academicpress.com

Academic Press
A Harcourt Science and Technology Company
525 B Street, Suite 1900, San Diego, California 92101-4495, USA
http://www.academicpress.com

ISBN 0-85661-104-2

A catalogue record of this book is available from
the British Library

Typeset by Kenneth Burnley, Wirral, Cheshire
Printed in China by Midas Printing Ltd.

00 01 02 03 04 05 ND 9 8 7 6 5 4 3 2 1

Contents

Apologia

This is an explanation of how this book came to be written, and my part in its writing. *Orkney Nature* is a much revised version of a book called *The Natural History of Orkney*, published in 1985 by Collins in their New Naturalist series. The original edition went out of print less than ten years later, despite continuing demand for it. Much has happened since the frst edition, and hence this new book rather than a simple reprint.

The Natural History of Orkney was written at the request of the New Naturalist editors, following the publication of *The Natural History of Shetland*, which I wrote with Laughton Johnston, one-time Nature Conservancy Council (now Scottish Natural Heritage) Officer for Orkney and Shetland.* My immediate reaction to the invitation to write about Orkney was to refuse: I knew less about Orkney than Shetland, and there are a number of distinguished naturalists resident in or regular visitors to Orkney. However, there was no single person likely to bring together the knowledge and understanding of Orkney into one book, which everyone I spoke to agreed was needed. The crucial factor in persuading me to compile the book was the co-operation of some of the best Orkney naturalists, who undertook to provide me with extended notes on subjects on which they were expert, and to allow me to reword these in my own style. The reason for this procedure was the criticism deservedly levelled at *The Natural History of Shetland*, where we included several 'guest chapters', that it was uneven and difficult to read. Whilst there may be a place for a multi-author book on Orkney, it would be a very different one from either *The Natural History of Orkney* or *Orkney Nature*. It is extremely difficult to achieve uniform and comprehensive coverage in a symposium volume.

Notwithstanding, both this book and its predecessor are the work of a whole group of people. It is said that Winston Churchill used to commission briefs from the greatest experts in the land for his historical books, and then

---

* *The Natural History of Shetland* has also been revised, and was published in 1999 by Poyser as *A Naturalist's Shetland*, with Laughton Johnston as the sole author.

rewrite them with his own turn of phrase (some say that he used to dictate them from his bath). I lay no claim to Churchillian eloquence but I want to acknowledge formally and gratefully that this book depends on and includes major contributions from the following:

Miss E. R. Bullard, botanist and doyen of Orkney naturalists, who largely wrote the botanical sections in the first edition, and who has provided the checklist of flowering plants for this book.

Professor R. M. M. Crawford, Professor of Botany at the University of St Andrews, who has written his own perspective on the Orkney flora (Chapter 3), drawing on Elaine Bullard's expertise.

Dr John Flett Brown, professional geologist now returned to his roots in Orkney, for input on geology and landscape; he is largely responsible for Chapter 2 with help and criticisms from Dr Adrian Hall of Fettes College. The chapter on rocks in the original book was drafted by Dr John Parnell, of Queen's University, Belfast; he has added his expertise to the revised chapter.

Eric Meek, Royal Society for the Protection of Birds Officer for Orkney, who was responsible for the systematic list of birds in the first edition, and has completely re-written the chapter on birds for this book (Chapter 8).

Andrew Dorin, formerly of Scottish National Heritage, for Chapter 12 and advice on conservation matters.

Ms Liz Charter, Conservation Officer to the Department of Agriculture, Fisheries and Forestry of the Isle of Man, and previously the Founder Director of the Orkney Farming and Wildlife Advisory Group, has re-written Chapter 6 on freshwater habitats, adding her own expertise to that of Dr Paul Hepplestone, formerly Senior Biology Master at Kirkwall Grammar School, who wrote the chapter in the first edition.

The chapter on sea and shore (Chapter 4) was substantially written by Dr John Baxter of Scottish Natural Heritage, with input from Dr David Raffaeli of Aberdeen University. I received substantial help in Chapter 5 (seals and whales and otters) from Professor John Harwood and Dr Callan Duck of the NERC Sea Mammal Research Unit and from Dr Hans Kruuk of the Institute of Terrestrial Ecology.

In the first edition, the chapters on birds, naturalists and conservation were largely written respectively by David Lea, formerly Orkney representative of the RSPB; Eoin Ross, Librarian of Kirkwall Grammar School; and Dr Peter Reynolds of SNH. All these have now left Orkney, but their inputs still persist.

Many others have contributed to a lesser, but substantial extent. They include: Chris and Jean Booth; Sydney Gauld; Dr Martin Gorman; Edward Milner; Clive Mitchell; Alan Skene; Willie Thomson; Richard Welsby (who went to a great deal of trouble to find appropriate photographs); Jack Saxon, doyen of Caithness and Orkney fossil fish, who illustrated some Devonian fish specially for the book; Dr Morton Boyd, former Director of the Nature Conservancy Council in Scotland, who painted an Orkney scene, used on the jacket; John Holloway of Stronsay who made the sketches at the beginning and end of chapters; Tommy Lee, who drew the endpapers; and a host of others.

A full Bibliography is provided at the end of the book. References to literature cited and relevant published works are listed at the end of each chapter.

This book is written for those who know or want to know about Orkney's structure and scenery, its animals and birds, its people past and present. It is not a guide book, but it should help those unfamiliar with the islands to discover what is where. It is concerned with the processes that have shaped the islands and their environment, living and non-living, rather than a mere cataloguing of its inhabitants, human and non-human. But above all it is for those who love sky and sea, nature in its fullness, solitude and plenitude.

The Orcadian poet Robert Rendall (1898–1967) wrote:

> But, John, have you seen the world, said he,
> Train and tramcars and sixty seaters,
> Cities in lands across the sea –
> Giotto's tower and the dome of St Peter's?
>
> No, but I've seen the arc of the earth,
> From the Birsay shore* like the edge of a planet,
> And the lifeboat plunge through the Pentland Firth?
> To a cosmic tide with the men that man it.

And then in a poem called, simply, 'Birsay':

> Here on this rocky coast I roved, and here
> Beside the sea in happy boyhood played,
> Ere I had felt the bonds of ruthless trade
> Or mourned time's loss through many a wasteful year.
> Along these cliffs, when summer skies were clear,
> I watched the waves with thunder long delayed
> Break on the shore; or saw the colours fade
> From evening clouds, and knew that night was near.
> Here once again, where grow the wild sea-pinks,
> With idle steps I go, and mind at ease
> From life's mad haste. O look! The red sun sinks
> In golden floods of light; and with the breeze
> Comes faintly now across the grassy links
> The ageless music of the rolling seas.

* At the northern edge of the largest Orkney island.

Hugh MacDiarmid wrote in *The Islands of Scotland* (1939), 'The Orkneys are known to most people probably by only two events – the death of Lord Kitchener aboard the sunk *Hampshire*, and the submersion (and subsequent salving) of the German Fleet'. So, read on and learn more . . .

Launching the boat on a Birsay shore.
Photo: Richard Welsby

Chapter 1

Like Sleeping Whales

The weather is good, if you like a temperate climate. Thermometer and barometer measure our seasons capriciously; the Orkney year should be seen rather as a stark drama of light and darkness . . . In the course of a single day you can see, in that immensity of sky, the dance of sun, cloud, sea-mist, thunder, run: the endless ballet of the weather.

(George Mackay Brown, *An Orkney Tapestry*, 1969)

Islands are properly approached by sea. Unfortunately for many, the sea which separates Orkney from mainland Britain is the Pentland Firth, a boisterous mill-race of a channel where the Atlantic is forced into an ungenerous 6 miles (10 kilometres). George Mackay Brown (1921–96), master wordsmith whose home overlooked the ferry terminal in Stromness, wrote that its crossing

> is looked on as a fearsome experience by some people who are visiting Orkney for the first time. In Scrabster [on Scotland's north coast] they sip brandy or swallow sea-sick tablets. The crossing can be rough enough – the Atlantic and the North Sea invading each other's domains twice a day, raging back and fore through the narrow channels and sounds, an eternal wrestle; and the fickle wind can be foe or ally. But as often as not, the Firth is calm . . . (Brown 1969:17)

Orkney is not as spectacular and precipitous as its northern neighbours Shetland and Faroe, nor like Skye and some of the Hebrides to the south and west. The highest point (the Ward of Hoy) is only 1,565 feet (477 metres)

Figure 1.1
Due north from
John O'Groats.
Photo: R. J. Berry

above sea level, and there is no land outside Hoy over 900 feet (273 metres). From the air the islands give a superficial appearance of a peaceful agricultural undulation. From even further away an observer from a satellite would see a central large island (always called the Mainland) surrounded by nearly 100 other islands, ranging from skate-shaped Hoy, down to mere tidal rocks (or skerries).

Figure 1.2
Satellite image of Orkney, as seen from 560 miles above the earth.

When I first saw Orkney, I thought it much duller in both topography and biology than its Shetland cousin. But this first impression has proved false: Orkney grows on one. The casual visitor who comes for a few days solely to see the spectacular archaeological monuments of Maeshowe or Skara Brae, or the naval and now oil developments of Scapa Flow, or the Hen Harrier, Orkney Vole or *Primula scotica*, will get a taste of the islands, but not an adequate flavour. Orkney reveals her charms gladly, but gradually, like a shy lover.

Bede described Orkney as 'lying in the ocean beyond Britain . . . at its back, where it is open to the boundless seas'. Like most early writers, he ignored the more distant Shetland; to him, Orkney was the *terra incognita* of the north. More evocatively, Orkney has been called a herd of sleeping whales, peaceful mounds with awful potentials. George Mackay Brown imagined how they appeared to the earliest colonists: 'The first Orkney peoples . . . sailed north into the widening light . . . Beyond the savage

Figure 1.3
The sea meets
Orkney on all sides,
with more sleeping
whales in the
distance.
Photo: Richard Welsby

bulk of Cape Wrath there was empty ocean until in a summer dawn they saw the Orkneys like sleeping whales . . .'

Although the Latin word for a whale is *orca*, the islands are not named after whales, but more probably from the Celtic *Inse Orc*, the Isles of Boars. The Orcs may have been a Pictish tribe which lived there. The suffix '-ey' is Old Norse for 'island': hence Orkney, and properly not 'the Orkneys' or 'Orkney Islands'. The Roman author Diodorus Siculus (a younger contemporary of Julius Caesar) called the promontory where, he said, Britain terminated in the north, Orkan; and later Latin writers refer to Orkney under the plural of that name, Orcades.

Humans arrived in Orkney around 3500 BC, around two millennia after the Ice Sheet finally retreated from Scotland, and the islands have been bound to human history ever since – Neolithic farmers, Bronze Age craftsmen, Iron Age builders, Viking warriors, Scottish adventurers, mediaeval traders, British servicemen, and many others. All of them have left their mark, most notably those who stayed to fight the land and the climate to herd animals and grow crops. For this reason the natural history of Orkney is inextricably linked to its human history: the voles which are the prey of harriers and kestrels were brought by early settlers over 4,000 years ago (p. 133), and the curlews which congregate on Orkney fields in their hundreds have increased as the hill land has been claimed by modern-day farmers. But Orkney is not simply farmland. It is hill and moor, sea and dune, loch and marsh, water and sky in the fullest sense. Eric Linklater (1965), himself an Orcadian, wrote about it thus:

> There is, indeed, a power in the land, or in the broad sky enclosing it that may take perpetual captive those who are rash enough to open their eyes to the endlessly flowing line of its hills, their ears to the curlew's cry and the bourdoun of the sea, their hearts to the northern peace. On a fine morning, when the winds are still and the lakes relume an azure sweep of sky – vacant but for a curd of cloud, a mallard and its mate – there is a hush like the drifting of the young earth, not wakened yet, in the innocence of time . . . You too fall silent and catch with livelier ear the small bright talk of linnets in the heather, the creaking fall of a lapwing, the tentative voice of a plover or the thresh of a rising swan, and far away the Atlantic rolling its organ-tongue in a cavern of the western cliffs.

Figure 1.4
Kirkwall, dominated by St Magnus Cathedral.
Photo: Richard Welsby

Figure 1.5
Stromness, the
second town of
Orkney.
Photo: Richard Welsby

Orkney lies between 58° 41′N and 59° 24′N latitude, and 2° 22′W and 4° 25′W longitude. This means that it lies at approximately the latitude of Leningrad or the southern tip of Greenland. Kirkwall is nearer to Oslo than London, and, perhaps more relevantly, closer to the Arctic Circle than the capital of Norway; it is more or less equidistant from Reykjavik, Stockholm, Berlin, Brussels, and Paris. It is as far from London as London is from Rome.

The county stretches 53 miles (83 kilometres) from south to north, and 23 miles (37 kilometres) from west to east, occupying about 240,000 acres (100,000 hectares). It is divided into about 70 islands (the exact number depends on the definition of when a rock is regarded as becoming an island), of which sixteen were inhabited by 19,328 people at the 1991 census. The main Shetland group lies about 50 miles (80 kilometres) north of North Ronaldsay, in the main Orkney group, with Fair Isle (which administratively is part of Shetland) lying almost exactly halfway between Orkney and the southern tip of Shetland proper. The main island of Orkney is known as 'the Mainland' (Pomona on some older maps), and contains more than half the land area, the only towns (Kirkwall and Stromness), and three-quarters of the population. A twice-daily car ferry connects Stromness with Scrabster in Caithness, and there are regular flights to Inverness, Aberdeen and other Scottish cities from Kirkwall Airport. In every way, the Mainland dominates Orkney.

It is impractical to give the detailed locations of all the places mentioned in the text of this book. Readers are recommended to refer to the Ordnance Survey 1:50,000 series, sheets nos 5, 6 and 7, or Bartholomew's 1:100,000 Orkney Leisure Map (previously sheet no. 61).

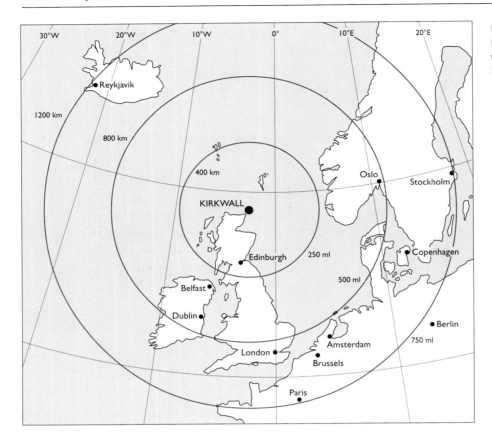

Figure 1.6
Distances of Orkney from other places in Europe.

Islands and people

About 330 BC, the Greek explorer Pytheas of Marseilles circumnavigated Orkney and claimed to have sighted the edge of the world (*ultima thule*). On a clear day it is possible to see three points of land from the northern limit of Orkney: Fair Isle, Fitful Head, and Foula, all of them in Shetland. The most distant of these is Foula, which is therefore claimed by its inhabitants as being the 'edge of the world'. In AD 43 the Roman fleet of Claudius entered into a non-aggression pact with the Orcadians; Tacitus records in his *Life* of Agricola, that after the battle of Mons Graupius in 89, a Roman fleet subdued Orkney.

But all that was before even Orkney folk history (although there are plenty of stories in Orkney about trolls, selkies, and the like). Later travellers left more detailed records, beginning with the Vikings in the ninth century and continuing, most notably among earlier visitors, with James Wallace in 1693 and John Brand in 1701. However, the first complete description was by John Tudor in a book *The Orkneys and Shetland* (1883). He begins by describing the isolation of the Northern Isles, which is a part of their attractive mystery; and by drawing attention to misconceptions which are still common:

Lying to the north of the most extreme northern point of the British Mainland, exposed to the full force of the Atlantic rollers and the hardly less turbulent surges of the wild North Sea, and surrounded by some of the fiercest tideways in the world, one cannot wonder that till comparatively recent years, the Orkneys and Shetland should to the average Englishman, or Scotsman too for that matter, have been geographical expressions and nothing more.

Most people know better now-a-days: but still even educated people are apt to be somewhat confused in their ideas about the two groups, and to have a vague impression: that the Orkneys and Shetland are one and the same thing; that they consist of some scattered islands not much larger than the Scilly Isles; and that they are inhabited by a semi-civilized race, who live chiefly on sea-fowl and their eggs, and are in urgent need of missionaries to convert them from their semi-heathen practices.

Figure 1.7
Western cliffs of Hoy, with St John's Head and the Old Man of Hoy.
Photo: Richard Welsby

Weather

James Wallace in 1700 commented that 'notwithstanding this Country [Orkney] is so far removed to the North, the Air is temperate and wholesome, agreeing well with those Constitutions that can endure a little Cold'.

Figure 1.8
Summer on the
shore.
Photo: Richard Welsby

More poignantly a Second World War serviceman called it: 'All bloody clouds and bloody rains.'[1] Robert Louis Stevenson's great lyric that has the lines, 'Blows the wind today, and the sun and the rain are flying . . . Standing-stones on the vacant wine-red moor . . . the howses of the silent vanished races . . .' might well refer to a typical Orkney day.

In fact, the Orkney climate is remarkably equable; technically it is called 'hyperoceanic' (p. 50), a description it shares with the Western Isles and Shetland, and the peninsulas of the extreme west and north coasts of Scotland.

Much of lowland Orkney is what meteorologists describe as 'fairly warm and rather dry', a category absent in Shetland and the Hebrides; this gives way at about 100 feet (30 metres) to a 'cool and moist' climate, which occurs at sea level in Shetland and the Western Isles.

In Orkney, the most important factors are wind, which is felt to its full extent because of the smooth relief; and the long hours of daylight in summer (in midsummer, it is never really dark, whereas in midwinter the sun is above the horizon for barely six hours).

Perhaps the most surprising fact about Orkney weather is its mildness. During the months of December, January and February, the average daily maximum temperature in Kirkwall is similar to that in Edinburgh and Glasgow, and less than 1°C lower than London, while the daily minimum in the same months is on average higher than in Edinburgh, Glasgow and even

---

1 The poem ends: 'Best bloody place is bloody bed
        With bloody ice on bloody head
        You might as well be bloody dead
        In bloody Orkney.' (*Orcadian*, 2 April 1998)

London. The first air frost in Kirkwall occurs on average on 20 November (earliest recorded 1951–72, 13 October), and the last on 23 April (latest recorded 30 May). Snow or sleet falls on an average of 64 days a year, but rarely lies long. It covers half or more of the ground at Kirkwall Airport on only fifteen days a year on average (compared with 28 at Lerwick in Shetland, sixteen in Edinburgh, but only twelve in Stornoway and four in Tiree in the Hebrides). Not surprisingly, Lerwick temperatures are generally similar but slightly lower than in Kirkwall. The summers are cool, similar to Shetland, but also to Lapland and Alaska. Orkney has a growth season (mean temperature above 6°C) of five to six months, similar to the Pennine or Welsh plateaux. In contrast, lowland England has seven to eight months suitable for growing corn crops; compared to this the Orkney climate is marginal for cereals, and can be disastrous in bad seasons.

The mean monthly temperatures in southern Greenland, the Falkland Islands, and South Orkney (which is part of the British Antarctic Territory) are given for comparison in Table 1.1. The enormous influence of the Gulf Stream is obvious. Port Stanley in the Falklands is cooler than Kirkwall, despite being more than 7° latitude nearer the equator (about the latitude of London in the northern hemisphere).

Figure 1.9
Snow-covered
Hoy Hills.
Photo: Richard Welsby

Table 1.1   Average monthly temperatures °C – mean of daily minimum and maximum

	Jan	Feb	Mar	Apr	May	Jun	Jul	Aug	Sep	Oct	Nov	Dec	Annual
Lerwick, Shetland 60° 8′N 1° 11′W	3.0	2.8	3.8	5.4	7.6	10.1	12.7	12.9	10.6	8.5	5.8	4.0	7.1
Kirkwall, Orkney 58° 59′N 2° 58′W	**3.7**	**3.6**	**4.7**	**6.1**	**8.5**	**10.7**	**12.5**	**12.7**	**11.1**	**9.0**	**6.1**	**4.4**	**7.7**
Cape Wrath, Sutherland 58° 37′N 5° 01′W	4.3	3.9	5.1	6.3	8.3	10.7	11.8	12.3	11.3	9.5	6.7	5.3	8.0
Stornoway, Hebrides 58° 12′N 6° 23′W	4.3	4.4	5.7	6.9	9.3	11.6	13.2	13.3	11.7	9.3	6.9	5.4	8.5
Lairg, Sutherland 58° 01′N 4° 35′W	1.1	1.7	4.1	6.5	8.9	12.3	12.7	12.7	11.4	8.1	3.9	1.9	7.1
Kew, London 51° 28′N 00° 10′W	4.2	4.6	6.7	9.4	12.4	15.9	17.6	17.3	14.3	11.1	7.6	5.4	10.6
Nanortalik, Greenland 60° 10′N 45° 05′W	−3.3	−2.4	−1.7	0.7	4.0	5.5	6.5	7.0	5.8	2.7	−1.0	−2.2	1.8
Stanley, Falkland Island 51° 42′S 57° 52′W	9.0	9.4	8.4	6.0	3.8	2.3	2.1	2.6	3.5	5.6	7.5	8.4	5.7
Signy Is, South Orkney 60° 43′S 45° 36′W	0.7	1.1	0.4	−1.8	−6.1	−8.7	−10.4	−8.5	−4.7	−2.3	−1.1	−0.2	−3.5

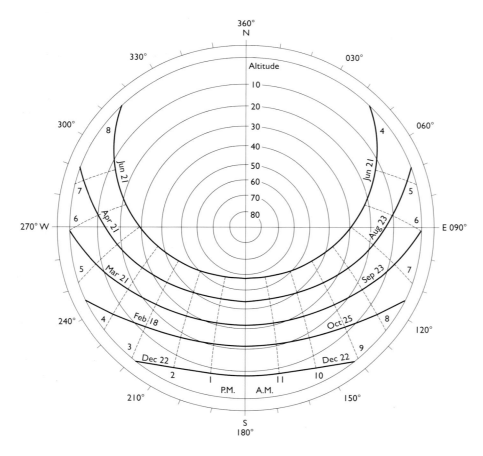

Figure 1.10
The height of the sun at Kirkwall at different times of the year. At mid-winter the sun is above the horizon for less than six hours a day.

Table 1.2   Mean rainfall (inches)

	Jan	Feb	Mar	Apr	May	Jun	Jul	Aug	Sep	Oct	Nov	Dec	Annual Total
Lerwick	4.52	3.31	3.09	2.71	2.20	2.20	2.53	2.76	3.75	4.44	4.63	4.44	40.49
Kirkwall	**4.35**	**3.02**	**3.24**	**2.26**	**1.94**	**1.91**	**2.20**	**2.93**	**3.80**	**4.32**	**4.75**	**4.62**	**39.33**
Cape Wrath	4.29	3.31	3.07	2.84	2.40	3.19	3.55	3.86	4.37	5.20	4.65	4.81	45.55
Stornoway	4.18	2.68	2.29	2.33	2.29	2.56	3.08	3.35	3.75	4.38	4.50	4.06	39.45
Lairg (Central Highlands)	4.02	3.23	2.68	2.88	3.27	3.11	3.59	4.33	3.59	4.14	4.18	4.57	43.58
Kew	2.14	1.55	1.46	1.81	1.81	1.72	2.44	2.24	1.98	2.25	2.45	2.06	23.95

Table 1.3   Duration of bright sunshine (monthly total, in hours)

	Jan	Feb	Mar	Apr	May	Jun	Jul	Aug	Sep	Oct	Nov	Dec	Annual Total
Lerwick	25	54	86	137	158	152	131	116	99	62	33	15	1,067
Kirkwall	**30**	**60**	**94**	**139**	**173**	**158**	**136**	**129**	**104**	**73**	**38**	**22**	**1,155**
Stornoway	37	66	108	153	186	173	132	135	106	76	48	26	1,244
Edinburgh	41	68	99	149	176	183	169	147	120	91	52	37	1,332
Kew	48	65	112	162	203	214	197	183	143	102	58	43	1,529

Table 1.4   Average number of days with gales

	Jan	Feb	Mar	Apr	May	Jun	Jul	Aug	Sep	Oct	Nov	Dec	Annual Total
Lerwick	7.9	5.3	5.9	2.0	1.1	0.9	0.5	0.4	2.1	4.3	4.5	8.5	43.5
Kirkwall	**3.9**	**3.5**	**3.7**	**1.8**	**0.9**	**0.6**	**0.3**	**0.6**	**1.2**	**2.9**	**4.1**	**5.6**	**29.1**
Wick	2.1	1.5	1.7	1.1	0.2	0.1	0.2	0.3	0.7	1.3	1.3	1.9	12.2
Tiree	7.6	4.5	3.6	1.5	0.6	0.4	0.3	0.7	1.7	3.4	4.5	6.4	35.2
Leuchars (St Andrews)	2.1	1.2	1.3	0.4	0.4	0.4	0.1	0.2	0.6	0.8	0.8	1.3	9.5

Table 1.5   Wind strength

Strength (Beaufort Scale)	0	1	2	3	4	5	6	7	8	9	9+
Wind speed 9knots)	0	1–3	4–6	7–10	11–16	17–21	22–27	28–33	34–40	41–47	48+
% through year											
Lerwick	2.5	3.6	10.1	21.9	30.4	15.1	10.2	4.4	1.5	0.2	0.1
Kirkwall	**2.8**	**5.7**	**10.8**	**22.6**	**31.3**	**14.1**	**8.5**	**2.8**	**1.0**	**0.2**	**0.1**
Stornoway	5.8	7.5	7.7	15.2	26.3	16.4	12.0	5.9	2.6	0.4	0.1

The other point to make about temperatures in Orkney is the comparatively small change between summer and winter. The difference between the average daily maximum at Kirkwall in January and in July is 9.7°C (9.3°C in Lerwick), whereas in Edinburgh it is 12.9°C, and 15.5°C at Kew. Orkney has winter temperatures like those of the Black Sea, and summer ones like the White Sea.

The rainfall over most of Orkney ranges from 35 to 40 inches (890 to 1,020 mm), more than Edinburgh and London, but less than Glasgow and Torquay. It is spread relatively evenly throughout the year (Table 1.2), with rain falling on a mean of 241 days each year, ranging from sixteen days in each of the driest months of May and June, to 25 days in December and January. Except in sea mist, visibility is extremely good. Temperature inversions are rare due to the small land area and frequent winds, so persistent fog is not common. The haars or cold sea mists which bedevil the Scottish mainland are relatively uncommon in Orkney. Thunder only occurs on four or five days a year, compared with seven or eight days in Edinburgh and Glasgow, and fifteen to twenty days in southern England. This means that lightning, and lightning-induced fires, are rare in Orkney. Even nearby Caithness has much more lightning than Orkney, due to convection currents over the land.

Orkney has more sunshine than Shetland, but less than most other places in Scotland (though Fort William and Braemar have less than Kirkwall (Table 1.3)). But on the debit side, even Manchester has more hours of sunshine than Kirkwall (1,334 hours on average compared with 1,155).

Finally, wind, the most noticeable feature of Orkney weather: gales may occur at any time of the year, although most commonly during the winter months (Table 1.4). The highest gust ever recorded in Britain at a low-level site was 136 miles per hour (61 metres per second) at Kirkwall on 7 February 1969. A gale only slightly less ferocious removed 7,000 poultry houses and 86,000 hens on 15 January 1952. Calm conditions are relatively infrequent (Table 1.5). Wind directions are fairly evenly distributed around the compass, although the commonest blow is between south and west. Easterly winds increase during spring and early summer.

The natural history of Orkney

Geologically Orkney is an extension of Caithness, but the isolation and exposure of Orkney means that there are fewer species of animals and plants there than might be expected if the Pentland Firth did not exist, and if Orkney habitats were more sheltered. This does not mean that Orkney is a biological desert – far from it – but it means that the stresses of natural selection and the vagaries of colonization have significantly affected the islands' flora and terrestrial fauna. The consequences of these pressures will appear during descriptions of different groups in the following pages.

Orkney's natural environment has been surprisingly neglected by naturalists when compared with other areas of the British Isles. *The New Orkney Book* (1966), produced by the Orkney Education Department as background material for use in Orkney schools, compares the Orkney flora disparagingly with that of Sutherland. Perhaps this is because Orkney has never had an ecologist of the calibre of, for example, C. B. Crampton, whose detailed descriptions of Caithness vegetation (published in 1911) provide an invaluable background to present-day studies. The Orcadian botanists of

Figure 1.11
Orkney's land mass
has sunk, leaving
'ayres' or 'oices'
between higher land.
Copinsay from the air.
Photo: Richard Welsby

Crampton's time were primarily collectors and taxonomists, and their notes give little indication of vegetation types. Again, professional insect collectors visited Shetland regularly in the latter part of the nineteenth century, but paid relatively fleeting visits to Orkney. E. B. Ford comments in his New Naturalist on *Moths* (1955) that:

> the moths of Orkney either resemble those of the mainland or are distinct forms: they are not generally transitional to the Shetland forms . . . however, we have far less information on the entomology of Orkney than of Shetland, for collectors who have penetrated so far tend to go on to the latter group where rare species and unusual forms are known to exist.

Shetland has long been a mecca for ornithologists, but once again bird-watchers have tended to bypass Orkney despite the fact that the group has the second-biggest seabird colony in the UK on Westray – only St Kilda has more birds – and 88 regular breeding species compared to 64 on Shetland.

Work carried out in Orkney has rarely appeared in accessible publications. The most important early works were Buckley and Harvie-Brown's *Vertebrate Fauna of the Orkney Islands* (1891) and Magnus Spence's *Flora Orcadensis* (1914), but these were not followed up until two local people produced short books in the 1970s, Eddie Balfour on *Orkney Birds* (1972)

Figure 1.12
Sanday, flattest of the main islands.
Photo: Richard Welsby

and Elaine Bullard a *Checklist of Vascular Plants in Orkney* (1975). There are other works of course, ranging from Low's *Fauna Orcadensis* (written in the 1790s), to Robert Rendall's *Orkney Shore* (1960) and William Groundwater's *Birds and Mammals of Orkney* (1974). More recently we have had the *Lepidoptera of the Orkney Islands* by Ian Lorimer (1983, 1998), *Birds of Orkney* by Chris Booth, Mildred Cuthbert and Peter Reynolds (1984) and *Mammals of Orkney* by Chris and Jean Booth (1994), but it is nonetheless true that Orkney has been much more poorly provided with natural history literature than most other parts of the United Kingdom. Certainly nowhere else as intrinsically interesting as Orkney is so starved of relevant writings. The precursor of this book (a New Naturalist on *The Natural History of Orkney*, 1985) sought to bring together the main facts and trends of the Orkney fauna, flora and landscape).

The first comprehensive account of Orkney geology was published by Ben Peach and John Horne in 1880. This formed the basis of the Geological Survey's *Memoir of the Orkney Islands*, published in 1935, supervised by Sir John Flett, a native Orcadian who became Director of the Geological Survey of Great Britain. This was succeeded by the Geological Survey's volume on *Orkney and Shetland* (1976) in the British Regional Geology series, by a geophysical survey of Orkney (1968) and a *Geochemical Atlas for Orkney* (1978), relevant for agricultural planning. The geochemical survey coincided with a more detailed exploration for uranium deposits which provided much local controversy, but little economic interest.

The first major publication on general natural history for nearly a century was the *Natural Environment of Orkney* (edited by Rawden Goodier, 1975), the proceedings of a two-day meeting sponsored by the Nature Conservancy Council (now Scottish Natural Heritage). This book draws heavily on that symposium, but is more inclusive. Its aim is to summarize as far as possible all that is known about Orkney natural history so that residents and visitors, amateurs and professionals alike will be guided and, hopefully, stimulated to learn more about 'the sleeping whales' that bask in the waters off the north of mainland Scotland. There they will learn of the environment that shaped Orkney written about by Robert Rendall:

> God, Who in days of old
> Created the sea
> And the skies – O there behold
> What beauties be –
> These treeless islands set
> Where the wild-goose flies,
> Lest men should e'er forget
> The sea and the skies.
> (From *Country Sonnets*, 1946)

Biological history

The two horns of the Orkney South Isles enclosing Scapa Flow approach within 6 miles (10 kilometres) of the mainland of Scotland, with Hoy to the west and South Ronaldsay to the east. The Pentland Skerries and Stroma lie in the Pentland Firth itself. This turbulent channel has been a major factor in the misinterpretation of the Orkney fauna and flora, because of uncertainty about when it came into being. During the Pleistocene, Orkney was fully glaciated. At the maximum glaciation, ice from Norway probably covered the whole of Shetland, Orkney, and Scotland; the final glacial period was a much more local affair, with ice passing over Orkney in a north-easterly direction, and meeting the local Shetland ice cap between Orkney and Fair Isle. As the ice melted, the sea-level rose, and so did the land, released from the weight of overlying ice. Was there then a period when dry land existed between Caithness and Orkney, allowing the islands to be colonized by terrestrial organisms?

If there was a land-bridge, its subsequent breaching would have isolated the Orkney animals and plants, so that the present populations persist as relics of formerly much more widespread ones; if there was no post-Pleistocene land-bridge, the Orkney fauna and flora will have opportunistically reached the islands at any time since the climate ameliorated, and hence will be much younger. Moreover, a colonizing group will almost certainly carry less genetical variation than its ancestral population, and possess a different spectrum of inherited traits. It may then show a significant amount of differentiation by chance. This has happened, for example, with field mice (*Apodemus sylvaticus*) in Shetland and the Hebrides which are all more closely related to Norwegian animals than Scottish ones and which were once divided into three distinct species: *A. fridariensis* on Shetland, *A. hirtensis* on St Kilda, and *A. hebridensis* on many of the other Hebrides. It is now accepted that the field mice were carried to the different islands as commensals by human colonizers, and in some cases their establishment may have been comparatively recent.

Figures 1.13 and 1.14
Land-bridges were artificially made during the Second World War to protect the Fleet anchorage in Scapa Flow. These 'Churchill Barriers' now carry a road linking islands south of the Mainland.
Photo: Richard Welsby

Are the Orkney animals and plants merely survivors of those species which made their way across a land-bridge from Scotland – and therefore a typical segment of the north Scottish fauna and flora limited through extinction and the failure of late arrivals to get over the bridge – or are they a unique assemblage of colonists who have managed to reach the islands by a variety of means and establish themselves there?

The traditional understanding is that Orkney has a relict fauna and flora, but this is based on a mis-reading of biological facts rather than any geological evidence for a post-Pleistocene bridge. Most of this can be laid at the feet of a distinguished mammalogist, M. A. C. Hinton, who worked at the Natural History Museum in London. He recognized that the Orkney Vole has no living relatives in Great Britain. However he classified it as a close relative of an extinct vole, *Microtus corneri*, which he believed to be widespread in the tundra of southern England during the Pleistocene. He argued that *M. corneri* followed the retreating ice sheet northwards through England and Scotland, and into Orkney where it evolved into the Orkney Vole, *M. orcadensis*. A subsequent wave of immigration brought another vole species, *M. agrestis*, across the land-bridge where the Straits of Dover are now, and this new vole (he believed) out-competed *M. corneri/orcadensis* which thus became extinct on the mainland of Britain. Because the Pentland Firth bridge had disappeared by the time that *M. agrestis* got to the north of Scotland, the Orkney voles were protected, and survived as a relict.

This story is recounted by Harrison Matthews (in his New Naturalist on *British Mammals*, 1952), although he obviously had doubts, because he notes, 'it may be the whole story, but on the other hand it may have to be modified in the future when more detailed research has been done on the genetics of voles'. However, geographers tended to be taken in by the biologists' assumptions. In the New Naturalist on the *Sea Coast* (1953), J. A. Steers wrote:

> Probably the islands were separated from the mainland before the advent of the ice, but the depths in the Pentland Firth today suggest that eustatic movements of sea level would have been sufficient to cause a junction with the mainland, probably at the time the Dogger Bank was land. At this time *there must have been a connection to account for the similarity of fauna between the islands and the mainland* (my italics). The islands as we now see them are, therefore, of post-Glacial origin.

More work on the genetics of Orkney voles has now been done (p. 134), but other considerations show that Hinton's interpretation is wrong.

The Orkney Vole is not in fact a distinct species, but belongs to *Microtus arvalis*, which is widespread in continental Europe. *M. arvalis* and *M. agrestis* live together over large areas of Europe; there is no reason to expect

Figure 1.15
Sea transport remains
key to island commu-
nities. Here an oil
tanker lies at anchor
in Scapa Flow, waiting
to load North Sea
crude from the
terminal on Flotta.
Photo: Richard Welsby

that *M. arvalis* would become extinct through competition with *M. agrestis* in Britain.

The range of *M. agrestis* extends further north in Scandinavia than that of *M. arvalis*. It would therefore be expected to colonize tundra-habitats before *M. arvalis*. (*M. arvalis* is not related to a tundra-living *M. corneri*. Indeed, this latter species is a rather doubtful one: some of the fossil skulls attributed to it belong to a form called *M. oeconomus*, which does not now occur in Britain.)

If the 'relict' theory is true, *M. arvalis* might be expected to be on other islands which have been separated from Britain in post-glacial times. However, it occurs elsewhere in Britain only on Guernsey (where it may indeed be a relict); it is not found, for example, on any of the Hebrides.

It seems almost certain that voles colonized Orkney by some other route than via Caithness. We do not know how they managed to get to the islands. Since their closest relatives today are in south-east Europe (p. 133), it seems likely that they were introduced by humans, although it is not impossible that they arrived on a floating tree-trunk or some other form of raft. The method they used is irrelevant; the important point is that they cannot be cited as evidence for a land-bridge.

There are, not surprisingly, other geographical puzzles in the Orkney fauna, but it is the origin of the Orkney Vole that has provided the base for biological speculation about a land-bridge.

Land between Orkney and Caithness?

Is there geological evidence for a land-bridge? The two deep channels around Orkney (the Westray and Stronsay Firths separating the North Isles from the Mainland and Rousay, and the Pentland Firth), were once river valleys draining eastwards into a north-flowing river, probably originating around the time of the volcanic episode in the Tertiary which produced the mountains of Skye and Mull. The Pentland Firth is not a recent breach in the Caithness rocks.

The Admiralty Chart gives the current depth of the Pentland Firth as 53 fathoms (105 metres). It is generally assumed that the rise of sea level produced by the Pleistocene ice melting was about 300 feet (100 metres), which would imply that there might just have been dry land between Scotland and Orkney in post-glacial times. The Hudson Bay area of Canada seems to have risen more than 900 feet (300 metres) as a result of being relieved of an ice cap nearly two miles thick. Orkney never carried ice of this thickness. An Orkney land-bridge cannot be completely ruled out, but there is no good evidence for it from either biology or geology.

The most direct data comes from topographic studies of the sea floor of the Pentland Firth. Most of the sea cliffs around Shetland continue down into the sea to a depth of about 45 fathoms (90 metres), where the sea floor becomes flat. Around Orkney, and westwards along the north coast of Scotland, the slope extends to 35 fathoms (70 metres) below sea level. The sea rose so fast after the melting of the ice sheets of the last glacial period that little cliff erosion took place. The result was a coastline substantially as we

Figure 1.16
Hoy Sound at sunset.
Photo: Charles Tait

know it today; the coast of north and north-east Scotland, Orkney and Shetland seems to have developed over a long period due to marine erosion at a number of levels within a height range of about 260 feet (80 metres) above the break of slope. The lack of any substantial wave-cut platform at the present sea level shows that the present cliffs owe little of their retreat to erosion by the sea at its present level. The current coastal profile was largely created before the glaciation.

An interesting feature of the Caithness coast is a raised wave-cut rock platform along the foot of the cliffs, about 10 feet (3 metres) above sea level. This is substantial enough to protect the cliffs behind it from much marine erosion, and it carries beach material and relic stacks. A similar platform occurs around Scapa Flow. It probably represents the main late-glacial shoreline formed during the so-called Loch Lomond Readvance; it must be the result of a unique period of marine erosion occurring during renewed glacial conditions after the last main glaciation. This suggests that immediately after the main deglaciation, while the sea level was still low, rivers cut into the valleys filled with glacial till. As the sea level rose in response to the melting of ice elsewhere, these valleys filled with mud and sand. The rate of isostatic rise of land as it was released from the overlaying weight of ice increased and eventually matched the eustatic rise of the sea (as water was freed by the melting of the ice) at about the time of the Loch Lomond Readvance. The wave-cut platform was formed. The isostatic rise continued as the eustatic rise decreased, with the net result that sea level fell again relative to the land. Peat started to form down to sea level. After some time, sea level again rose and drowned peat in Caithness, Orkney and Shetland. The still-rising sea is cutting into the wave-cut platform in the northern part of Orkney at the present.

It would be wrong to be dogmatic about the existence of a land-bridge: in the *Lepidoptera of the Orkney Islands* (1983), Ian Lorimer quotes J. D. Peacock of the British Geological Survey as believing that 'it is highly unlikely Orkney was connected to the mainland after the arctic Loch Lomond Re-advance, 10,000 to 11,000 years ago', while Patrick Bailey in his *Orkney* (1971) gives his opinion that the Pentland Firth remained dry land up to the Boreal period, about 9,500 years ago. All that it is safe to say is that any land-bridge cannot have persisted for long in conditions when animals and plants could pass over it.

Figure 1.17
Like sleeping whales:
the Green Holms in
the Stronsay Firth.
Photo: Charles Tait

Further reading

GENERAL

Older works: Barry, 1805; Brand, 1701; Low, 1879; Tudor, 1883; Wallace, 1693, 1700.

Modern works: Bailey, 1971, 1995; Brown, 1969, 1981; Clouston, 1932; Fenton, 1978; Linklater, 1965; Marwick, 1951; Miller, 1976; Schei and Moberg, 1985; Tait, 1997; Thomson, 1980; Withrington and Grant, 1978.

The Orkney Islands Council publish an annual *Orkney Economic Review* with data about life and activity in the islands.

There have been two *Orkney Books*, the original one edited by Gunn (1909); the later one by Shearer, Groundwater and Mackay (1966). Older Orkney literature is listed by Cursiter (1894).

There is also a *Shetland Book* (edited by Cluness, 1967), a *Caithness Book* (edited by Omand, 1972) and a *Sutherland Book* (edited by Omand, 1982).

SHETLAND
General: Cluness, 1951; Cowie, 1871; Nicolson, 1972.

Natural history: Berry and Johnston, 1980; Evans and Buckley, 1899; Goodier, 1974; Johnston, 1998; Spence, 1979; Schei and Moberg, 1988; Tulloch, 1978; Tulloch and Hunter, 1972; Venables and Venables, 1955; Williamson, 1965.

FAROE
General: Schei and Moberg, 1991; West, 1972; Williamson, 1948; Wylie, 1987.

Natural history: Jensen, 1928–72; Rasmussen, 1952; Reinert, 1971; Williamson, 1948.

ORKNEY
Natural history: Baikie and Heddle, 1848; Balfour, 1972; Barne *et al.*, 1997; Berry, 1985; Booth and Booth, 1994; Booth, Cuthbert and Reynolds, 1984; Buckley and Harvie-Brown, 1891; Bullard, 1975, 1995; Dunn, 1837; Goodier, 1975; Groundwater, 1974; Low, 1813; Meek, 1995; Rendall, 1960; Spence, 1914.

Weather: Douglas, 1952; Plant and Dunsire, 1973.

ISLAND BIOLOGY
General: Berry, 1977, 1983a; Carlquist, 1974; Darling and Boyd, 1964; Lack, 1969, 1976; MacArthur and Wilson, 1967; Mayr, 1954; Whittaker, 1998; Williamson, 1981.

The Royal Society of Edinburgh have held two symposia, one on the Natural Environment of the Outer Hebrides and the other on the Natural Environment of the Inner Hebrides. These are published in the Proceedings of the Royal Society of Edinburgh, series B, volumes 77, 1979, and 83, 1983 respectively.

BIOLOGICAL HISTORY OF ORKNEY
Berry, 1985; Berry and Rose, 1975; Bullard, 1975; Chapman and Crawford, 1981; Childe, 1931; Corbet, 1961, 1979; Davidson, Jones and Renfrew, 1976; Downes, 1988; Flett, 1920; Flinn, 1974; Goodier, 1975; Hoppe, 1965; Huxtable *et al.*, 1976; Lorimer, 1983; Matthews, 1952; Moar, 1969; Peach and Horne, 1880; Renfrew, 1979, 1985; Renfrew, Harkness and Switsur, 1976; Ritchie, A., 1993, 1996; Ritchie and Ritchie, 1974; Ritchie, J. N. G.,1978; Sadler and Buckland, 1998; Steers, 1953; Traill, 1888.

Chapter 2

Rocks and Scenery*

Orkney is really a piece of the Caithness plateau, scissored from Scotland by
the Pentland Firth and dissected by the channels between individual islands.
It is best imagined as an undulating plateau tilted to the north and east, with
a major central structural depression (Scapa Flow) behind the residual
massif of Hoy. As the sea has risen relative to the land, a mosaic of islands,
firths and straits has been produced. For the discerning eye, the rocks of fore-
shore and hill provide a fascinating story of moving continents, changing
climates and evolving life forms.

Most of the land of Orkney is not particularly old by Scottish standards.
The foundation rocks are the northernmost British remnants of the Caledonian mountain belt which arose between 600 and 400 million years ago,
when the southern continent of Gondwan collided with the North American
continent of Laurentia. The debris from their erosion washed into the seas
surrounding the mountains, and formed sediments which compacted to
become the Old Red Sandstones of the north and east of Scotland.

The Old Red Sandstones were formed about 380 million years ago when
fish were first becoming common. They are often red in colour (as in Devon-
shire and Herefordshire), but in Orkney the colour can easily be
exaggerated. The cliffs of Hoy are magnificently red, as are the stones of St
Magnus Cathedral in Kirkwall quarried from the Head of Holland; but
brown, grey and ochre are more usual colours.

Many of the rocks are flagstones, layers of rock divided into thin and

* This chapter was written by John Flett Brown (see p. viii).

regular beds. Some are so finely
divided that the layers can be split
off readily for roofing flags; others
are thicker and make good paving
stones; others again are slab-like,
and have been used by builders for
over 4,000 years, since the time of
Skara Brae. They are derived from
numerous narrow belts of intensely
shattered rock, some of which
contain metalliferous minerals.

Orkney sandstones tend to be
fairly soft. Although mill-stones used
to be made from some of them (especially from Yesnaby, on the west
Mainland) they were tough enough
to grind only bere, primitive barley;
Millstone Grit from the Pennines had
to be imported to deal with oats.

Orkney geology has been increasingly studied in relation to the
exploration for oil in the North Sea
and Atlantic margin. The offshore
equivalents of some of the Orkney
rocks may yield oil (see p. 47), but
commercial amounts of oil are
extremely unlikely to be discovered
below Orkney itself.

Figure 2.1
Much of Orkney is
fertile, with a pre-
dominantly farmed
landscape.
Photo: Richard Welsby

Lake Orcadie

During the Devonian Period, North America and Northern Europe formed
a single 'Continent of Euramerica'. Britain was part of this land-mass, lying
about sixteen degrees south of the Equator with mountains in the north west
and a marine 'Devonian Sea' to the south, covering what is now south-west
England. Between the mountains and the sea was a vast desert plain 600
miles long and 120 miles wide (1,000 kilometres by 200 kilometres) stretching from Greenland through Shetland, Orkney, Caithness and the Moray
coast to western Norway. The lowest part of this was a basin occupied by a
large, shallow freshwater lake known as 'Lake Orcadie'. Several large rivers
flowed into it from the western mountains carrying sand and mud to gradually fill the lake basin.

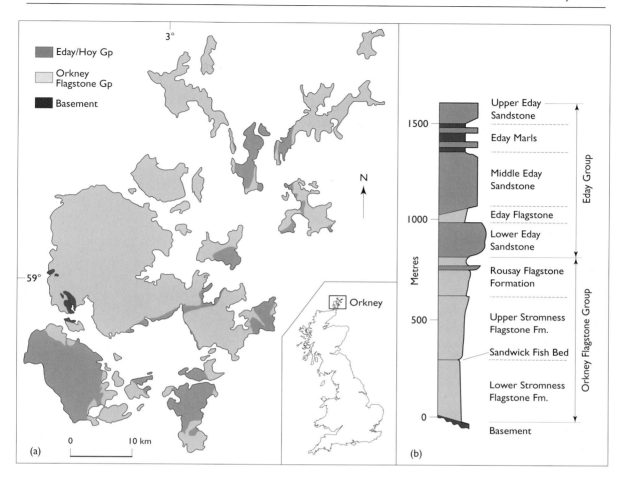

Figure 2.2
Geology of Orkney, after J. E. A. Marshall.

In the semi-arid and sub-tropical climate, evaporation was high and rainfall seasonal. Extensive sand and mudflats were produced at the margins of the lake as a result of the fluctuations in the area covered by water. Super-imposed on this cycle of wet and dry periods were longer climatic cycles, lasting 100,000 years or so. These started with a relatively wet period with the lake lapping up to the edge of the western mountains, and were followed by a drier period, with the lake margin retreating towards the centre of the basin. This long-term cyclicity is now considered to be controlled by the eccentricity of the earth's orbit around the sun (Milankovitch Cycle), which changes from near-circular to an ellipse and back over 100,000 years with consequent variation in the seasonal flux of solar radiation.

These cycles are easily traced in the sedimentary rocks of the well-exposed coastal sections in Orkney where the major cycles are represented by deposits from 15 to 50 feet (5 to 15 metres) thick. Each cycle starts with a finely laminated dark grey to black muddy-flagstone with fossil fish frag-ments, and ends with lake margin sediments consisting of sands, silts and light-grey mud with occasional thin bands of wind-blown desert sands.

Repeated cycles of lake deposition and desert continued for 7 million years until the upper-middle Devonian. At this time Lake Orcadie retreated so far that the water body was broken into many small lakes in a predominantly desert landscape. The final dry period lasted about 3.5 million years, interrupted by intervals of increased rainfall when the lake temporarily increased in area. It is characterized by sandstone deposits derived from the large braided river channels that continued to flow from the western mountains and from sand dunes that migrated across the desert.

Figure 2.3
A modern Orkney loch – Stenness, on the Mainland.
Photo: Richard Welsby

Tectonic history

Before the formation of the Orcadian Basin and Lake Orcadie, the tectonic history of the Orkney region started with the compressive phase of Caledonian Mountain-building involving thickening of the crust and major thrust faults (such as the Moine Thrust). This thrust movement ceased 450 million years ago. In the next 20 million years considerable erosion took place before the first lower Devonian sediments of the region were preserved. Collapse of the over-thickened crust took place on faults closely related in position and trends to the existing Caledonian Thrusts. Continued movement on these growth faults formed a series of half-graben structural basins that rapidly filled with immature erosion deposits (conglomerates and breccias). This period took the basins to near sea level through complex cycles of erosion, reworking and deposition, eventually levelling to form, by middle Devonian times, the relatively flat landscape unconformity of the Orcadian lake basin.

During the deposition of the Middle Devonian lake sediments, local unconformity and sediment thickening indicate continued tectonic activity. Evidence from the organic matter in the Middle Devonian rocks indicates that the Orcadian Basin continued to subside until the late Carboniferous/ early Permian when the African Continent collided with southern Europe, and the Orkney region experienced uplift and erosion. Orkney lies to the west of a major zone of faulting; this is an extension of the Great Glen Wrench Fault of the Scottish mainland. Tectonic inversion, possibly related to movement on the Fault System, has created local compressions, faults and folding and reactivated many older normal faults producing reversed faults and decollement zones. This tectonic inversion was eventually associated with decoupling of the normal fault system from its root zone and isolation from subsequent tectonic activity in the region.

Most of the folds affecting the Orkney rocks are gentle, open structures. The few major folds have a northerly axis, the most important being the contemporaneous Eday and Deerness Synclines. The more substantial faults are the Borwick-Navershaw, North and East Scapa and Brims-Risa Faults. Small-scale folding and faulting is common throughout Orkney, with normal fault movements of less than 10 metres.

Figure 2.4
Coastal rocks.
Photo: Richard Welsby

Fossils

The Devonian rocks of Orkney contain relatively few fossil species, due to the isolation of the lake in its surrounding arid desert. Despite this, the freshwater Lake Orcadie is very important for the understanding of the evolution of fish species, with successive forms well preserved in the rocks of the west mainland and elsewhere. They are originally marine genera whose presence in a freshwater lake environment must have been the result of rapid adaptation following the initial colonization through a network of rivers and lakes.

Figure 2.5
Pseudomorphs of salt crystals, Berstane Bay.
Photo: John Flett Brown

Diversification in this environment gave rise to a community of small herbivores, mud-grubbing scavengers and omnivores, with large carnivorous predators at the top of the food pyramid. When these animals died, their carcasses drifted to the bottom of the lake where, if the remains were covered quickly by sediments, they would change from flesh and bone to rock as the lake sediments hardened under the weight of succeeding layers. Periodically the fish suffered mass mortality, probably caused by increased salinity in hot, evaporating conditions. Fresh colonization took place when renewed access from the sea was established during wetter periods.

Although collecting is strictly controlled from the major type localities of the 'Sandwick Fish Bed' such as Cruaday Quarry in Sandwick, the coastline exposures of dark grey laminites provide abundant material for fossil hunters. In the deep-water parts of a cycle, plant fragments are often found associated with fish remains.

Fossil fishbeds have also been recorded on North Ronaldsay, Westray, Papa Westray, Rousay, Eday, Sanday, Stronsay, Shapinsay, South Ronaldsay and Hoy. The most common species are the crossopterygians *Glyptolepis paucidens*, *Osteolepis macrolepidotus* and *Gyroptychius agassizi*; the placoderms *Coccosteus cuspidatus*, *Homosteus milleri* and *Pterichthyodes* spp.; the acanthodians *Cheiracanthus murchisoni*, *Mesacanthus peachi*, *Diplacanthus striatus*, *Rhadinacanthus longispinus* and *Cheirolepis trailli*; and the dipnoan (lung-fish) *Dipterus valenciennesi*. The actual composition of the fauna differs somewhat in different deposits (Table 2.1).

The profusion of fossil fish around Stromness was known more than a century and a half ago: an extensive collection by Professor Traill (p. 229) was classified by Louis Agassiz, better known for the recognition of glaciation in the USA. He reported on these fish at one of the early meetings of the British Association. By 1837 the Stromness Museum was exhibiting over

Figure 2.6
Devonian fish from the Sandwick Fish Beds, now existing only as fossils. At the top right, *Cheirolepis* is chasing a pair of *Diplocanthus*. Below it, *Dipterus* cruises along. Below *Dipterus*, *Osteolepis* is in pursuit of two more *Cheirolepis*, while *Coccosteus* has her mouth open for either a *Cheirolepis* or the single *Mesacanthus*. Bottom right is *Pterichthyodes*.
Drawing by Jack Saxon.

100 fossil fish specimens. Such fossils became widely known through the writings of the Scottish stone-mason Hugh Miller, whose *Footprints of the Creator* was sub-titled *The Asterolepis of Stromness* (rather ironically, since the fossil that Miller wrote about is not an *Asterolepis*!). Miller's work was part of the background when Charles Darwin was working towards his theory of evolution by natural selection. Darwin was Secretary of the Geological Society, in the years when Miller was most active; Miller was an outspoken anti-evolutionist on mainly religious grounds. He fought a long

Table 2.1   Stratigraphy of the Middle Devonian fossil fish

Eday group	*Watsonosteus, Tristichopterus, Pentlandia, Microbrachius, (Dipterus valenciennesi).*
Rousay Flags	*Millerosteus, (Dickosteus), (Gyroptychius milleri), Thursius pholidotus, (Osteolepis panderi), (Pentlandia), Glyptolepis paucidens, Homosteus milleri, Dipterus valenciennesi, Asterolepis, Acanthodii.*
Upper Stromness Flags	*(Coccosteus), Dickosteus, Gyroptychius milleri, (Thursius pholidotus), Osteolepis panderi, Glyptolepis paucidens, Homosteus milleri, Dipterus valenciennesi, Cephalaspis, Acanthodii.*
Sandwick Fish Bed	*Coccosteus, (Thursius macrolepidotus), Osteolepis macrolepidotus, Gyroptychius agassizi, Glyptolepis paucidens, Homosteus milleri, Dipterus valenciennesi, Pterichthyodes, Acanthodii. Cheirolepis, Rhamphodopsis.*
Lower Stromness Flags	*(Coccosteus), Thursius macrolepidotus, (Gyroptychius agassizi), (Glyptolepis paucidens), (Homosteus milleri), (Dipterus valenciennesi).*

and bitter rearguard action against the 'Infidels' of science, experiencing considerable inner conflict which contributed towards his suicide at the age of 54.

A small branchiopod crustacean, *Asmussia murchisoniana*, whose living descendants are found in brackish waters, occurs commonly in the Rousay Flags. Shallow water sediments and riverbank deposits occasionally contain very rare trace fossil tracks ('footprints') of lobster-like arthropods. In some areas, particularly within the Eday Marls, 'U'-shaped worm burrows filled with sand have been observed.

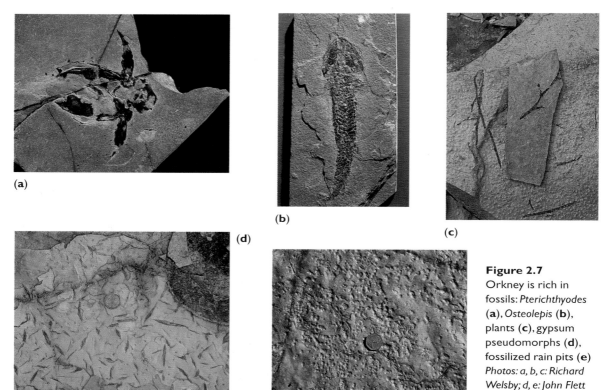

(a)

(b)

(c)

(d)

(e)

Figure 2.7
Orkney is rich in fossils: *Pterichthyodes* (**a**), *Osteolepis* (**b**), plants (**c**), gypsum pseudomorphs (**d**), fossilized rain pits (**e**)
Photos: a, b, c: Richard Welsby; d, e: John Flett Brown

Figure 2.8
Stromatolites.
Photo: John Flett Brown

In the shallow water mudflat environment at the lake margin, extensive growths of algal mats occurred. They provided a potential food source for fish and were only preserved from grazing in areas where the local environment was too harsh for fish to survive. In these places, sticky organic films grew on the sediment surface. They were then covered by fine-grained sediment, which is preserved. Repeated seasonal growth and death of the algae form a distinctive convex corrugated layered structure known as 'stromatolites'. The best-known of these in Orkney occur at the classic 'Horse Tooth Stone' locality at Yesnaby; this is protected as a Site of Special Scientific Interest, but many other collectable examples can be found in coastal exposures.

Stratigraphy

The original investigations into the sedimentary rocks of Orkney and Caithness by Roderick Murchison (1859) led to a simple three-fold classification of the Old Red Sandstone into:

1. Lower Old Red Sandstone (sandstones and conglomerates of the southwest Mainland);
2. Middle Old Red Sandstone (grey flagstones of the Mainland and islands);
3. Upper Old Red Sandstone (red and yellow sandstones of Hoy and Eday).

This early interpretation had to be modified when angular unconformity was recognized between the sands and conglomerates at Yesnaby and the overlying flagstones, and between the flagstones and sandstones in north Hoy. This appeared to fit the tectonic picture from other parts of Scotland and led to their classification into Lower, Middle and Upper Devonian epochs.

Since no unconformity existed between the Eday sandstones and the Middle Old Red Sandstone flagstones, the Eday Sands were initially assigned to a Mid-Devonian age and thus deemed older than the Hoy sandstones, which were given a late Devonian date. This stratigraphic interpretation was adopted by Peach and Horne (1880) and is still shown in many current publications.

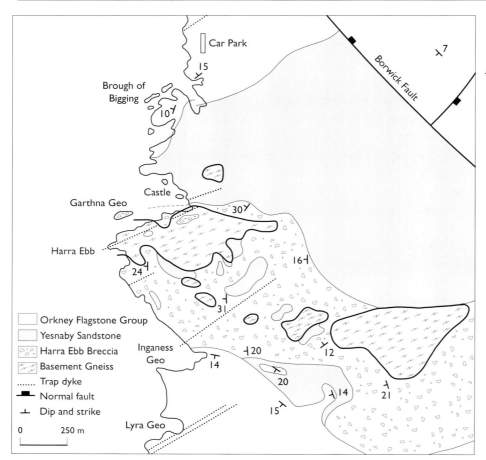

Figure 2.9
Geological sketch
map – Yesnaby.
John Flett Brown

However, our understanding of the Orcadian Devonian sedimentary rocks is currently being radically revised following increased research activity, in part spurred by economic interest from the oil industry. Recent detailed stratigraphic sections, sedimentology and palaeogeographic reconstructions of the sandstones in the South Isles have shown that the Eday Group sandstones are equivalent to the Hoy Group. The new work has also recognized contemporaneous fault movements on the North Scapa and Bring Fault systems and volcanic eruption at the base of both the Eday and Hoy sandstones; the current belief is that the North Hoy Unconformity is a local rather than a regional feature.

The modern interpretation of the stratigraphy of Orkney uses five subdivisions.

1. Precambrian Basement Complex

The Basement rock exposed at Graemsay, Stromness and South Yesnaby consists of a pinkish-grey granite-gneiss complex including sillimanite-gneiss, hornblende-schist, mica-schist and psammitic-schists interleaving with unfoliated migmatite granites. It is complexly veined by white quartz, aplites and pegmatites with muscovite, biotite, orthoclase, quartz (Rose and Cairngorm), garnet and occasional tourmaline and beryl. The absolute age of the Basement has not been established but its similarity to rocks of the Moinian succession in the Altnaharra district of Sutherland has led to it being considered of 'Moine age' (1,500 million years).

Before burial by the Devonian sediments of Lake Orcadie, the basement rocks formed a range of small, steep-sided hills running north to north west. These hills eventually stood out as islands within the lake and were surrounded by locally derived beach deposits of sands, conglomerates and breccias.

2. Lower Devonian Sediments

The oldest sedimentary outcrop is found to the north and east of the Yesnaby exposure of basement rock. The Harra Ebb formation consists of breccias, conglomerates, sands and mud deposited on an uneven surface of eroded basement gneiss. These in turn were tilted and eroded before the dune sands

Figure 2.10
Yesnaby cliffs and 'castle'.
Photo: Richard Welsby

of the Yesnaby Sandstone formation (clearly shown in the sea stack of Yesnaby Castle) were formed. The dune sands pass upwards into reworked fluvial sands with trace fossils of burrowing organisms. These strata were finally tilted about ten degrees to the west before being overlain by the Middle Devonian lake sediments.

3. Lower Middle Devonian Sediments

The Orkney Flagstone group is 2,200 feet (752 metres) thick, and consists of grey and black thinly bedded flagstones clearly laid down in an extensive lake of variable salinity. It has three parts:

Lower Stromness Flagstone Formation

A basal breccia beach deposit fringing the Granite Gneiss Complex in the Stromness area and reworked Yesnaby Sandstone at Yesnaby, passing upwards into 700 feet (277 metres) (43 cycles) of lake cycle flagstones. The top of the formation is marked by the distinctive Sandwick Fish Bed, 30 to 100 feet thick (10 metres to 30 metres) which is exposed on the coast and in several quarries in the west Mainland.

Upper Stromness Flagstone Formation

750 feet (285 metres) (25 cycles) of lake cycle deposits with a higher content of fluvial river sand and sheet flood deposits coming from the north west. The top of the formation is less distinct than the base. The top lies at the transition from a series of very sand-rich and thick cycles to a distinct set of much thinner cycles.

Rousay Flagstone Formation

500–600 feet (170–190 metres) (18 cycles) of lake cycle deposits similar to the underlying Upper Stromness Flagstone Formation. Near the top of the Formation at Sacquoy Head is a distinctive pebbly sandstone known as the Sacquoy Sandstone.

4. Upper Middle to Upper Devonian Sediments

The Eday Group including the Hoy sandstones (up to 2,500 feet, 800 metres thick) is composed largely of yellow and red sandstones with intervening grey flagstones and red/green marls. It comes from two major river systems flowing into the lake basin, one south east over Eday and a second much larger one north west over Dunnet Head (Caithness), Hoy and the South Isles. The alluvial plains from these river systems overlapped and merged in the East Mainland and South Isles. Contemporary tectonic movements and extensional faulting in the region early in their formation released alkaline volcanic deposits of ash and lava flows near the base of the Lower Eday (Hoy) Sandstone.

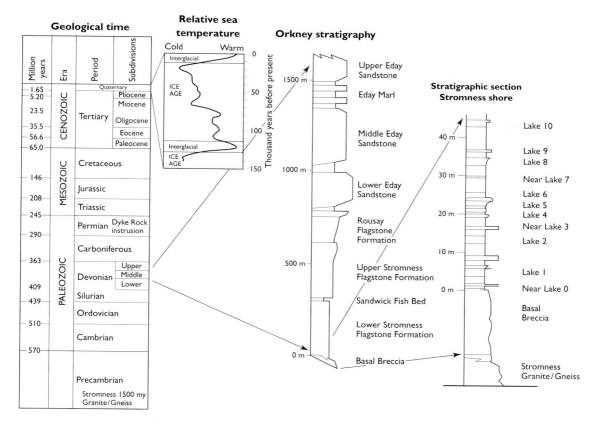

Figure 2.11
Orkney stratigraphy.
John Flett Brown

There are five separate lithostratigraphic units in the Eday Group above the basal volcanic sequence:

Lower Eday Sandstone
This was formed during an arid period when there was local faulting and folding. It varies from 100 feet (35 metres) at the margin to nearly 600 feet (180 metres) in the core of the Eday Syncline basin.

Eday Flagstones
These mark a return to wetter conditions with the establishment of up to twelve lake cycles. These lakes were best developed in eastern Orkney where they rapidly transgressed the alluvial plain. The lakes formed during this phase were local in extent although probably linked through stream and river systems allowing migration of fish between lakes. Westwards from South Ronaldsay the lake cycles pass laterally into aeolian (desert) deposits. No lake or marginal lake deposits have been found in Hoy.

Middle Eday Sandstone
In Eday the alluvial sands related to the northern river system returned after only four lake cycles. This Middle Eday Sand is confined to the northern part

of Orkney and thins towards the south east. The sandstone disappears in Newark Bay (Deerness) with the Eday Flagstones passing directly into the Eday Marls.

Eday Marl
This is a distinctive unit of green and red silt and mud, subjected to extensive turbulence, desiccation and oxidation. The recent discovery of large halite pseudomorphs (rare marine microfossils), beds of saddle dolomite, anhydrite altered to limestone and beds with worm burrows and casts on ripple surfaces indicate a marginal-marine salt-flat environment.

Upper Eday Sandstone
This represents a return to sandy river deposits forming a wide alluvial plain. Aeolian desert deposits are absent in eastern Orkney but can be found in central Hoy. The uppermost preserved fluvial sands of the Eday Group in Hoy and Dunnet Head (Caithness) could be as young as Lower Carboniferous as observed in the reservoir sand of the Clair Oil Field.

5. Post Devonian Rocks
No sedimentary rocks younger than Devonian have been definitely identified in Caithness, Orkney or Shetland. The 1,500 feet (500 metres) of red conglomerates on a metamorphic basement at Kirtomy and Tongue in Sutherland might be Permian to Triassic in age. However, Permo-Triassic sediments outcrop on the sea bed 10 miles (15 kilometres) west and 15 miles (20 kilometres) east of Orkney, and Carboniferous sediments outcrop on the Rona Ridge in the vicinity of the Clair Oil Field.

Figure 2.12
Schematic geological cross-section – West Mainland, Orkney.
John Flett Brown

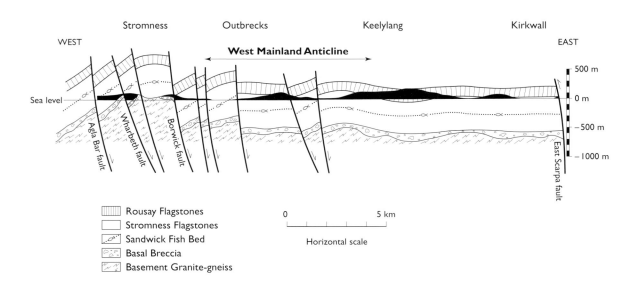

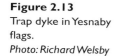

Figure 2.13
Trap dyke in Yesnaby flags.
Photo: Richard Welsby

Despite the fact that no younger sedimentary rocks have been found in Orkney, geochemical analysis of organic carbon in the laminites of the Orkney Lake Sediments shows that they are consistent with being covered by at least 2,000 metres of younger rock. Tectonic inversion in the early Permian uplifted the Orkney basin to its present level, with consequent erosion of the younger sediments. After this the Orkney region was isolated from major tectonic activity and probably remained as a non-depositional palaeogeographic high during the remainder of its geological history.

Over 200 'Trap Dykes' of igneous origin cut the Devonian sediments of Orkney in a NE–SW direction with a small group in south-east Orkney running N–S. This suite of dykes is part of a set of nine similar dyke swarms found in the Highlands and Islands, widely distributed both in space and time. These hard, black rocks often follow the line of fractures. They are notable in containing an exotic collection of mantle-derived xenolith inclusions, indicating rapid transport of host liquids from great depths. It is possible that they represent volcanic activity which never reached the surface. The age of the Orkney dykes is 252 ± 10 million years, placing the time of their intrusion in the late Permian, a period of renewed tectonic movement in the sedimentary basins to the west of Orkney but post-dating the deformations associated with the basin inversion.

The Ice Age and after

The low-lying rolling landscape of modern Orkney is the result of sculpturing by vast sheets of ice moving at various periods across the islands during the last Ice Age. In fact the term 'Ice Age' may mean two very different things. It may describe long intervals of earth history (tens to hundreds of millions of years) during which glaciers waxed and waned; but it can also describe shorter time periods (tens of thousand of years) during which glaciers were near their maximum extent. These shorter intervals are more accurately called 'glaciations'.

In the past 2.4 million years there have been over twenty glaciations, each lasting about 100,000 years and consisting of several stadial (shorter cold periods) and interstadial episodes. Relatively long warm periods (interglacials) of about 15,000 years occur between each glaciation. We are presently approaching the end of the current interglacial.

Such glacial to interglacial oscillations are estimated to involve a potential exchange of up to 50 million cubic kilometres of water between the oceans and the ice caps, which could produce a global change in mean sea level approaching 500 feet (150 metres) with consequent changes in salinity and temperature.

Several major 'ice age periods' have occurred before the current cycle, notably ones 600 and 300 million years ago. The causes of such ice ages are complex and involve a combination of factors such as continental distribution, volcanic activity, jet stream directions in the upper atmosphere and the

Figure 2.14
The rolling landscape of Orkney: a Westray farm.
Photo: Richard Welsby

astronomical orientation of the earth. However, a major factor in the Quaternary Period is fluctuation in the amount of 'insolation' (incoming solar radiation); this is the most likely cause of the large-scale and small-scale variations in the Earth's climate.

This solar variable or Milankovitch cycle relates to three major components of the earth's orbit about the sun:

1. The orbital eccentricity of the earth around the sun varying from a circular to an elliptical orbit with a change in seasonal incoming solar radiation of about 30 per cent takes 95,800 years.
2. Changes in the inclination of the earth's axis from the vertical between 21.39 degrees and 24.36 degrees with a periodicity of 41,000 years. Any increase in axial tilt results in lengthening the period of winter darkness in polar regions. These changes cause significant variation in the insolation at high latitudes.
3. The precession of the equinoxes over a period of 21,700 years requires the northern hemisphere to be tilted towards the sun at successively different points on the earth's annual orbit. This affects the lengths and the absolute temperature of summer and winter.

A high degree of correlation exists between the combined insolation curves and the fine structure of observed stadial and interstadial episodes within the last major glaciation (115,000 years) as observed in the relative sea temperature curves.

Proof of early glaciation in Orkney is elusive as the last major ice advance (30,000 years ago) removed most of the evidence. However, a sequence of glacial sediments has been found in boreholes drilled in the sea bed to the east and west of Orkney. Although the 'Ice Age' started around 2.4 million years ago, there is no evidence of glaciation in Scotland until about 850,000 years ago. It has been suggested that that the first presence of small glaciers on Hoy may possibly date from this period.

About 750,000 years ago there appears to have been a switch to more extreme climatic oscillations with the first of several extensive glaciations in the outer Moray Firth. This early Cromerian glaciation may be the first time that the Scottish ice sheet reached Orkney.

During the Anglian glaciation 440,000 years ago, Orkney was almost certainly covered by ice sheets, although no glacial sediments of this age are known. At this time the Scottish and the Scandinavian ice sheets may have been confluent. Approximately 300,000 years ago, the Saalian ice sheet was present in the northern North Sea, indicating that Orkney was again covered by ice.

The Devensian Ice Age which started approximately 115,000 years ago is characterized by at least four ice advances (stadials) interspersed by shorter intervals of ice retreat involving changes in global sea levels of between ten and twenty fathoms (20 to 40 metres).

The late Devensian glaciation built up and advanced from about 30,000 years ago, reaching its maximum around 24,000 years ago. The ice retreated and thinned around 15,000 years ago, finally leaving Orkney about 13,000 years ago.

The ice sheet carried rock materials, sand and muds derived mainly from local sources with occasional erratics (rocks transported by ice and deposited far from their point of origin) from the bed of the North Sea (chalk, flints and shells) and from as far away as Norway (granites and metamorphic rocks). The rock materials concentrated in the base and margins of the ice sheet acted like sandpaper and efficiently eroded the land surface. Rock steps observed on many Orkney hillsides (well seen on Rousay) are testimony to this differential erosion of soft and hard rock layers. Rocks embedded in the ice left scratch marks (striations) on the bedrock. The striation orientation shows the direction of movement of the ice sheet. The flow direction in Orkney fluctuated from a generally SE–NW direction to an E–W direction.

A large erratic of hornblende gneiss found near Saville at the north end of Sanday is thought to have come from Norway. This does not necessarily mean that the Norwegian ice travelled over Orkney; the rock may have been dropped from the Scandinavian ice at an earlier stage of glaciation and picked up by the Moray Firth ice and brought to Sanday. The huge Cubbie Roo's Stone in the upper Woodwick valley (north Mainland) must have been transported at least from the Head of Holland, about 30 miles (50 kilometres) away. On Flotta, laurdalite, a rock characteristic of Norway but unknown in Britain, occurs on a beach with many other foreign rocks, none of which occurs in the till at the back of the beach. However, the most likely explanation is that these were ships' ballast, as are the labradorite blocks once common behind the Inner Holm and now found in many Stromness gardens.

Figure 2.15
Ice scratch marks on Rousay.
Photo: John Flett Brown

The rocks, sand and mud frozen in the ice sheet were deposited as the ice melted, forming a layer of boulder clay (or till) in most of the low-lying areas of Orkney. This boulder clay varies from a few inches (centimetres) thick to 50 to 60 feet (20 metres). Small rounded hills ('morainic mounds') of boulder clay cover substantial regions of Orkney. Oriented hummocky moraines in areas such as Rousay, Stenness and Harray with many 'kettle holes' (hollows in boulder clay left by late melting ice blocks) indicate that sheets of ice

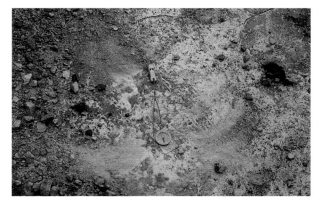

Figure 2.16
Boulder clay at Birsay.
Photo: John Flett Brown

probably continued their east–west flow until finally melting.

In Orkney, boulder clay illustrates a clear relationship between the till lithology and the local bedrock source. Although the Orkney boulder clay at any one place is uniform in texture and composition, more than twenty multiple till sections have been recorded. Differences in colour reflect the bedrock composition up-ice and the contrasts between individual units relate to changing ice movement patterns. Classic localities are to be found at Den Wick (Deerness) with two superimposed tills and at Scara Taing (Rousay) where there are three separate till lithologies. The absence of soil horizons or weathered surfaces between these tills indicates that melting of a single ice sheet 13,000 years ago was probably responsible for deposition of these multiple tills.

The north-west end of the island of Hoy exhibits the classical form of a valley glacier. The two deep valleys either side of the Ward Hill are U-shaped valleys formed by the presence of local glaciers. The Trowie Glen was a hanging valley glacier where deeper erosion by the ice was prevented by the presence of the glacier in the main valley. Several small corries are also present at Enegars Corrie (shaped like an armchair overlooking Stromness), Quoyawa facing Graemsay, and the Nowt Bield opposite the Dwarfie Stone. Other glacial features such as truncated spurs and terminal moraines are common. An excellent exposure of a lateral moraine is seen at the east end of the

Figure 2.17
Glacial shaping at the north end of Hoy.
Photo: Richard Welsby

Figure 2.18
Volcanic ash overlain
by lava flow,
Rackwick.
Photo: John Flett Brown

Rackwick beach where the angular rock debris, which fell from the valley side on to the edge of the glacier, is observed.

Linking all these features on Hoy is difficult since they were sculpted over a long period beginning 850,000 years ago and may well have been actively reworked during each succeeding ice age when the ice sheets first advanced and then retreated.

Towards the end of the Devensian period the short cooling period of the Loch Lomond stadial (11,000 years ago) marked the last fling of the Ice Age. On Hoy there is evidence for this phase of local glaciation with the presence of small end moraines at Dwarfie Hamar and the interior of Enegars' Corrie.

There seems to have been a long period of very cold climate when the

Figure 2.19
Wind stripes on Hoy.
Photo: Richard Welsby

Figure 2.20 a and b
Caves, mud-cracks and wave-rippled rocks.
Photo: Richard Welsby

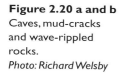

ground was still without vegetation, evidenced by frost shattering, churning and solifluction on the top of the boulder clay deposits and rock surfaces. It is from this time that the bare rocky 'pavements' and 'patterned ground' of the summits of the Hoy hills originate, and also the great gashes cut by torrents of meltwater in the glens. Arctic tundra conditions continued to between 10,000 years and 9,000 years ago when the temperature rose to around that of the present.

Post-glacial sea-level change in Orkney is only beginning to be studied. Relative sea-level change is the combination of global sea-level rising, opposed by elevation of the land surface following removal of the weight of the ice. In Orkney, the sea level appears to have risen faster than the land since the last glaciation. This is responsible for the archipelago's present drowned topography with its partially inundated valleys and submerged peat bogs.

In the Wick Valley (Caithness) the sea level started to rise 8,500 years ago and this marine transgression (17 feet or 5.5 metres) culminated 7,900 years ago. Two subsequent marine transgressions, reaching 0.5 and 0.9 metres above the first, at 4,000 and 1,200 'radiocarbon years' ago also occurred. Mathematical modelling suggests that about 6,000 years ago the sea level in Orkney was between one and two metres above the present datum. There is some evidence around the Stromness shore to indicate an undated raised beach platform at about this level.

Raised beaches, formed when the land rises faster than the sea, are common in Caithness and Sutherland with distinctive wave-cut platforms backed by cliffs and caves. In Orkney the only high-level raised beach is at Muckle head (north-west Hoy). This is around 20 feet (6 metres) above sea level and is covered by the late Devensian boulder clay. It is obviously connected to one of the earlier interstadial sea-level rises in the region and not the present fluctuations.

The coast

Modern Orkney has an extensive shoreline approximately 500 miles (800 kilometres) long, almost half that of mainland Scotland and comparable to that of Shetland. Cliffs exceeding 50 feet (15 metres) in height make up nearly a fifth of this shoreline, whilst sand or shingle beaches make up another 10 per cent. The remaining 70 per cent consist of low rock and boulder clay cliffs and rocky shores. The interior coasts of the island group consist of sheltered marine environments, while the outer fringes are exposed to strong erosional wind and waves.

The westward-facing coasts of Hoy, West Mainland and northern Westray are fully exposed to the destructive forces of the open Atlantic, with deep water extending close inshore and waves breaking directly on the cliffs. A solid rock wave-cut platform, sometimes of great width with many rock pools, forms on these exposed shores, with boulder beaches being created in the bays from the broken cliff debris. In places wind-blown sand has collected behind the beaches to form extensive dune and machair areas.

Major storms have lifted rocks to form boulder beaches on some cliff tops. Good examples are to be found on the westward-facing cliffs at Sacquoy Head, Rousay. At the Nev in Westray a storm beach, 400 yards (400 metres) long, 50 feet (7 metres) wide and 15 feet (5 metres) high has formed on top of a 40-foot (13-metre) cliff. At the Brough, Stronsay, blocks several tons in weight have been thrown up more than 20 feet (7 metres) on southeast-facing cliffs, illustrating the power unleashed by storms from the Atlantic and the North Sea. All these cliff-top storm beaches show weathering and lichen cover, indicating they have built up over hundreds or thousands of years (Hall, 1996). We still have to learn how many major storms are represented in these cliff deposits, but it is safe to assume that they are relatively rare phenomena; more recent ones may even be recorded in the local historical archives.

One of the best-known features of Orkney is the Old Man of Hoy, a sea stack standing on a plinth of Rackwick Lava. At 400 feet (137 metres), it is the tallest sea stack in Britain, forming the remaining leg of a one-time two-legged stack and arch, named and sketched by the landscape painter William Daniell in 1819. Early in the nineteenth century a severe storm destroyed the local fishing fleet and washed away one leg of the Old Man. The debris still lies between the stack and the shore. Blaeu's map of 1663 (probably drawn in 1600) shows only a headland with the Fort of Braburgh on the point. Murdoch Mackenzie's hydrographical map (1750) of Hoy likewise only shows a headland. This suggests the Old Man may be the result of relatively recent erosion and no more than 250 years old.

The Old Man of Hoy is only one of the many sea stacks and 'castles' along

Figure 2.21
Geos, South Waas.
Photo: Richard Welsby

the Orkney shoreline. On the west coast of Mainland from Black Craig (near Stromness) northwards, there is an endless succession of headlands, bays and geos, with caves, gloups or blowholes, arches and sea stacks in every stage of development and destruction.

All these features start with sea caves whose formation begins from geological weaknesses such as stratification, joints, cracks, faults and dyke intrusions. Wave-induced erosion of the rocks along the fracture line at the base of the cliff produces a small opening following the weakness, and develops according to the dip of the bedding planes and the line of the fractures. Enlargement proceeds by hydraulic action of the waves enhanced by the pneumatic action of trapped air and the abrasive action of sand and pebbles. When long caves are formed, collapse of the roof at the inward end forms a gloup, while total collapse of the roof forms a geo. Where the waves succeed in excavating a line of weakness bisecting a promontory, the caves may join to form an arch (as at the Hole o' Row, Skaill); subsequent collapse of the roof will then form an isolated sea stack.

Within historical times, the sea has encroached on some shores such as the Bay of Skaill, exploring weaknesses of rock structure and exploiting valleys formed by the moving ice sheet. The actual rate of retreat of the coast is not easy to measure. Absence of the seaward part of the brochs at Borwick, Sandwick and Breckness and the near-total disappearance of that at Stromness Kirkyard suggests at least 80 feet (25 metres) over the last 2,000 years. The boat slip at the Brough in Birsay shows a loss of nearly 100 feet (37 metres) since Viking times. The Brough may even have been joined to the Mainland at that time. Within living memory at Birsay, Skaill and Warebeth, 15 to 30 feet (5–10 metres) of sand and boulder clay shore have been lost. This loss is episodic and depends on a combination of factors including storm direction and the absence of cushioning sand in the intertidal zone, allowing the waves to break on the shore face. An average rate of 30 feet (10 metres) per century seems to be a reasonable estimate for erosion on the exposed coastlines.

Not all the actions of the sea, wind and wave are destructive. Perhaps the best example of coastal build-up is on the south-east side of the fourth

Figure 2.22
Gloup and arch: Vat
of Kirbister, Stronsay.
Photo: Richard Welsby

Churchill Barrier linking South Ronaldsay to Burray. The expanding beach is formed by refraction of waves round Grim Ness creating an offshore sand bar and filling in the lagoon behind it, with beach and blown sand piling up on the Barrier. Mackenzie's map (1750) shows the north end of Sanday as a group of small rocky islets joined by spits, bars and tombolas formed by shoreward movement of sands. The enclosed lagoons have since filled with blown sand, and the whole is now an integral part of the main island. The almost enclosed Cata Sand, on the eastern side of Sanday, will no doubt be similarly incorporated.

The present 1–2 mm per year relative rise of sea level in Orkney renders these areas of sand dune infilling vulnerable. Even more importantly, sand extraction for building removes the plant cover and affects the local wind direction, turning natural accretion into erosion with consequent loss of dunes.

Refraction of waves round an island can also throw up a loop of storm beach boulders to enclose a small loch such as those at Torness (Stronsay), Vasa Loch (Shapinsay), the south end of Copinsay and many others. Bay-mouth bars (ayres) are formed due to a combination of factors including sea-level rise, storm beaches and wave refraction. An example of a bay cut off from the sea in this way is the Peedie Sea in Kirkwall. The old mill (now a warehouse) on the ayre used to be operated by the ebb and flow of tides in the lagoon. The ayre now has the main road to Stromness running along it. Other good examples of ayres are the Long Ayre of Tankerness near Kirkwall Airport, at Finstown, Millsand and Holm (Mainland), Skaill and Fribo (Westray), and Echnaloch (Burray).

Minerals

As early as 1666, John Speed recorded the presence of lead ore in Orkney. Several mineral veins have been worked, but all were small and rapidly exhausted. Most veins were mined for lead sulphide ore (galena). The two biggest mines, at Warebeth, west of Stromness, and Manse Bay on the north-east coast of South Ronaldsay, were worked in the latter half of the eighteenth century. Other lead mines were at Selwick in north Hoy, near the Low Light on Graemsay, at North Hill on Sanday, and in south-west Rousay. The lead and zinc ores at Rousay, Selwick and Warebeth were notably rich in silver (up to 76 ounces per ton).

Many uneconomic occurrences of galena in Orkney occur in or next to stromatolite beds. Metals entered the Orcadian Lake in the rivers draining the surrounding hills, and were concentrated during sediment deposition. When the algae died and were degraded, metal-organic complexes were formed, from which sulphide minerals were deposited.

Copper has been mined on the shore at Wha Taing, Burray, and east of the lead mine on Rousay. Iron ores have been worked in northern Hoy, and fist-sized lumps of haematite are abundant in the Bay of Creekland near the old mine. In northern Hoy, manganese has also been found and exploited.

Uranium occurs in fault zones from secondary hydrothermal concentration of the placer deposits in the basal breccias of south-west Mainland. The quantity is small and there is no likelihood of mining in the foreseeable future, but it remains as a strategic national resource.

Hydrocarbon potential

Many laminite (fishbed) horizons in Orkney are carbon rich (Marshall *et al.*, 1985; Hillier and Marshall, 1992), and if deeply buried would in time produce petroleum. Where such carbon-rich rocks have been intruded by hot igneous intrusions, small quantities of oil are formed. Sandstones through which this oil migrated and left bituminous residues are found near major faults, particularly the North Scapa and Brims-Risa faults.

In the Yesnaby area the basal sand is full of solid bitumen and was once an oil reservoir containing 225 million barrels of oil. Other sandstone beds throughout Orkney show past evidence of hydrocarbons. Such rocks in the offshore areas are attractive oil exploration targets. The major discovery of oil in the Devonian and Carboniferous sands of the Clair field to the north west of Orkney confirms that such basal sands may hold commercial quantities of hydrocarbons.

Further reading

Agassiz, 1834; Astin, 1985, 1990; Astin and Rogers, 1991; Baxter and Mitchell, 1984; Black, 1978; Bott and Browitt, 1975; Brown, 1975; Coward, Enfield and Fischer, 1989; Enfield and Coward, 1987; Fannin, 1969; Flett, 1897, 1898, 1920; Flinn, 1969a, 1969b, 1973, 1978, 1981; Gallagher *et al.*, 1971; Geikie, 1877; Goodier and Ball, 1975; Hall, 1996; Halliday, McAlpine and Mitchell, 1977; Hansom and Evans, 1995; Heddle, 1878; Hill, 1996; Hillier and Marshall, 1992; House and Gale, 1995; Institute of Geological Sciences, 1978; Jameson, 1813; Jarvik, 1948; Kellock, 1969; Laing, 1877; Leask, 1928; McQuillin, 1968; Marshall, 1996; Marshall, Brown and Hindmarsh, 1985; Marshall, Rodgers and Whiteley, 1996; Mather, Ritchie and Smith, 1974, 1975; Michie and Cooper, 1979; Miles and Westoll, 1963; Miller, 1849; Muir and Ridgway, 1975; Murchison, 1859; Mykura, 1975, 1976, 1991; Parnell, 1983a, 1983b, 1983c; Peach and Horne, 1880, 1883; Richardson, 1965; Rodgers and Astin, 1991; Saxon, 1991; Saxton and Hopwood, 1919; Steavenson, 1928; Upton, Mitchell, Long and Aspen, 1992; Watson, 1932; Watts, 1971; Wilson *et al.*, 1935; Wilson and Knox, 1936.

Chapter 3

Land Plants in an Oceanic Environment*

Orkney never fails to astonish summer visitors for the verdure of its land-scape and the number of cattle grazing on highly productive pastures. This vigorous pastoral activity is particularly striking for those who have travelled to Orkney via the bleak moorlands of Sutherland or the desolate expanse of the Flow Country of Caithness. Here, to the north of some of Scotland's most deserted landscapes, is a land supporting an active agricultural economy and a substantial level of human settlement. It is soon apparent that the coastline and its inlets, the bogs, moorlands and hills support a highly diverse natural flora in a wide range of habitats. Hoy is particularly noteworthy for the astonishing contrasts that can be found in the relatively short distance from shore to hilltops. At sea level, herb-rich pastures and fields of oats, barley and potatoes can be found, while a low-lying gully at Berriedale in North Hoy is the home of Britain's most northerly natural woodland. A short walk above this brings one to Arctic-type tundra vegetation between St John's Head and the Cuilags at an altitude of only 1,100 feet (335 metres). However, Arctic species grow at much lower levels in the more exposed sites. On the walk past the Old Man of Hoy, Arctic Bearberry (*Arctostaphylos alpinus*) grows in profusion at an elevation of

---

* This chapter has been written by R. M. M. Crawford (see p. viii).

only 330 feet (100 metres), and in the lower corries Purple Flowering Sax-ifrage (*Saxifraga oppositifolia*) and Alpine Meadow Rue (*Thalictrum alpinum*) descend towards sea level although elsewhere they are normally confined to high altitudes. On Westray, Alpine Moss Campion (*Silene acaulis*) mingles with the Scottish Primrose (*Primula scotica*) at an altitude of only 270 feet (82 metres).

The existence in Orkney of both productive grasslands and low-lying mountain tundra vegetation is due to a single key environmental factor, a hyper-oceanic environment (see Chapter 1). One aspect of this is the lack of large temperature differences between summer and winter. Figure 3.1 shows the distribution of 'Conrad's index', a measure based on annual temperature range modified by latitude, ranging from 0 for maximum oceanicity to 100 for maximum continentality. It has values of nearly zero in Thorshavn (Faroe: 62° 2′N, 6° 4′W) to almost 100 for Verkoyansk in central Siberia (67° 33′E, 133° 24′E). In the British Isles the index ranges from 12.5 at

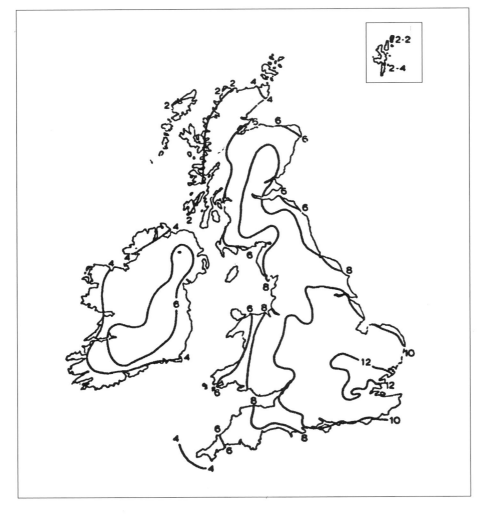

Figure 3.1
Conrad's continental-ity index averaged for 1941–70. (Redrawn from Chandler and Gregory, 1976.)

Figure 3.2
Ragwort in Orkney is nearly always the Marsh Ragwort, or its hybrid with the Common Ragwort. Only in dunes and links are the soils dry enough to provide a suitable habitat for the Common Ragwort.
Photo: Richard Welsby

Heathrow to less than 4 on the western and northern coastal fringes including the Northern Isles of Orkney and Shetland. Such conditions can be described as 'hyper-oceanic'.

A significant consequence of oceanicity for Orkney is freedom from both summer drought and winter frost. Grass can grow almost throughout the year. Due to latitude, oceanic cooling and high relative humidity, the evaporative power of the atmosphere is so low that grass growth is hardly ever reduced by water shortage, even at the height of summer. This results in green pastures filled throughout the summer with flowering buttercups to an extent that does not occur further south. Moreover, Orkney lies in a rain shadow area to the north of Scotland and this, coupled with the excellent drainage provided by the underlying Old Red Sandstone, protects the islands from the worst dangers of excessive precipitation. Waterlogging and bog growth are not as extensive as in either Shetland or the Western Isles. Nevertheless, the constant high level of humidity maintains a moisture level in pastures sufficient for the Common Ragwort (*Senecio jacobea*) to be excluded in favour of the Marsh Ragwort (*S. aquaticus*) or the hybrid between the two species (Figure 3.2). In sharp contrast to further south, the Common Ragwort is confined in Orkney to only the very best-drained sites in dunes and links.

An often overlooked feature of the North Atlantic oceanic environment is the high lapse rate (the rate at which air cools with increase in altitude). The prevailing winds in Orkney are from the south west, but their origin is Arctic. They blow south over Greenland before turning to the north east as they pass over the North Atlantic Drift. This warms only the lower regions of the total air mass and there is a sharp fall in temperature with altitude. Such ocean-warmed Arctic winds are described as polar maritime. Depending on the

season, the lapse rate can be as much as 0.8°C per 100 metres, markedly more than the 0.5–0.6°C in less oceanic regions. This vertical cooling, coupled with increased wind chill factor in the highly exposed Orkney hills, causes an abrupt falling-off in agricultural productivity with altitude, and accounts for the existence of tundra-type vegetation at relatively low altitudes. There is probably no other place in the world where the vegetation zones are so telescoped altitudinally. It is possible to stand in Hoy at just over 1,000 feet (305 metres) in Arctic-type tundra with dwarf vegetation sheltering in the lea of wind-formed terracing and look down on farm crops below.

Figure 3.3
View from Ward Hill on Hoy with tundra vegetation in the foreground and active agriculture only 1,000 feet (305 metres) below.
Photo: R. M. M. Crawford

The treeless landscape

Everyone who visits Orkney is struck by the almost total absence of trees. This has characterized the islands for many centuries. Plant remains taken from under the Standing Stones of Stenness suggest that Neolithic man lived in a landscape almost 5,000 years ago that was not very different from that of Orkney today (Dickson and Dickson, 1975), if we ignore recent agricultural improvement. However, both Orkney and Shetland were forested before this. Even on Unst, the most northerly of the Shetland Islands, there was a significant tree cover during the mid-post-glacial period 8000–5000 BP

(Bennett *et al.*, 1992). In Orkney a woodland vegetation began to expand around 8000 BP (Bunting, 1996b) and appears to have been particularly dominant in the exposed west Mainland with willow, birch, alder and hazel, and an under-storey of tall herb species similar to the communities that can still be seen today in Berriedale Wood (Chapman and Crawford, 1981). This mixed woodland vegetation persisted in both Shetland and Orkney until about 5000 BP, approximately the time when Neolithic settlers were becoming well established in the Northern Isles.

Whether or not the disappearance of the trees was due entirely to human disturbance is still an open question. There is evidence both in Orkney and Shetland that some reduction in forest cover was beginning to take place before the arrival of man. There is a natural succession, particularly where the summers are cool and humid, for tree communities to be replaced with wet moorlands and bogs. This process can be greatly accelerated by even a small amount of human disturbance, particularly in maritime environments, where merely opening up the tree canopy allows the ground to become wetter and hence initiates bog growth, thus rapidly creating conditions inimical to the regeneration of trees (Crawford, 1997b). The early farmers in these oceanic lands had neither the knowledge nor the technology to resist such a change. Clearance of peat deposits both in Shetland and Ireland has provided striking examples of old field systems where walls were built on mineral soils and then abandoned as the land was overwhelmed by the growth of peat (Davidson and Carter, 1997; Whittle *et al.*, 1986).

Trees can still be grown in Orkney if care is taken with their early establishment. For example, the grounds of Balfour Castle on Shapinsay support Horse Chestnuts (*Aesculus hippocastanum*) remarkable for the size of their leaves. Elsewhere on the islands, Ash (*Fraxinus excelsior*), Beech (*Fagus sylvatica*), Swedish Whitebeam (*Sorbus intermedia*), Wych Elm (*Ulmus glabra*) and Gean (*Prunus avium*) are found. Given sufficient time, a source of seed and adequate drainage, the natural process of succession could reconstitute the mid-postglacial tree cover, starting from willow and alder scrub and progressing to birch and hazel woodland. At present little natural regeneration is taking place. Even in North Hoy, where there has been little or no grazing for over half a century, trees are not spreading out of the gullies into the moorland because of the height of the ungrazed heather and the underlying deep layer of water-saturated mosses, including *Sphagnum*. Heather burning and the provision of native birch seed could achieve much for woodland restoration. This would encourage the re-establishment of the former native woodland, and with it increase the diversity of both birds and vegetation. Without such management, decades of climatic warming assisted by chance fires to remove the heather and dry out the ground vegetation will be needed before unaided natural succession restores something resembling the mutually self-sheltering tree communities that once covered the North

Atlantic archipelagos from Orkney to Iceland. There is even the danger with climatic warming that bog growth will increase and jeopardize an opportunity for woodland restoration.

Despite the modern aids that have allowed the 'improvement' of so much former moorland and bogs for agricultural production, these lands can easily succumb to the hyper-oceanic Orkney climate and revert to their former state. Rushes may invade improved pastures and, with their rolled-up leaves reducing transpiration, the soil becomes wetter. This allows mosses (in particular *Sphagnum spp.*) to invade and rapidly nullifies the effects of drainage and re-seeding. Once this type of wetland vegetation is established it is only a matter of time until peat formation is resumed. Such a successional change in the vegetation can be summed up as '*paludification*' (Latin – *paludosus*: marshy, swampy). Throughout the boreal regions of the Northern Hemisphere to which Orkney belongs, there is an ever-present tendency for paludification and this is likely to be accelerated by climatic warming. Although Orkney might benefit from a warmer climate to increase agricultural productivity generally, at present milder winters are tending to be accompanied by higher precipitation. Winter waterlogging will be a hazard in agriculture, and in conservation the danger of renewed blanket bog growth may hinder attempts to re-establish trees.

Figure 3.4
Berridale Wood, North Hoy, photographed in 1975. Despite the absence of grazing there has been little evidence of tree colonization out of the gully.
Photo: R. M. M. Crawford

Plant diversity

Figure 3.5 compares the number of native species of flowering plants, plus those introduced through human intervention, in Orkney, Shetland and Faroe. The numbers are only approximate because distinguishing true species from micro-species presents many problems due to the extent of variation that can take place between populations, as well as the ability of plants to vary their chromosome numbers (polyploidy).

Species richness declines with increase in both latitude and habitat size, so Orkney and its neighbouring archipelagos are poorer in plant species than the mainland of Britain. Orkney has less than 30 per cent of the flowering plants found on mainland Britain but nevertheless supports considerable ecological diversity as well as geographical interest.

Peripheral areas are of great biological interest in terms of species distribution, as the more variable conditions outside the core area induce fluctuating selection, which maintains high genetic diversity (Safriel *et al.*, 1994). Plants have a remarkable ability to produce specialized populations

Figure 3.5
Approximate number of native flowering plants and introduced species found in the North Atlantic archipelagos of Faroe, Shetland and Orkney as based on estimates from local floras and excluding micro-species.

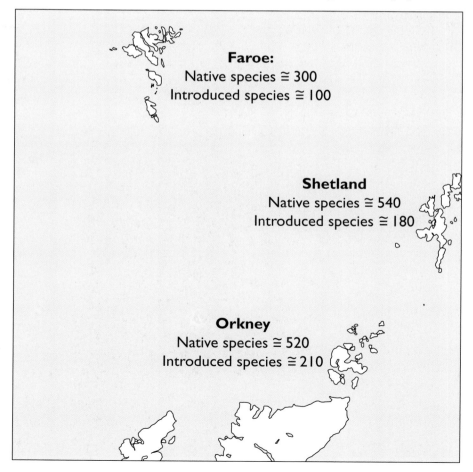

Faroe:
Native species ≅ 300
Introduced species ≅ 100

Shetland
Native species ≅ 540
Introduced species ≅ 180

Orkney
Native species ≅ 520
Introduced species ≅ 210

(or ecotypes) that are adapted to particular habitats. A particular feature of marginal habitats, like those around the coastline of Orkney, is the variety of ecotypes. What the flora may lack in species diversity is to some extent compensated for by the degree of variation that exists within species. Any walk along the cliff tops, particularly those exposed to salt spray and erosion, will reveal very extensive variation both in the form and size of many of the common species. Sea Plantain (*Plantago maritima*), Buck's-horn Plantain (*P. coronopus*) and Sea Thrift (*Armeria maritima*) all show enormous variations in size. The plantain populations vary greatly in their degree of hairiness (Figure 3.6). Not all of this variation is inherited. When Sea Plantains are transferred from cliff tops to glasshouses even the most dwarfed plants can grow considerably larger and produce leaves that are much less hairy than those in their original exposed site.

Orkney is a particularly good location for seeing a spectacular display of Eyebrights (*Euphrasia spp.*), which are semi-parasitic annuals that draw water and nutrients from a range of other plants that live in short grass swards. In Orkney, Eyebrights flourish particularly well in the links and dune heaths near the shore. The species aggregate (*Euphrasia officinalis* agg.) appears to be particularly adapted to soils that are mildly acidic to neutral in pH and are protected from excessive exposure to wind and salt spray. There are twenty sub-species of Eyebrights in the British Isles and eleven of them, together with their fertile hybrids, occur in Orkney (Bullard, 1995). The proliferation of the Eyebrights illustrates the phenomenon of the evolution of peripheral ecotypes, since the majority occur in the Hebrides and Northern

Figure 3.6
Hairy dwarf form of Sea Plantain (*Plantago maritima*) growing near the cliff edge at Yesnaby.
Photo: R. M. M. Crawford

Isles. *Euphrasia micrantha* is common in wet heaths, flushes and sometimes salt marshes, while *E. heslop-harrisonii* is a species of well-drained sea banks with short turf (Bullard, 1995). In Orkney the Arctic Eyebright (*E. arctica* ssp. *borealis*) becomes the dominant flowering population towards the end of the growing season. This capacity to have forms differing in their precise habitat requirements not only allows this group of inter-fertile species to extend their range, but also means that they can adjust to climatic and environmental change with great rapidity. The hybrids represent a survival strategy which ensures that even if one parent becomes locally extinct, the re-establishment of the suppressed parent is possible by back-crossing when environmental conditions return to normal. This phenomenon has been noted for a number of Arctic genera where it allows survival, even when there are marked changes in length of growing season (Crawford, 1997a).

The composition of the plant communities in Orkney also varies enormously. There are few areas anywhere in the world where examples can be found of both alpine and Arctic plants growing alongside plants of more temperate habitats. The Oyster Plant (Figure 3.11, *Mertensia maritima*), which is a typical plant of Arctic coasts, has its most thriving British populations on Orkney shores and can be seen taking advantage of the new sand accretions on the east side of the fourth Churchill Barrier in the South Isles. One of Britain's few endemic species, the Scottish Primrose (*Primula scotica*), grows mainly at the interface between maritime heath and cliff top salt-tolerant thrift (*Armeria maritima*) – dominated communities. This restricted distribution is particularly surprising given that the whole of Orkney is so maritime that plants normally associated with coastal habitats such as Sea Arrow Grass (*Triglochin maritimum*) can be found growing on inland bogs.

Natural plant communities

As so much of Orkney is near the sea, it is logical to begin a description of the natural vegetation communities from the shore. Coastal plants can all be classified as pioneers; they were among the first colonizers after the Pleistocene glaciation. When the ice retreated these coastal plant communities would have begun to spread uphill. With time, other species have colonized the islands but they are mainly grasses, shrubs and eventually trees occupying the middle ground between the shore and the mountain tops. Many species from the original post-Pleistocene vegetation survive on the tops of mountains as well as by the sea; more complex communities are inhibited in both these extreme habitats by the rigours of the environment. Notable examples of this disjunct species distribution include Thrift (*Armeria maritima*) and Sea Plantain (*Plantago maritima*). Further information on rare plants that occur near the sea and their specialized habitats together with location maps can be found in the Joint Nature Conservation Committee's Orkney volume in the series on the *Coasts and Seas of The United Kingdom* (Barne *et al.*, 1997).

The following account examines the range of communities that survive in Orkney and highlights both the advantages and disadvantages of the maritime environment on the diversity of plant life.

Dunes and links

One of the great pleasures in exploring Orkney is to discover the variety of the wildlife on its many beaches and adjacent dunes and links. Sandy beaches can be found on most of the islands with the most spectacular sand spits on Sanday (Figure 3.8). Most of the sand that forms dunes in Orkney is rich in shell fragments and there is no significant increase in alkalinity on moving inland; when the sea salts have been removed by rainwater the shell fragments maintain a high pH. The plant communities that develop on these shell sand dunes and their hinterland support a diverse herbaceous flora and usually erode to form flat, herb-rich plains, sometimes referred to as *machair* (Scots Gaelic – a low-lying plain) in sharp contrast to the acid dune heaths that are formed inland from dunes which lack a shell component. In Orkney, these areas of machair and dunes are more usually termed *links* (from Scots – linch/linchet, an unploughed strip between fields or serving as a boundary).

The sandy beaches of Orkney differ from most of those around the Scottish mainland through having been subject to rising sea levels for some considerable time (Chapter 2). Orkney has no true raised beaches (p. 43); if such beaches ever did form they are now below sea level. The rate at which the sea level has been rising is not known with any precision, although there appears to be considerable variation between localities (Smith *et al.*,

Figure 3.7
Bay of Bombasty, Stronsay
Photo: Richard Welsby

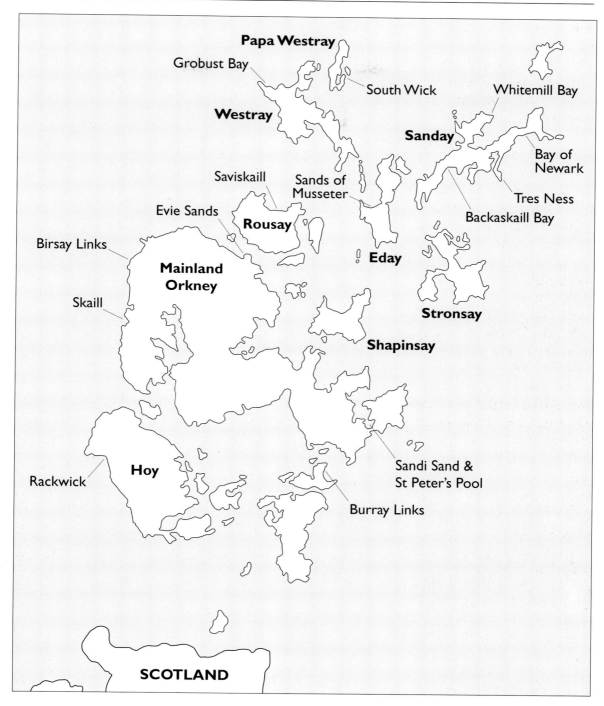

Figure 3.8
Location of coastal sites in Orkney with sandy beaches forming either dunes or links.

1996). The majority of the dunes and their associated links show signs of having had a long history of erosion. Tres Ness Point in Sanday is a spectacular example of a once prosperous farm on links, which is now a mere isolated spit of sand and in imminent danger of disappearing altogether (Figure 3.9). Similarly, the links at Birsay and at Grobust in Westray have

been retreating steadily for many years, a process greatly accelerated by sand extraction and motor cycle scrambles (see Figure 3.25). The overwhelming of Neolithic coastal settlements by sand as at Skara Brae (4500 BP) may have been facilitated by the intensity of human coastal disturbance (Ritchie, 1979).

Three grass species are mainly responsible for the anchoring of mobile sand to form the Orkney dunes. Two of these species are widespread in the British Isles: Sand Couch Grass (*Elytrigia juncea*) and Marram Grass (*Ammophila arenaria*). The former is particularly sensitive to rapid vertical accretion, and experimental studies have shown that both newly germinated seedlings and fragments of rhizome cannot tolerate sand burial deeper than 127 mm. Marram grass is the main species in building up height in dunes and can withstand and thrive with vertical sand accretion rates of up to one metre per annum. However, as the sand level stabilizes, the plant loses vigour just when it might reasonably be assumed to be in a position to flourish on the more sheltered leeward slopes.

The third key dune grass species which can aid dune expansion in Orkney is Sea Lyme Grass (*Leymus arenarius*). This is a species of northern distribution on coasts from the Arctic southwards to Britain and north-west Spain. In Orkney it occurs at a number of locations, including Whitemill Bay and Tres Ness in Sanday, Bay of Mocklett and South Wick in Papay Westray, and at Aikerness in Evie. It extends its rhizomes laterally with great vigour, withstands drenching with salt spray, and is highly successful in consolidating

Figure 3.9
Tres Ness Point in Sanday: once the site of a thriving cereal-producing farm, now in danger of disappearing due to coastal erosion.
Photo: R. M. M. Crawford

coastal accretion. However, the species appears to be a specialist for areas with modest increases in sand depth and loses vigour rapidly as dunes increase in height.

In mid- to late summer the drift line in front of the dunes can develop a luxuriant community of annual species, particularly when seaweed and other flotsam and jetsam accumulate and provide shelter from desiccation plus nutrients for young seedlings. One of the most spectacular species in this habitat is Sea Rocket (*Cakile maritima* – Figure 3.10). In the same habitat other annual plants such as the Spear-leaved Orache (*Atriplex prostrata*) and Sea Sandwort (*Honkenya peploides*) are usually found. A notable biennial to perennial species with striking white flowers which manages to survive successfully in the driftline community is the Sea May Weed (*Tripleurospermum maritimum*).

One particularly northern species which can be seen in profusion in parts of Orkney is the Oyster Plant (*Mertensia maritima*) so called as its leaves are said to taste of oysters (Figure 3.11). This species can be found on beach strand lines on the high Arctic shores of Spitzbergen and finds its southern limit on the coasts of Scotland. In common with many high Arctic species, this plant has a high respiration rate which fuels rapid growth in the short growing seasons of high-latitude habitats. In the long days of the far north this high respiration rate can be sustained due to the fact that the plants have long periods of high metabolic activity. Further south, the species is unable to fix enough carbon during daylight hours to compensate for high respiration rates during the hours of darkness (Crawford and Palin, 1981). It is therefore not competition, but maladaption of an Arctic physiology to

Figure 3.10
A shore colony of Sea Rocket (*Cakile maritima*) near Tres Ness, Sanday.
Photo: R. M. M. Crawford

warmer southern climates with short days that limits the southern distribution of the Oyster Plant. Another coastal species that is restricted in the same way is Scot's Lovage (*Ligusticum scoticum*, Figure 3.12).

On the landward side of the dunes there is usually some development of links. Frequently this land has been modified in some way, either for agriculture or for recreation. Links are favoured areas for golf courses. Fortunately, in the latter case the rough still preserves some of the characteristic native flora including both the Primrose (*Primula vulgaris*) and the Cowslip (*Primula veris*). The coastal occurrence of these species is particularly common in both Orkney and Shetland and they are found in the sand dunes at Gurness and in the Bu of Burray. The hybrid between these two species, the False Oxlip, is rare in Orkney. In mainland Britain, Primroses and Cowslips are characteristic of woodland clearings, where they are protected from being overgrown by more competitive herbaceous species. However, in the treeless islands of the north, it is the skeletal soils and exposure factor near the sea that protect them from more vigorous competitors. The sensitivity of primulas to habitat is discussed below in relation to the Scottish Primrose (*P. scotica*).

Buttercups are a distinctive feature of the Orkney links and their diversity is greater than appears at first sight. The Common Buttercup (*Ranunculus acris*) is dominant in the hollows and lower areas of the links, while on the drier ridges it is replaced by the Bulbous Buttercup (*R. bulbosus*). This species derives its name from its corm (a swollen – and buried – stem base). At a distance the two species of buttercup look very similar. They can, however, be easily distinguished by their sepals, which are reflexed in the

Figure 3.11
The Oyster Plant (*Mertensia maritima*) growing on the shore near the 4th Churchill Barrier.
Photo: R. M. M. Crawford

Figure 3.12
Scot's Lovage (*Ligusticum scoticum*), a species of predominantly Arctic and sub-Arctic distribution growing on the shingle bank at Marwick Bay.
Photo: R. M. M. Crawford

Bulbous Buttercup. Orkney is the northern limit of the Bulbous Buttercup species; it does not occur in Shetland. The grass cover in the links is predominantly Red Fescue (*Festuca rubra*) which grows in close association with the Sand Sedge (*Carex arenaria*) and the Glaucous Sedge (*C. flacca*). Colour is added by the yellow flowers of Lady's Bedstraw (*Galium verum*) and Bird's Foot Trefoil (*Lotus corniculatus*). From midsummer onwards, pastures are dotted with the minute white flowers of the Limestone Bedstraw (*Galium sterneri*) and the semi-parasitic annual Eyebrights (*Euphrasia spp.*). Links are also the preferred habitat of the Field Gentian (*Gentianella campestris*) as well as the related Felwort or Autumn Gentian (which in Orkney is *G. amarella* ssp. *druceana*).

Winter flooding can cause the land behind the dunes to be waterlogged for several months, with wet hollows usually referred to as dune slacks (Norwegian *slakke* – a damp hollow). This seasonal flooding creates totally different over-wintering and summer growing conditions from those in the dunes and results in a markedly different flora. Species that can survive prolonged winter flooding gain by not having to compete with non-flood-tolerant species and thus get easier access to the water table in summer. The water of the dune slacks is nearly always fresh as the dunes themselves block drainage from the land. Occasional incursions of salt water after extreme high tides or

storms may lead to salt-loving plants colonizing the slacks. The Sea Milkwort (*Glaux maritima*) is a very good indicator of occasional salt-water floods (Figure 3.13). Dune slacks are also a habitat for yet another buttercup species, the Lesser Spearwort (*Ranunculus flammula*), often accompanied by Common Sedge (*Carex nigra*) and Silverweed (*Potentilla anserina*), and for the Frog and Early Marsh Orchids (*Coeloglossum viride* and *Dactylorhiza incarnata*).

Figure 3.13
Sea Milkwort (*Glaux maritima*), a salt-loving plant which can be found at Orkney either in saltmarshes or in the sea spray zone at the top of coastal cliffs, *Photo: R. M. M. Crawford*

Cliffs

Orkney's cliffs are botanically as well as scenically exciting (Figure 3.14). However, it is the inaccessibility of cliffs to grazing animals rather than their height that makes the cliffs probably the least disturbed of all habitats by human activity. Cliff faces which are almost vertical or exposed to extreme conditions lack any significant vegetation cover, but in early summer the flowers on the tops and faces of Orkney's coastal cliffs are spectacular. There is a variety of communities depending on the degree of nutrient enrichment by sea spray, freedom from desiccation on north-facing sites, access to water through seepage, and variation in rock types. This variation in vegetation is maintained due to constant physical disturbance which prevents certain species becoming dominant and thus allows a variety of species to coexist (Cooper, 1997). In each type, vegetation builds up with time and then becomes unstable and erodes, thus setting up a successional cycle and preserving biodiversity.

Working upward from the base of the cliffs, a succession of plant communities can often be observed. Lichens, in particular the bright orange *Xanthoria parietina*, are found immediately above the high-water mark. Above this, crevices and ledges provide a habitat for Sea Plantain (*Plantago maritima*), Buck's-horn Plantain (*Plantago coronopus*), Rose-root (*Sedum rosea*) and Sea Aster (*Aster tripolium*). Cliff faces are the preferred habit of species that can tolerate sea spray and summer drought but not inundation or competition. Such species include Thrift (*Armeria maritima*), Sea Campion (*Silene uniflora*), and Scots Lovage (*Ligusticum scoticum*). All these are common in most parts of Orkney, either in rock crevices on the cliffs or in the boulder-strewn debris below. Towards the upper areas of cliffs and extending onto the cliff top, particularly where there is no grazing (as on sea stacks), there may be a tall-herb community with Wild Angelica (*Angelica sylvestris*), Red Campion (*Silene dioica*), the Common Primrose (*Primula vulgaris*), Foxglove (*Digitalis purpurea*) and Sorrel (*Rumex acetosa*). Later in the summer Grass of Parnassus (*Parnassia palustris*) appears. In more sheltered gullies and away from sea spray, as high on the Hoy cliffs, there are a number of species more typical of woodlands with large stands of the Greater Woodrush (*Luzula sylvatica*), and Honeysuckle (*Lonicera periclymenum*). Sometimes, as in The Pinnacles and cliffs around Waukmill Bay, woody species such as Rowan (*Sorbus aucuparia*) and even aspen (*Populus tremula*) are found (Bullard, 1995). On drier cliffs like the sandstone block cliffs facing Scapa Flow, a heath-type vegetation can be found with Heather (*Calluna vulgaris*), Bell Heather (*Erica cinerea*), Crowberry (*Empetrum nigrum*), Wood Sage (*Teucrium scorodonia*) and Golden Rod (*Solidago virgaurea*).

Dense bird colonies affect the cliff vegetation in parts. Too much disturbance and excess guano can eliminate flowering plants entirely. However, the more

Figure 3.14
Cliffs of North Hoy viewed from the south. Despite the large extent of sheer vertical rock face on these enormous Old Red Sandstone exposures, the green areas indicate the ability for survival of a number of plant communities.
Photo: R. M. M. Crawford

normal consequence of large nesting colonies of auks or fulmars is to favour species which respond to large inputs of nitrogen. Most striking of these is Scurvygrass (*Cochlearia officinalis*). In cliff-top areas where colonies of Greater Black-backed Gulls congregate, the habitat is marked by luxuriant growth of grasses such as Yorkshire Fog (*Holcus lanatus*) along with Sorrel (*Rumex acetosa*) and other docks (*R. obtusifolius, R. crispus*), and often Stinging Nettle (*Urtica dioica*). Puffin colonies are often associated with colonies of Mayweed (*Triplospermum maritimum*) and Orache (*Atriplex spp.*).

Salt marshes

Rising sea levels lead to dune erosion but favour salt-marsh development. The balance between accretion and erosion in salt mashes is delicate, and exposure to waves and the effect of tidal flow on sediment deposition are both critical. On rapidly rising coastlines, there is little opportunity for salt-marsh development. Falling coastlines, or rising sea levels, can allow marsh development, so long as the rate of change is not excessive and does not exceed the capacity of the vegetation to consolidate silt deposition and raise the level of the salt marsh. The sediments anchored in salt marshes vary from clay-rich muds to sandy gravels. Orkney has no large river mouths providing suitable sources of mud, so Orkney salt marshes are made up of small units. These are more stable than sand dunes. Typical sites for salt-marsh development are in bays that lie behind sandy spits or 'ayres' (p. 46).

In the British Isles the salt-marsh species of southern-eastern regions differ markedly from those of the north west, with the traditional dividing line lying from the Solway to just south of the Firth of Forth (Figure 3.15). Orkney lies in the Western Scottish region where the salt marshes are characterized by relatively few salt-requiring species but have instead rich fen-like communities in the upper regions of the marsh. High rainfall and constant seepage of fresh water from terrestrial communities provide conditions for a wide range of species, with many freshwater plants mixed with typical salt-loving forms.

Salt-marsh vegetation zonation

Species composition across salt marshes is influenced mainly by variations in salinity and inundation. They are flooded to varying degrees up to twice a day, depending on the season and the tidal cycle. Nearest to the sea, the salinity is rarely greater than that of sea water (3.4 per cent), while in salt marshes bordered by freshwater streams, the salt content is lower. Higher up, and particularly as the growing season progresses, salt-stress hazard increases as evaporation makes the rooting region of the soil progressively more saline. Consequently, there are differences in salt tolerance, not just between species, but between populations within species. In Red Fescue (*Festuca rubra*) and common salt-marsh grass (*Puccinellia maritima*), the

Figure 3.15
Geographic division of
the salt marshes of the
British Isles. (Redrawn
from Adam, 1990).

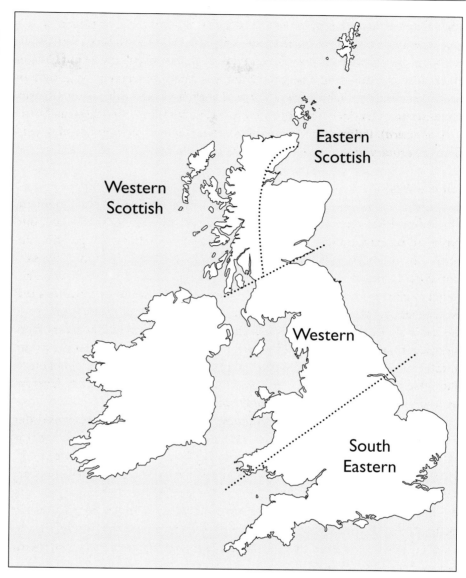

up-marsh populations are often more salt tolerant than those that grow
lower down the marsh. In Orkney this effect is fairly small due to the continual seepage of fresh water from the land.

Salt marshes provide an excellent opportunity to see different strategies
adopted by plants to limit their exposure to salt. In succulent species such as
the Sea Sandwort (*Honkenya peploides*) and the Sea Milkwort (*Glaux
maritima* – Figure 3.13) the leaves increase in succulence as the growing
season progresses; this has the effect of diluting the concentration of salt to
which the tissues are exposed. In Thrift (*Armeria maritima*) and Orache
(*Atriplex spp.*) salt glands, which actively secrete salt, form a mealy texture
on the surface of the leaf.

The lower salt marsh

Open mudflats support a large diatom flora which binds the sediment parti-cles together with a copious mucous excretion. The only flowering plants to inhabit these open flats in Orkney are the Eelgrasses (*Zostera spp*). These can be readily observed on the mudflats of St Peter's Pool in the East Mainland. They are much grazed by wildfowl.

Common Glasswort or Marsh Samphire (*Salicornia europaea*) along with Annual Sea-Blite (*Sueda maritima*) are early colonizers of bare mudflats and this is a community likely to expand if sea levels rise. The most conspicuous species in the lower regions of the marsh is Sea Aster (*Aster tripolium*) which in Orkney, in common with a number of other salt-loving plants such as Thrift and Sea Milkwort (Figure 3.13), can also be found in the salt-drenched vegetation that grows on cliff tops.

The upper salt marsh

Thrift (*Armeria maritima*) is more common on rocky outcrops near the sea, but also occurs as a mid-marsh species. Although tolerant of salt, the species as a whole has a wide distribution in environmentally-stressed habitats, from mountain tops to cliffs and salt marshes. It is highly variable and the plants in salt marshes have broader leaves than those found on mainland Scottish mountains and in the Hebrides. In the upper salt marsh, characteristic species are Salt Marsh Rush (*Juncus gerardii*), Scurvy Grass (*Cochlearia officinalis*) and Sea Arrow Grass (*Triglochin maritimum*). Other widespread species are Creeping Bent Grass (*Agrostis stolonifera*), Marsh Foxtail (*Alopecurus geniculatus*) and Salt Marsh Grass (*Puccinellia maritima*).

Freshwater marshes and bogs

Centuries of intensive agriculture have resulted in much of the former wetlands of Orkney being drained, and peat removed from many of the lowland bogs. However, there are still areas where extensive areas of bog and marsh remain (Figure 3.16). Striking examples of these ancient wetlands are to be seen in the West Mainland at Loch of Banks near Twatt and at the Loons (Figure 3.17) in Marwick (loons – Old Norse *lon*: a flat meadow strip alongside water). Marshes are defined as wetlands on mineral soils where the water table does not rise above the surface during the summer. If flooded above the surface in summer they would be termed swamps. Bogs consist of organic soils where peat has accumulated usually over the surface of an original mire. Due to a long history of peat cutting, all the lowland bogs (i.e. *raised bogs*, as their surface rises up above the surrounding landscape) have been extensively cut over for peat.

Because of this, Orkney wetland basins are characteristically mosaics of marsh and bog. The Loons in Marwick are possibly the best example of an ancient bog and mire complex (Figure 3.17). Where the peat has not been

Figure 3.16
Location in Orkney of
some typical mires and
bogs.

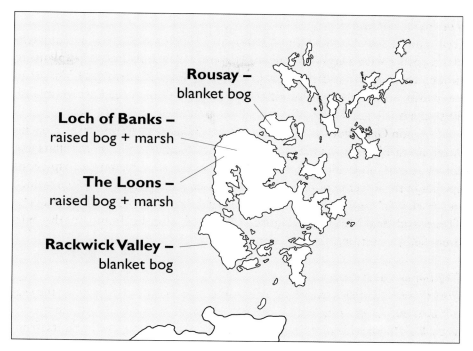

Rousay –
blanket bog

Loch of Banks –
raised bog + marsh

The Loons –
raised bog + marsh

Rackwick Valley –
blanket bog

disturbed, the accumulated sediments provide a continuous pollen record that can be traced back over 12,000 years (Moar, 1969). Due to the calcareous nature of much of the underlying rock, the water that wells up in these lowland basin marshes is rich in minerals and can have pH values often greater than 7.5, particularly in old peat cuttings. In contrast, adjacent uncut peat remnants have a pH range lying between 4.2 and 5.5. Consequently, such areas have a rich flora due to the juxtaposition of plants that favour mineral-rich, non-acid soils with those that can survive on nutrient-poor acid peat. Comparatively little peat cutting has taken place since the Second World War and consequently these lowland marsh and bog areas have become a refuge for both plants and birds.

The Loons are now an RSPB reserve and access is restricted during the nesting season. On the peat-bog areas, early summer provides colourful displays of the Northern Marsh Orchid (*Dactylorhiza purpurella*) and the Early Marsh Orchid (*D. incarnata*). The marsh areas also have large colonies of Bogbean (*Menyanthes trifoliata*) and extensive Reed beds (*Phragmites australis*). The Black Bog Rush *(Schoenus nigricans)* is common and its pale grey-green foliage is a useful indicator of calcareous flushes where it produces tussocks that provide a habitat for such characteristic Orkney species such as the Grass of Parnassus (which is not a grass but a saxifrage, *Parnassia palustris*) and the Butterwort (*Pinguicula vulgaris*). The oceanicity of the Orkney environment is also evident even in the inland marshes, as plants such as Sea Arrow Grass (not a grass but a member of the Juncaginaceae, *Triglochin maritimum* – Figure 3.18) and Sea Plantain (*Plantago*

maritima) grow and flower successfully even although they are some miles from the sea.

Where high atmospheric humidity results in constant saturation of the soil, blanket bog develops. This can cover any terrain irrespective of its topography and does not need to begin in a marsh which is a necessary beginning for the formation of raised bogs. Blanket bog appears only to have become widespread after the arrival of man and the extensive deforestation of Orkney that took place about 5,000 years ago (p. 52). In recent years much of this blanket bog has been removed by hill reclamation. Nevertheless, a considerable area remains in North Hoy, particularly on the slopes of the hills south of Rackwick, as well as in Rousay and some parts of the West Mainland. The vegetation of these bogs is very similar to that of heather moors and raised bogs but is distinguished by the greater frequency of species such as Moor Mat Grass (*Nardus stricta*), Heath Rush (*Juncus squarrosus*) and numerous sedges. In some places, Cloudberry (*Rubus chamaemorus*) and the Lesser Twayblade (*Listera cordata*) occur. On flatter ground where open pools of water develop, more flood-tolerant species such as Bog Asphodel (*Narthecium ossifragum*) and Creeping Cotton Grass (*Eriophorum angustifolium*) provide colour, mixing yellow flowers of the former with the white cotton heads of the latter.

Figure 3.17
View of the Loons, Marwick, from Ravie Hill. This ancient basin wetland is a rich mosaic of lake, marsh and bog vegetation.
Photo: R. M. M. Crawford

Heathlands

From the Neolithic Age until the end of the Second World War heathlands dominated the vegetation of Orkney. Their extent has traditionally been

Figure 3.18
Sea Arrow Grass
(*Triglochin maritimum*)
growing near the cliffs
at Yesnaby.
Photo: R. M. M. Crawford

attributed to human disturbance which began around 5000 BP (Renfrew, 1979). Recent research, however, suggests that in exposed western regions of the archipelago some peat development can be dated to as early as 7000 BP, much earlier than any record of substantial human impact (Bunting, 1996a). In Caithness some peat development, possibly caused by local Mesolithic use of fire, has been dated to as early as 8500 BP (Peglar, 1979). The effect in Orkney appears to have begun with the replacement of tall-herb communities by heathland without any substantial decline in tree cover. This suggests it was due to natural soil change, perhaps coupled with alterations in climate.

In oceanic climates, exposure, together with increased nutrient leaching as a result of salt spray, can accelerate podsolization. Nutrient-deficient soils eventually become underlain by an iron pan which impedes drainage and results in peat formation. This produces a natural succession from forest to heath and bog without human intervention, especially in areas where there is a high level of leaching. As tree cover is reduced, there is less interception of precipitation by the forest canopy and transpiration activity is reduced. This initiates a positive feed-back process accelerating leaching and hindering the regeneration of trees. The pollen record in Orkney shows a further decline in the presence of trees starting about 5400 BP, with local variation in different parts of the islands.

Maritime heath

A particular aspect of heathland development in Orkney is the formation of maritime heath in western areas exposed to gales and frequent inundation

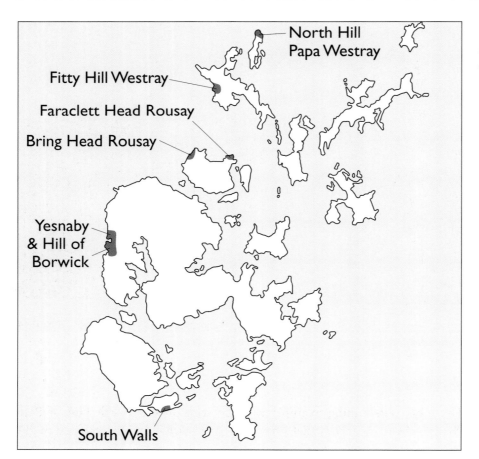

Figure 3.19
Distribution of maritime heath in the Orkneys.

North Hill
Papa Westray

Fitty Hill Westray

Faraclett Head Rousay

Bring Head Rousay

Yesnaby & Hill of Borwick

South Walls

Figure 3.20
Maritime heath on North Hill, Papa Westray, after a period of wet and stormy weather.
Photo: R. M. M. Crawford

Figure 3.21
Maritime heath,
inundated by sea spray.
Photo: Richard Welsby

with salt spray. Maritime heath is not unique to Orkney and can be found on western and northern coasts in other parts of the British Isles, such as on the Old Red Sandstone exposure at Tarbat Ness in Easter Ross. Orkney with its maritime climate and dominant Old Red Sandstones provides suitable habitats for some of the largest remaining areas of maritime heath in Britain. The most outstanding example is to be seen on the North Hill of Papa Westray. Here, as at the other sites, maritime heath is mainly confined to thin soils overlying Old Red Sandstone flagstone (Figure 3.19).

Botanically, maritime heath consists of a mosaic of cliff-top and heath species. Among the former are Sea Plantain (*Plantago maritima*) which can be found in various forms, from dwarf hairy plants only an inch or so (2–3 cms) in diameter to much larger non-hairy forms. The dwarf-hairy plants (ecotypes) predominate in the sites most exposed to salt spray. In early summer these areas often have a striking display of flowering of the Spring Squill (*Scilla verna*). The most characteristic feature is the mixture of heath species, Heather (*Calluna vulgaris*), Bell Heather (*Erica cinerea*) and Crowberry (*Empetrum nigrum*) together with a number of sedges (*Carex flacca, C. panacea*). The heather plants are usually dwarf prostrate forms as opposed to the bushier forms found in inland heaths. Such heathlands in Orkney are sometimes termed *maritime sedge heaths* because of the large sedge component in their flora (Figure 3.20). The nearer to the cliff edge, the greater is the component of salt-loving plants, and eventually the sward is dominated by Sea Thrift, Sea Plantain and Sea Arrow Grass. Another characteristic species is Creeping Willow (*Salix repens*), a prostrate form of a group more normally thought of as bushes or trees. Other common species associated with maritime heaths include the Eyebrights (*Euphrasia spp.*) together with Thyme (*Thymus polytrichus*), Tormentil (*Potentilla erecta*) and Mountain Everlasting (*Antennaria dioica*).

Primula scotica

The transition zone between maritime heath and the thrift-dominated sward of the cliff tops is the major habitat for the coastal occurrence of the Scottish Primrose (*Primula scotica*) in Orkney. The Scottish Primrose deserves extra attention in this discussion of Orkney plants as it one of the very few species endemic to the British Isles. It occurs in Orkney, Caithness and Sutherland and nowhere else in the world (Figure 3.22). In Orkney the Scottish Primrose is now confined to fewer than fourteen coastal and one hill site. At the beginning of this century it was recorded from over 30 sites including both hillside and coastal locations. Grazing improvement has now destroyed all inland hill sites, with the exception of Fitty Hill in Westray, and is steadily encroaching on the remaining coastal areas. Electric fences move ever nearer to cliff edges, and livestock grazing on improved pastures nearby deposit nutrient-enriched dung onto the nutrient-poor habitats occupied by the Scottish Primrose, destroying them for ever.

In Orkney, *Primula scotica* is mostly confined to the seaward side of maritime heath habitats, although there is still a site on Papa Westray where it grows on shell-sand links. Where the Scottish Primrose came from, and why it is confined to so few hyperoceanic sites in Orkney and northern Scotland, is not clear. It is morphologically similar to the Scandinavian *P. scandinavica* but has a smaller rosette and a shorter flowering stalk, rarely exceeding 60 mm. It is, however, quite distinct genetically, being a hexaploid

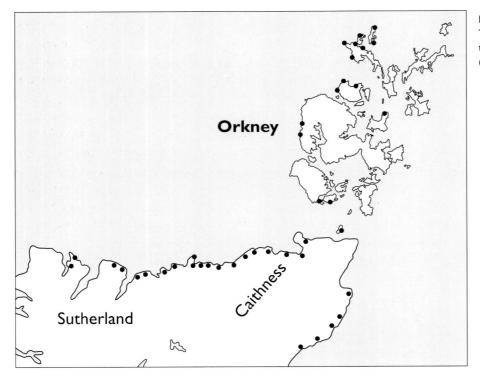

Figure 3.22
Total distribution of the Scottish Primrose (*Primula scotica*).

Figure 3.23
The Scottish Primrose
(*Primula scotica*).
Photo: R. M. M. Crawford

(2n = 54) whereas *P. scandinavica* is an octoploid (2n = 72). The latter species also has a much more extensive range from 60°N to 70°N. It is also morphologically and genetically distinct from the English Bird's Eye Primrose (*P. farinosa*) which is a diploid (2n = 18).

Primula scotica has two main flowering periods. The most spectacular display and the one that contributes most seed is in late May and early June. There is a second flowering of some individuals in August. Individual plants can either produce long or short flowering stalks (Figure 3.23) but in the August flowering most plants flower with short stalks. Summer storms and gales can have a disastrous effect as they often result in the destruction or loss of most of the seed production.

Between 1966 and 1982 a prolonged observation of flowering, seedling recruitment and mortality in the Scottish Primrose was carried out at marked sites at Yesnaby by the Orkney Field Club (Bullard *et al.*, 1987). It had been thought for many years that the Scottish Primrose was short lived. However, this study showed conclusively that many plants can live for twenty years or more. It was also found that many plants remained vegetative for years at a time; some individuals were observed to have died after eight years of vegetative growth without succeeding in flowering even once. The long-term study also showed that as well as being restricted to a very narrow ecological site (the transition zone between cliff-top salt vegetation swards and maritime heath), *P. scotica* also has a very narrow climatic window for reproduction. During the period from 1966 to 1982, only in four years between 1970 and 1973 with mild winters was there an increase in the Yesnaby population. If warmer winters result from global climatic warming, it is to be hoped that this very rare species, which is clearly highly vulnerable both in terms of habitat specialization and climatic requirements, will be encouraged.

The Scottish Primrose may be further 'at risk' from its low genetic diversity. A study of five sites in Orkney and nine from the Scottish Mainland revealed variation between individuals at only one of fifteen enzyme-encoding genes examined, and a survey of DNA sequence variation found no genetic diversity at all, either within or between four populations (Glover and Abbott, 1995). Individual plants exhibited a 'fixed' level of heterozygosity, indicating that *P. scotica* is of allopolyploid origin. Thus, despite the high level of heterozygosity per individual and the biochemical diversity that this can provide, there is an almost complete lack of genetic diversity both within and between populations. Notwithstanding, another study which examined the growth and form of plants raised from seed collected from different populations revealed considerable variation (Ennos *et al.*, 1997). This study of character responses looked at aspects of plant variability that are multi-genically controlled; they do not appear to be so severely limited as enzymatic variation that is under the control of individual genes. Genetic variability within Scottish Primrose populations has important implications for its conservation, and further research is needed to know why the species is so limited in its present distribution and what aspects of variation may be involved in its long-term survival.

Tundra-type vegetation

The summits of the North Hoy hills – Ward Hill at 1,565 feet (477 metres) and the Cuilags at 1,420 feet (433 metres) – are the highest points in Orkney and support a vegetation which is often referred to as *tundra*. Strictly speaking, this term describes areas where there is a perma-frost zone in the underlying soil, and the situation in Orkney is more accurately called *fell-field*. Nevertheless, the exposed conditions of these hills together with cool oceanic summers certainly produces a tundra-like vegetation. In it the strong winds produce step-like turf-banked terraces interspersed with sections of

Figure 3.24
Stiff Sedge (*Carex bigelowii*) growing at 1,410 feet (430 metres).
Photo: R. M. M. Crawford

bare ground. The form of these terraces varies with the degree of exposure, and sometimes they become wind-*stripes* when they take on a ripple-like cross-section. In certain places islands of vegetation termed *hill dunes* stand out above the bare ground and migrate with the direction of the wind, showing erosion on the exposed site and colonization on the sheltered face. The vegetation in these areas is dominated by wind-pruned dwarf Heather (*Calluna vulgaris*), not a typical Arctic or tundra species. It forms a low-growing vegetation mat with Arctic Rhododendron (*Loiseleuria procumbens*) and Crowberry (*Empetrum nigrum*). Associated with these terraces and hill dunes is a hardy combination of alpine and Arctic species. Particularly striking in autumn is the Arctic or Black Bearberry (*Arctostaphylos alpinus*) with its blood-red leaves, and in places the Common Bearberry (*Arctostaphylos uva-ursi*). Also growing in the shelter of terraces is the high alpine Stiff Sedge *Carex bigelowii* (Figure 3.24). Sheltering close to the ground, and only emerging to show a few pairs of terminal leaves and catkins, is the Least Willow (*Salix herbacea*). Dwarf Prostrate Juniper (*Juniperus communis* ssp. *nana*) also occurs. Oceanicity at this altitude is not ameliorated by any extensive snow cover. Drought and wind resistance are the adaptations most needed for plant survival on these exposed hill tops; only the most hardy and drought-resistant species can survive.

Conservation

Orkney superficially gives the impression of an area where intense pastoral farming is the dominant feature of the landscape. Such a judgement under-estimates the variety of natural plant communities that survive in Orkney and which deserve active conservation. Much of the biodiversity of these islands comes from the influence of oceanic conditions. Some of these effects can be considered as favourable in providing freedom from drought, frost and extending the growing season. Unfortunately both plants and soils are adversely affected by drenching with salt and dangers of flooding, particularly during long, mild winters. Climatic change tendencies in Scotland suggest that oceanic regions are likely to become even more oceanic as winters become warmer, with increased rainfall and high westerly winds. The native plant populations of Orkney, whether they live by the shore, or in bogs, or on the mountains and moorlands, have many adaptations that allow them to withstand these conditions. The diversity of plants that survive today is all the more remarkable when it is remembered that Orkney has been heavily farmed for over 5,000 years. The current trend in Orkney away from arable farming to greater use of pasturage could be considered as potentially beneficial to the preservation of natural plant communities. However, increasing use of artificial fertilizers, weed-killers and regular

Figure 3.25
Erosion of the links at Birsay initiated by sand extraction and aggravated by motor cycle scambling.
Photo: R. M. M. Crawford

re-seeding to maintain pasture productivity poses a threat to the long-term survival of many species. The facility with which electric fences can be moved to encompass marginal areas for pasturage can bring nutrients through dung deposition into areas where floral biodiversity depends on minimal competition from dominant nitrogen-demanding species. The rate of loss of sites where *Primula scotica* can be found is a case in point.

The ancient rights of the Norse system of land tenure (*udal land-law*) allows relatively unrestricted access to shores for obtaining supplies of sand and gravel. There are consequently many areas of links and storm beaches where such disturbance, together with rising sea levels, is destroying whole communities (Figure 3.25). It is usually forgotten, or not realized, that these areas have little ability to recover as there are no longer adequate supplies of off-shore sand and gravel to bring about replenishment.

In areas such as North Hoy there has been no significant grazing for many years, and these offer the hope that the natural woodlands that once covered the islands might become re-established. Unfortunately, the dominance of tall stands of heather growing through large amounts of *Sphagnum* moss inhibits the establishment of young tree saplings. It is therefore unlikely that there will be any natural tree-regeneration in times measured by human life-spans unless some encouragement is given through active heather burning and some re-seeding (Figure 3.4).

Despite these problems, there are many positive aspects in present-day Orkney that should foster the restoration of plant biodiversity. Climatic warming may well create more favourable conditions for agriculture and for the conservation of many species, including *Primula scotica*. The oceanic climate will counter the danger of drought that threatens more southern areas and this will be beneficial both to grazing and plant diversity. It is to be hoped that future management of the land, coupled with scientifically-based nature conservation practices, will be in harmony with the ecology of the many plant communities that inhabit these islands.

Further reading

Adam, 1990; Barne *et al.*, 1997; Bennett *et al.*, 1992; Bullard, 1972b, 1975, 1995; Bullard and Goode, 1975; Bullard *et al.*, 1987; Bunting, 1996 a, b; Burnett, 1964; Chapman and Crawford, 1981; Cooper, 1997; Crampton, 1911; Crawford, 1997 a, b; Crawford and Palin, 1981; Davidson and Carter, 1997; Dickson and Dickson, 1975; Dunn, 1837; Ennos *et al.*, 1997; Glover and Abbott, 1995; Goodier and Ball, 1975; Macdonald, 1967; McVean and Ratcliffe, 1962; Moar, 1969; Nicol, 1938; Peglar, 1979; Prentice and Prentice, 1975; Renfrew, 1979; Ritchie, J., 1954; Ritchie, W., 1979; Safriel, Volis and Kark, 1994; Shirreff, 1814; Smith, De La Vega and Dawson, 1996; Spence, D. H. N., 1974, 1979; Spence, M., 1914; Wallace, 1700; Whittle *et al.*, 1986; Wright Smith and Fletcher, 1942.

Chapter 4

Sea and Shore*

The sea was the great mother: she gave them, sometimes lavishly, sometimes stingily, from her stores of fish, whale, salt, tangle, driftwood. Winter after winter she hurled freighted ships on the rocks and crags; while the cargoes of rum or wheat or apples lasted, life in this island and that was a long winter festival. But the sea did not give for nothing; another of her names was 'the widow-maker'. From time to time the sea took a single life to herself, or at a stroke a whole ship's crew. And this was her due.

(George Mackay Brown, 1981)

In many ways the sea may have been less important to Orkney than to many other island groups. That may seem an odd statement, since the sea has formed, protected, provided and isolated Orkney for thousands upon thousands of years. But we must remember that Orkney is first and foremost a farming community; the sea may help with fertilizer or building material or saleable harvest, but few people in Orkney depend on the sea in the same way as in Shetland or, the even more barren, basaltic Faroe. However, few natives or even many of the growing number of visitors can have failed to sense a feeling of vastness, where a seemingly limitless sky merges with

---

* This chapter was largely written by J. M. Baxter (see p. viii).

Figure 4.1
Kirkwall Harbour in a storm.
Photo: Scottish Natural Heritage

apparently endless sea. The sea exercises a powerful influence over Orkney and the character of both the land and people. Increasingly the sea is important to the local economy with the setting up of salmon and shellfish farms over the last twenty years and the developments associated with the oil industry, both to the east and more recently the deep waters off the continental shelf to the north and west of the islands.

The seas around Orkney hold an enormous interest for the natural historian and scientist which was unsuspected twenty or thirty years ago; we now know that faunally and florally they are among the most diverse in the United Kingdom. Our knowledge of them has grown immensely in recent years, first through the work associated with the coming of the oil industry and then with the establishment of the International Centre for Island Technology in Stromness. We have learnt also from other surveys, including that by the Marine Nature Conservation Review team and one of the maerl beds (see below).

Orkney consists of around 90 islands and skerries with a coastline length of around 550 miles or 880 kilometres (approximately 13.5 per cent of the total coastline of Scotland), ranging from towering near-vertical cliffs exposed to the full force of the North Atlantic waves to extremely sheltered rocky, sandy and muddy shores on some of the more enclosed areas of Scapa Flow and the northern islands.

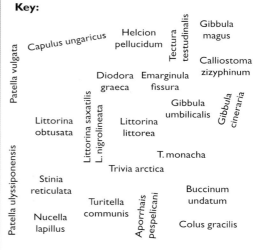

Key:

Patella vulgata

Patella ulyssiponensis

Capulus ungaricus   Helcion pellucidum   Tectura testudinalis   Gibbula magus

Diodora graeca   Emarginula fissura   Calliostoma zizyphinum

Littorina obtusata   Littorina saxatilis   L. nigrolineata   Littorina littorea   Gibbula umbilicalis   Gibbula cineraria

T. monacha

Trivia arctica

Stinia reticulata

Turitella communis   Aporrhais pespelicani   Buccinum undatum

Nucella lapillus   Colus gracilis

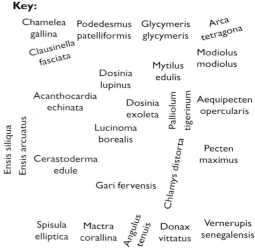

Key:

Chamelea gallina   Podedesmus patelliformis   Glycymeris glycymeris   Arca tetragona

Clausinella fasciata   Modiolus modiolus

Dosinia lupinus   Mytilus edulis

Ensis siliqua   Ensis arcuatus

Acanthocardia echinata   Dosinia exoleta   Palliolum tigerinum   Aequipecten opercularis

Lucinoma borealis

Cerastoderma edule   Chlamys distorta   Pecten maximus

Gari fervensis

Spisula elliptica   Mactra corallina   Angulus tenuis   Donax vittatus   Vernerupis senegalensis

Tides, wave exposure and weather determine the distribution of life on the shore. Like the air temperature, which varies comparatively little between summer and winter, the sea temperatures around Orkney change only from 5°C (41°F) in February to 13°C (57°F) in July. Since littoral organisms are sensitive to heat, light and desiccation, the Orkney climate can be regarded as friendly for them, and hence likely to favour the development of relatively rich and diverse communities. Probably their worst enemy is the seemingly ever-present drying wind.

Figure 4.2 a and b (opposite)
The marine molluscs of Orkney have been well studied (see p. 286). Some of the species found around Orkney are illustrated here.
a: Gastropods.
b: Bivalves.
Photo: Richard Welsby

Orkney has complex tides. It is assaulted on both sides – by the independent systems of the North Atlantic and of the North Sea. The two tides reach the Orkney coast with similar strengths, but from different directions and with different timings, the Atlantic peak arriving two or three hours before the southward-travelling North Sea wave. This produces a net flow of water from west to east, and complex tidal interactions among the island sounds and in Scapa Flow. Some areas such as Hoy Sound and the Pentland Firth are subject to considerable tidal streams as a result (up to nine knots or 4.5 m/s in the Pentland Firth). Another consequence, particularly important for shore life, is the effect of all this on the rise and fall of the tide: crests and troughs of the progression may be flattened, and irregular gradients may result from uneven acceleration of the mid-tide water level. These complications may alter the usual vertical zonation of littoral organisms due to changes in the immersion period at some beach levels.

The mean tidal range for Stromness is 9 feet (3 metres) at spring tides and 4 feet (1.2 metres) at neap tides. Significantly low water of spring tides occurs during the early morning or late afternoon. Since the air temperature is cooler and the direct effect of insolation at these times is less than at mid-day, this favours the development of a particularly diverse sublittoral fringe community, with many species generally intolerant of emersion occurring above low-tide level on the shore.

Orkney is to some extent influenced by the current of the North Atlantic Drift which carries water north and east through the Faroe–Shetland Channel to the Norwegian coast. A branch of this stream enters the North Sea round the north of Shetland, but its strength varies annually. Another stream, which may be composed of Atlantic or more coastal waters, passes between Orkney

Figure 4.3
Waulkmill Bay.
Photo: Richard Welsby

and Fair Isle, and runs southward close to the Orkney coast. This current continues on into the Moray Firth, but only rarely enters the North Sea proper. Finally, a sub-surface flow from the Mediterranean moves up the west coast of Britain, becoming less marked as it moves north. This current may be sufficiently strong in some years to mix with coastal water on the continental shelf to the west of Orkney, before it passes through the Orkney–Fair Isle passage into the Moray Firth area. Thus, the west coast of Orkney is dominated with northward-flowing oceanic water from either the North Atlantic Drift or from the Mediterranean current; whilst the north and east coasts are likely to be influenced by mixed water from the Orkney–Fair Isle passage. Evidence from salinity patterns and from drift bottles indicates that the net flow through the Pentland Firth is westwards. The consequence is that Orkney is roughly encircled by a clockwise set of tidal streams.

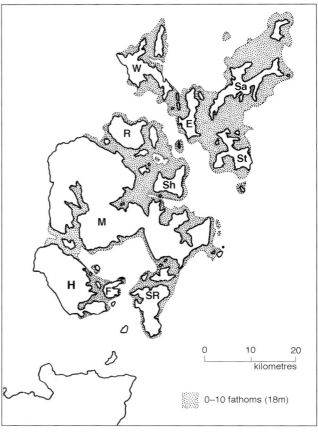

Figure 4.4
Sea depths around Orkney.

The sea water around Orkney is relatively free of sediment and the salinity remains essentially constant throughout the year at about 35‰. The sea depth increases rapidly to around 30–40 fathoms (60–80 metres), particularly on the

Figure 4.5
Sea shells on an Orkney beach.
Photo: Richard Welsby

Figure 4.6
Marram-covered dunes on Orkney.
Photo: Richard Welsby

west coast, although in many of the firths, sounds and in Scapa Flow itself, the water depth is rarely more than ten fathoms (20 metres). Large parts of the coastline have an extensive shelf of rock favouring extensive kelp forests to depths in excess of 25 metres. The floor of Scapa Flow is fairly flat with a variety of bottoms from mud to rock; the tidally scoured sounds have bottoms of sand, shell-gravel, maerl or rock; the more sheltered firths have some localized mud deposits, but mud is fairly uncommon in Orkney.

The littoral is largely slabs of bedrock or of large boulders, ranging from very wave-exposed, near-vertical bedrock areas to sheltered, egg wrack (*Fucus vesiculosus*)-dominated boulder shores. The grade of sand varies with the amount of wave action or tidal scour. Fine sands are found in the more sheltered bays like those on Sanday on the Scapa Flow coast of Hoy; they support an abundant and relatively diverse burrowing fauna which contrasts to that in the coarser grained, mobile sands of the more exposed shores with only a very sparse and limited fauna.

Studies of the plankton in Orkney waters clearly shows the significant influence of the warmer western currents, although the extent of this varies from year to year, and sometimes is virtually undetectable. Scapa Flow is rich in planktonic life, much of which must enter through Hoy Sound. It is an area particularly rich in meroplankton in the spring and summer months.

Shore biology

Rocky shores exhibit a classical zonation of flora and fauna, dependent on the type of rock, topography, slope and its exposure to wave action. The supralittoral fringe on the more exposed shores is particularly well developed in Orkney, with a diverse and abundant lichen flora including the whitish-green *Ramalina* sp. and the bright orange *Xanthoria* sp. and *Caloplaca* sp. On the most wave-exposed shores these can give a dramatic splash of colour. On the more shaded vertical walls the damp conditions permit the development of a conspicuous dark-green belt of Myxophyceae (blue-green algae).

The Acorn Barnacle *Semibalanus balanoides* and the Common Limpet *Patella vulgata*, often with a band of small blue mussels, *Mytilus edulis* below them, typically dominate the very exposed coasts. On the most exposed shores of Hoy and the west Mainland a second narrow band of another species of barnacle, *Chthamalus stellatus* may be found above *Semibalanus*, distinguished from the latter by its bright white colour. In general, these more exposed shores are relatively species-poor, with Dog Whelks *Nucella lapillus* found in cracks and crevices, and only a few species of Red Seaweed (Rhodophyceae) together with thong weed, *Himanthalia elongata* and Dabberlocks, *Alaria esculenta* on the lower shore. Interestingly, the Dog Whelks on Orkney are almost completely unbanded and white in colour, in dramatic contrast with the populations found on Shetland, which come in a variety of colours and banding patterns. Where there are cracks and crevices in the rock the resulting dampness provides ideal conditions for a range of small seaweeds such as Carrageen, *Mastocarpus stellatus*, Pepper Dulse, *Laurencia pinnatifida*, and *Cladophora* sp.; these create colourful scars across the rock surface.

The more sheltered shores in Orkney range from the semi-exposed shores of much of the northern islands to the very sheltered shores inside Scapa Flow and some of the other islands such as Otterswick on Sanday. They are dominated by fucoid algae. The typical algal sequence from the top to bottom of the shore, of Channelled Wrack, *Pelvetia canaliculata*, Spiral Wrack, *Fucus spiralis*, Bladder or Egg Wrack, *Fucus vesiculosus*, Egg Wrack, *Ascophyllum nodosum*, and finally Serrated Wrack, *Fucus serratus* may be

Figure 4.7
A typical colourful spring shore with lichens and thrift.
Photo: Scottish Natural Heritage

Figure 4.8
Rocky shore with Dog Whelks (and their egg case) and mussels.
Photo: Scottish Natural Heritage

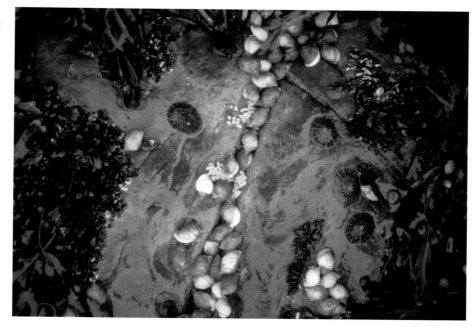

Figure 4.9
Sandy shore on Sanday.
Photo: Scottish Natural Heritage

indistinct, due to the broken nature of the shores giving varying degrees of localized wave exposure. On the most sheltered shores the cover of algae is almost complete, with the mid-shore being particularly heavily covered by substantial growths of Egg Wrack. Beneath this canopy of algae where the atmosphere is continually damp, and especially where the boulders are stable, a diverse associated fauna can develop, including sea anemones, sponges and a variety of molluscs including chitons, snails and sea slugs. The broken nature of the shores also leads to many rock pools that support a further range of plants and animals such as Sea Oak, *Halidrys siliquosa*, and delicate red seaweeds. In some locations more unusual communities can be found, such as the sheltered shores in the inner reaches of Otterswick Bay where the intertidal is dominated by dense growths of the green alga *Codium fragilis*.

Around the coast of Scapa Flow and some of the northern islands are sandy beaches nestled between rocky headlands

Figure 4.10
Codium forest, off
North Sanday.
*Photo: Scottish Natural
Heritage*

ranging in size from small pockets of sediment to large and extensive sand
flats such as those found on Sanday, Hoy, and Swanbister and Mill Bay on
mainland Orkney. The fauna of these sandy shores varies with the physical
and chemical conditions of the shore. Those that are subject to considerable
wave action and tidal scour comprise relatively coarse-grain sediments and
support larger species of animals; on more sheltered shores the sand tends to

Figure 4.11
Bay of Quoys, Hoy.
*Photo: Scottish Natural
Heritage*

be finer and contains high densities of the annelids such as the lug worm that are the architects of the miniature volcanic landscape created by their faecal casts and inhalent pits, as well as a variety of crustaceans and molluscs. These are important components of the diet of many seabirds and waders. In many of the finer sediment shores there is a pronounced black anaerobic layer present a few centimetres below the surface. More unusually, on certain beaches in Scapa Flow (especially Scapa, Waulkmill and Swanbister) the sands take on a distinctly purply-pink hue at certain times of the year due to blooms of sulphur-reducing anaerobic bacteria belonging to the genera *Thiocapsa* and *Chromatium*. The sandy beaches in Scapa Flow are also remarkable for a giant race of the edible cockle *Cerastoderma edule*. At the Bay of Quoys on Hoy there is a very unusual community of animals found nowhere else in Orkney, with vast numbers of maldanid worms together with the normally sublittoral worm, *Polydora antennata* and a remarkable range of small crustaceans. At extreme low-tide mark on some sandy shores dense populations of razor shells or 'spoots', *Ensis* sp. are found; they are considered a prize catch by many locals.

Extensive areas of mud are rare in Orkney and are usually associated with freshwater inflows or with urban developments such as at the Bridge of Waithe and Stromness harbour.

Sub-littoral animals and plants

The shallow sublittoral is well developed throughout Orkney with extensive kelp forests of *Laminaria digitata* in the sublittoral fringe and then cuvie, *L. hyperborea* extending to depths of seven or eight fathoms (15 metres) or more. These kelp forests are the habitat for a wide range of associated seaweeds and animals including the common Sea Urchin, *Echinus esculentus*, which is a voracious grazer and in some places can result in a significant reduction in the kelp density. In addition Topshells (*Gibbula* sp.) together with the beautiful painted Topshell *Calliostoma zizyphynum* are also important grazers. The rock between the kelp holdfasts are encrusted with sponges, sea mats, sea firs and anemones. The Edible Crab, *Cancer pagurus*, the Velvet Swimming Crab, *Liocarcinus puber*, and Lobsters, *Homarus vulgaris* are frequent, especially in areas where the rock is more broken, providing cracks and crevices for them to hide in. The extent and density of the kelp forest around some parts of the Orkney Islands is remarkable and after winter storms vast piles of cast kelp or 'tangle' are found on certain shores. There is a history of collecting tangle, which continues to this day, but these great mounds of shredded rotting seaweed are also important feeding grounds for over-wintering waders such as Purple Sandpipers and Turnstones.

In places exposed to extreme wave action, Dabberlocks *Alaria esculenta* replaces *L. digitata* in the sublittoral fringe. With its short stipe and flexible mid-rib it is well adapted to survive constant wave motion. In contrast, in some of the sheltered areas of Scapa Flow and the northern islands where the rocky sea bed is adjacent to more sandy areas the Sugar Kelp, *L. saccharina*, is found. In places where the sea bed is a mixture of sand and small boulders or cobbles the Bootlace Weed *Chorda filum* flourishes forming dense forests, with individual plants growing to over 16 feet (5 metres) in length. Other shallow areas support Seagrass beds made up of *Zostera marina*, one of the few flowering plants found in the marine environment. In the sand beneath the Seagrass the secretive Sea Potato, *Echinocardium cordatum*, a relative of the common Sea Urchin, can be found.

Where there is a reasonable flow of water in parts of Scapa Flow and more particularly in some of the sounds between the northern islands, there are beds of Scottish Coral or Maerl. This is a pink calcareous seaweed that grows as knobbly nodules or, when bound together by the holdfasts of kelp, into dinner-plate sized discs. Maerl grows extremely slowly at no more than half an inch (2–3mm) a year, but over time beds of dead maerl form, often metres deep with a thin veneer of live plants at the surface. Within the maerl a large variety of burrowing animals live including a wide range of bivalves and Sea Cucumbers.

Figure 4.12
(top left) *Echinus* grazed kelp, NW of Hoka Head, Scapa Flow.
(top right) Sea urchins, south of the Barrel of Butter, Scapa Flow.
(right) *Echinus* grazed rock and *Metridium*, NW of Hoka Head, Scapa Flow.
Photos: Scottish Natural Heritage

As the kelp forest gives way to kelp park with increasing depth, the rock surfaces become more and more densely encrusted in animals, together with delicate red seaweeds such as *Ptilota plumosa*. In more wave-swept areas there are dense growths of sea mats, such as Hornwrack, *Flustra foliacea*, together with a wide variety of sponges, anemones and soft corals such as Dead Man's Fingers, *Alcyonium digitatum*. In the more tide-swept areas such as Eynhallow Sound below the depths where seaweeds can survive, dense faunal turfs develop with a range of different animals competing for space. Dead Man's Fingers, Horned Wrack and the Bottlebrush Hydroid, *Thuiaria thuja*, an Arctic species, are found, along with massive growths of various sponges such as *Myxilla incrustans*, *Cliona celata* and the Elephant's Ear Sponge *Pachymatisma johnstonia*.

Where the sea bed is predominantly sand and gravel, but still with some

Figure 4.13
Aplysia on maerl, Wyre Sound.
Photo: Scottish Natural Heritage

current, Horse Mussel beds, *Modiolus modiolus*, and Brittle Star beds of *Ophiocomina nigra* and *Ophiura albida* are dominant. Associated with these are animals such as various burrowing sea cucumbers and the Sand-mason Worm, *Lanice conchilega*, that builds a delicate exo-skeleton of sand grains. The waters around Orkney are famous for their wonderful seafood and in particular the Great Scallop, *Pecten maximus* and the Queen Scallop *Chlamys opercularis*.

Figure 4.14
Alcyonium and *Crossaster* on sea floor, Egilsay Sound.
Photo: Scottish Natural Heritage

Figure 4.15
Sea Pens in soft mud,
Scapa Flow.
*Photo: Scottish Natural
Heritage*

In the deepest waters where the sea bed is more muddy, populations of the Slender Sea Pen, *Virgularia mirabilis,* are found together with other strange animals such as the echiuran worm, *Amalosoma eddystonense* and the tube-dwelling worm *Chaetopterus variopedatus*. In the Bring Deeps at a depth of 30 fathoms (60 metres) the sea bed comprises dead maerl gravel and appears to be a collecting place for all sorts of algal debris which rots slowly on the seabed attracting vast numbers of the large isopod *Idotea emarginata*.

Orkney has been a magnet for naturalists for many years. Probably most incomers are ornithologists, but even the most hidebound birdwatcher must surely be stirred by the ever-present sea, with its own life and rhythm and stresses. The sea has shaped the people of Orkney as much as it has moulded the coasts. No Orcadian can ignore it, although few can describe it as well as Orkney's own Robert Rendall:

> Even upon the margin of the deep
>> Life spills her myriad forms before our gaze
>> In tiny treasures – bright anemones,
> Worms, star-fish, crabs, and little fish that leap
> Across the pools. Look how storm waves heap
>> A fringe of shell along these sandy bays,
>> And how on golden bladderweed that sways
> With rhythmic motion periwinkles creep.

I step from stone to stone, and as I peer
　　Far into depths of pools inhabited
By swarming ocean creatures, I can hear
　　Echoes around me of the Voice that said,
Go, have dominion over great and small,
And name all living things that swim and crawl.

Further reading

Atkins, Jones and Simpson, 1985; Barne *et al.*, 1997; Baxter, 1982; Baxter, Jones and Simpson, 1985; Davies, 1985; Dunn, 1973; Jones, 1975; Lyle, 1929; McMillan, 1971; Mason *et al.*, 1985; Murray, Dalkin, Fortune and Begg, 1999; Nicol, 1938; Rendall, 1956, 1960; Sinclair, 1950; Tait, 1937; Thomson, 1983; Thorpe, 1998; Traill, 1890, 1892, 1895; Walker, 1950; Wilkinson, 1975; Winchworth, 1920.

Chapter 5

Seals and Whales and Otters

The sea mammals are among the most attractive and spectacular wildlife of Orkney. They are also among the most publicized – including otters (which are effectively sea mammals in north Scotland and the islands) for their shyness and vulnerability; whales for their rarity; and seals, ironically, because of their commonness and the periodic controversies about culling them.

Seals

Both of the resident British seals live and breed around Orkney: about 8,500 Common (or Harbour) Seals (*Phoca vitulina*) (26 per cent of the British population, about 5 per cent of the world population – 1997 data) and about 44,000 of the larger Grey Seals (*Halichoerus grypus*) (32 per cent of the British population and about 13 per cent of the world total – 1997 data). Common Seal numbers seem to have remained constant in recent years; Grey Seal numbers more than doubled between 1964 and 1982 and again between 1982 and 1997 (Figure 5.1). The main concentrations of Common Seals are on the islands in Scapa Flow (Switha, Cava, Flotta and the northern tip of Hoy), the coasts of Stronsay, Westray and North Ronaldsay, and the east side of Mainland; Grey Seals are scattered throughout the islands with the main breeding sites in the northern isles – on islets off Eday and north-west Stronsay.

Figure 5.1
Grey Seals on North
Ronaldsay.
Photo: Richard Welsby

Seals have long been an important resource for Orcadians, and are almost as close to everyday life as a farm animal. Folklore (which Orkney shares with both Shetland and the Hebrides) has it that seals ('selkies') possess magical powers and are able to cast off their skins and come ashore as beautiful (and seductive) people. Many an islander is said to have fallen in love with a selkie and gone to sea:

> I am a man upo' the land
> I am a selchie in the sea
> And when I'm far frae every strand
> My home is on Sule Skerry.

A rather more mundane approach is represented by the stories linked with Seal hunting. The Barrel of Butter skerry in the middle of Scapa Flow is said to have got its name from payments made by Seal hunters to the owner of the skerry. The *Old Statistical Account* refers to an annual sealing expedition to Sule Skerry: Pitcairn, writing a *Retrospective View of the Scotch Fisheries* (1787) describes between 500 and 1,000 seals being killed there in a couple of days. This expedition ceased after 1786, when the ship was swept away northwards and all but three of the crew of 30 or 40 lost. Netting was a common method of catching seals on the skerries off Hoy, Walls, North

Ronaldsay, Eday, Westray, Wyre and the Pentland Skerries. Nets were set up while the tide was rising, with the upper edge at such a height that the seals could swim over. When the tide fell sufficiently and enough of the net was clear, the seals were scared off the skerry and into the net. They were killed by clubbing or shooting.

Seal-skins were exported from at least the seventeenth century. With the hair on the outside they were used to make shoes, and covers for saddles and trunks. Oil was used in lamps, for feeding to cattle, and for dressing leather. A good-sized seal would yield about eight gallons (25 litres). The meat was eaten, usually after being salted and hung in the chimney to be smoked. Low commented in the *Fauna Orcadensis* that seals (he did not distinguish between the Common and Grey):

> are with us very numerous: they lie off-shore in the desert isles and sea rocks: they swim with vast rapidity: they are yearly caught about our coasts with net and shot for the sake of the skins and oil, though in North Ronaldsha they take them for eating: they say they make a good ham.

In the mid-sixteenth century the Swedish Church regarded seal-meat as fish, but it was later forbidden on saint days in Norway. The comparatively small amount of modern hunting has been almost entirely for skins.

Grey Seals

The Grey Seal can be found from the Baltic to Iceland and on the eastern coast of Canada. It is larger than the Common Seal, an adult male weighing up to nearly half a ton (300 kg), compared with just over 250 lbs (120 kg) for

Figure 5.2
Total production of Grey Seal pups for all sites in the Outer Hebrides and the Orkneys since the 1960s, when regular monitoring began. *Based on Hiby et al., 1996*

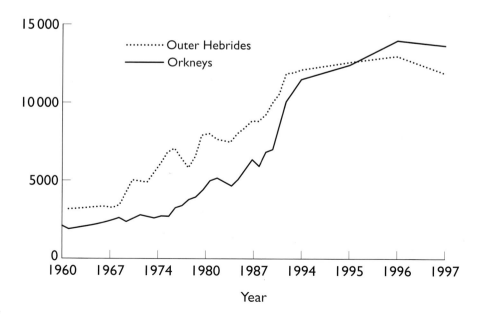

a male Common Seal. Its old Orkney name is 'haaf-fish', from the Old Norse *haf*, for ocean, presumably referring to its habit of frequenting off-shore skerries. The Common Seal used to be known as the 'tang' (or seaweed) fish.

There are two main groups of breeding Grey Seals on Orkney, the larger one being centred around Rousay, Wyre and the Westray Firth, and a smaller one around the southern approaches to Scapa Flow. There are a number of other breeding sites including Pentland Skerries, Auskerry and Seal Skerry near North Ronaldsay. Breeding females come ashore from late September to mid-November, giving birth to a single white-coated pup, weighing about 25 lb (12 kg). Three to four weeks later it has been weaned, moulted into its adult coat, and goes to sea. The females mate on land (with one or more males), and all the adults then disperse to feed.

Grey seals become sexually mature at around four years of age. Females have their first pups at five to eight years of age, but males do not achieve sufficient social status to mate until approximately ten years of age. In Orkney the peak numbers of pups are found ashore during the last week in October. At this time they can be counted on aerial photographs, and censused without being disturbed. Every year each island is photographed up to six times at ten to twelve day intervals. The data on pup production is combined for all sites, and used in a model to estimate the total population. This is then apportioned between areas using the pup production contribution for each area.

Since 1951, 3,000 Grey Seal pups have been tagged at breeding sites in Orkney. About 250 of these have been subsequently recovered, all but 27 within nine months of tagging. The recoveries show that Orkney seals may disperse as far south as Holland, north up to Norway and the Faroes, and west to the west coast of Ireland. Pups tagged in the Hebrides and the Farne Islands have been found in Orkney waters. However, data from North Rona shows that there is a high degree of site fidelity, with considerable likelihood of a seal returning to its birthplace to breed. There is a small amount of genetic divergence between seals from Orkney and the Hebrides, which suggests that the groups are isolated to some extent; satellite tracking shows that Hebridean seals tend to move to Orkney. Grey Seals are present throughout the year around Orkney, but most of the breeding islands are deserted during the summer months. Adults are seen hauled out throughout the year, although they spend longer ashore in February and March, when they undergo their annual moult.

Productivity of all the Orkney seal breeding sites increased during the 1960s and 1970s, except for the Muckle and Little Green Holms, where the 1964 figure (650 pups) was three times that of 1982. This decrease can probably be attributed to the large hunting effort there in the 1960s, but it represents emigration of breeding females, not their loss: pup productions on the islets of Spurness Sound between Stronsay and Sanday to the east of the

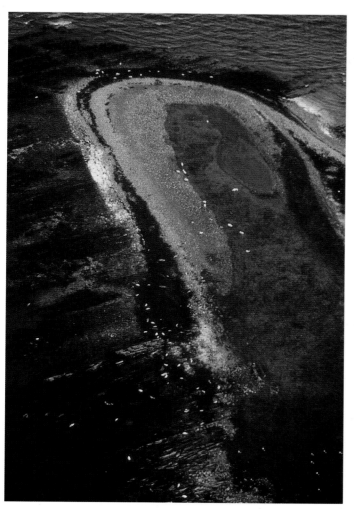

Figure 5.3
Grey Seal pups on the Holms of Spurness.
Photo: Sea Mammal Research Unit

Green Holms rose thirteen-fold (to 3,000 pups per year) over the same period, whilst in the Westray Firth productivity only increased three and a half times (to 1,600 per year). All the Spurness Sound colonies have expanded in the last twenty years, and at least seven new ones have been established since then. However, there was a slight decrease in pup numbers in 1998. From 1978 no licences for hunting have been issued for the Green Holms, but still there has been no increase in pups born there.

Ironically, the nadir of breeding on the Green Holms (and the year of most human disturbance) was in 1978, when protesters against seal hunting camped there for several weeks. A vivid account of this episode is given in a book *Let the Seals Live!* by Sue Flint (1979).

The rapid recent increase in the Orkney Grey Seal population is well documented. In the past there have been times when the species has been rare. Low recorded that on occasion seals (of uncertain species) had a 'murrain' (illness) which 'caused them to cough much, make a sort of plaintive noise, and when they died and drove ashore were much swelled, and appeared as if very fat, but when cut up were nothing but skin and bone'. This would have been around 1770. Apparently similar epidemics occurred in 1836 and in 1869 and 1870, 'since which time certain bays have been quite deserted by seals'. Whether it was disease or human predation that controlled numbers in past centuries we may never know. The first Grey Seal Protection Act was passed in 1914 prohibiting the 'killing, wounding or taking of any grey seals between 1st October and 15th November' (extended in 1932 to cover the period 1 September to 31 October). When it was before Parliament it was asserted that Grey Seal stocks around the whole of Britain had been reduced by over-killing to as few as 500. However, although there is no hard data, there are anecdotes which suggest that seals were already increasing at the end of the nineteenth century.

During the 1950s, the increase in seals in Scottish waters led to concern among both the commercial and salmon fishing communities about depredation and damage to fish, and about the apparently rising incidence of a worm (*Pseudoterranova decipiens*) parasitic in Cod and other fish, whose intermediate host is the Grey Seal. (Cod worm infestations increased in the 1960s, giving rise to the idea that they were dependent on seal densities. However, they remained relatively constant in the 1970s despite the continued growth in seal numbers.) This concern led in 1959 to the formation of a Consultative Committee on Grey Seals and Fisheries. One of the recommendations of this committee was that there should be an annual cull of Grey Seals in Orkney, in order to reduce the population by a quarter. From 1962 to 1982 an average of 834 pups were taken every year by local hunters, but this policy failed to stop the population increase. In 1976, the Department of Agriculture and Fisheries for Scotland and the Nature Conservancy Council proposed that the Scottish Grey Seal stock should be reduced to the mid-1960s level (around 35,000). The Natural Environment Research Council, who had the responsibility of giving scientific advice to the Government, recommended that the safest way of achieving this was to remove 900 cows and 4,000 pups every year for six years. Bad weather interfered with this programme in the Hebrides in 1977, and the focus was turned on Orkney in 1978, where it was proposed that 1,000 moulted pups and 450 adult cows plus their pups should be removed. The protests and obstructions that followed led to the Secretary of State abandoning the cull. Although licences to cull were issued until 1983, there has been no culling since 1978.

In his statement cancelling the 1978 cull, the Secretary of State for Scotland stated

Research has been undertaken over many years into seal behaviour, diet, etc. and there is no doubt that they are consuming considerable quantities of fish which has been put at a value of some £12m per annum. The simple facts of the matter are that seals eat fish as their main diet, mostly fish suitable for human consumption, and the more seals there are, the greater the damage done to fish stocks.

He went on to commission the Sea Mammal Research Unit to check and quantify the diet of Grey Seals. They found that the proportion of seal-damaged Salmon around salmon nets did not indicate a change in the number of seals attacking Salmon over the period 1959 to 1982. It was not possible to determine the actual number of Salmon eaten by seals, but certainly there was no increase in the fish attacked but not killed. More direct investigations of seal diets were carried out by analysing fish otoliths (ear bones) in seal faeces collected at various places round Britain. These showed that Sand Eels were by far the most important prey species, making up 50 per cent of the diet by weight. Next in order of importance were Ling and Tusk (12 per cent), followed by various *Trispoterus* species such as Poor Cod and Pout Whiting (7 per cent), Whiting (6 per cent), Haddock, Saithe and Pollack (5 per cent), and Cod (3 per cent). No Salmon remains were found, but if Salmon comprised only one or two per cent of the diet, their remains might well be undetected. If the mix of species represented by these analyses reflect the seals' diet, then in 1985 the seals were eating the equivalent of about 15 lb (6 kg) of Cod per day or 9 lbs of Sand Eels per day per seal. There was little seasonal variation in faecal contents, suggesting that the prey species were more or less the same at different stages of the year. Making apparently reasonable assumptions, seal consumption as a proportion of the commercial fisheries catch is highest for Tusk and Ling (45 per cent), followed by Sand Eels (11 per cent) and Whiting (5 per cent). For all other species, the seals are catching less than 5 per cent of the amount caught by commercial fishing.

This data does not support the contention that seals are direct and important competitors with commercial fishermen, or even salmon netters. However, there are still many imponderables, and the large consumption of Sand Eels raises questions about the effects of further increases in industrial fishing of this important prey of seabirds (see p. 168).

Common Seals

Common Seals are smaller than Grey Seals, up to about 6 feet (1.9 metres) long and weighing up to 250 lb (120 kg). Males are slightly larger than females. Pups are born in June and July. Unlike Grey Seals, they are born in their adult grey-brown coat; the white coat is moulted in the uterus, the occasional one which survives birth being shed within a day or two. At the high tide following their birth, the pups are capable of swimming off the pupping beach with their mothers. This makes it difficult to catch and tag Common Seal pups, and little is known about their dispersal. Pups may suck for up to six weeks, either on land or in the water. The relationship of the pups to their mother is closer than in the Grey Seal, with the pups following their mother closely, even, it is said, after weaning. The adults moult after the pups are weaned, having mated (usually) between weaning and moult. They are around the islands for the whole year, and it is assumed that most of their feeding is done closer to the shore than Grey Seals. Even so the estimated numbers of Common Seals are unlikely to be as accurate as for the Grey Seal, because the haul-outs of the former are much more scattered, and counting individuals is more difficult. They are surveyed in Orkney every five years, using a thermal imaging camera mounted in a helicopter.

The Common Seal was totally unprotected until the Conservation of Seals Act of 1970. In the years before this, there were drastic declines of the species in a number of areas, including Shetland, through over-hunting. Killing is now permitted in Orkney (but not Shetland) throughout the year, albeit only

Figure 5.4
Common Seals.
*Photo: Paul Thompson,
University of Aberdeen*

following the granting of a licence from the Department of Agriculture and Fisheries in the closed season (1 May–31 July).

The seal situation in Orkney is very different from that in Shetland. In the latter islands, the Grey Seal breeding beaches are almost all very exposed to wave action, many of them in caves, and a large proportion of pups starve or are drowned each year. In contrast to every other part of the country, Grey Seal numbers in Shetland seem to have remained fairly constant in recent years. As a result, Common Seals were hunted much more intensively than

Figure 5.5
Common Seals on Westray. These are difficult to count visually, and censuses are carried out using thermal imaging techniques.
Photo: Sea Mammal Research Unit

Greys in Shetland. Between 1972 and 1976 an annual average of 140 Common Seal pups were shot in Orkney, but only eight between 1977 and 1982. During the 1960s an average of 700 pups a year were taken in Shetland; by 1970 it was thought that about 90 per cent of the pups born each year were being taken by hunters. From 1972 no licences have been issued for shooting in Shetland.

As far as Orkney is concerned, Common Seal numbers have increased slowly in recent years. The minimum estimate in 1989 was 7,100, by 1993 the estimate was 7,900. Oil-related developments do not seem to have affected them; there have been changes in the distribution of seals around Flotta and the western fringes of Scapa Flow, but the total numbers have remained constant. When the Egilsay pier was rebuilt in 1972, the animals normally resident on the nearby Holm of Scockness deserted their regular beach for a less disturbed part of Egilsay. Once the construction work was finished, the Seals moved back to their regular site.

Other seal species

Vagrant seals of other species from the Arctic appear in Orkney from time to time, but they are very rare. In the nineteenth century, most reports were of the Walrus (*Odobenus rosmarus*), but some of these were probably transported in ships, for it is said that Arctic whalers used on occasion to bring back young Walrus. There is a story of a Walrus at Longhope which annoyed people crossing the bay on the way to church, by putting its tusks over the gunwale of the boat . . . history does not relate the end of the story. In the twentieth century, there have been two records of the Bearded Seal (*Erignathus barbatus*) (1987, 1988) and of the Hooded Seal (*Cystophora cristata*) (1998, 1999), and single reports of the Walrus (1986) and of the Ringed Seal (*Phoca hispida*) (1992).

Whales

It is not uncommon to see whales from land in Orkney, and nineteen different species have been recorded, fourteen of them since 1980 in the seas nearby. Of these, seven (26 per cent of the 27 UK species) are seen most years. Pilot or Caain' Whale (*Globicephala melas*) is the most common, but the schools in Orkney seem to be smaller than in Shetland, where the most recorded was of 1,540 whales which came into Quendale Bay, south Mainland on 22 September 1845. It has been claimed that 450 animals were killed at Westray in autumn 1843, but this was based on a newspaper article written in 1886 and must remain doubtful. There do not appear to be any contemporary accounts. Orcadians and Shetlanders have traditionally used only the blubber from stranded whales, unlike the Faroese who eat whale meat regularly. In Orkney, the blubber was boiled and turned into oil, while the carcasses were left to rot.

The earliest mention of whales being driven ashore in Orkney was of 114 grounded near Kairston, Mainland in 1691. There are a number of accounts from the nineteenth century: a school of 50 whales ran aground at Rothiesholm in Stronsay in November 1834, and yielded about £100-worth of oil; early in 1841, 287 whales came ashore on the west side of Eday and yielded a return of £398. In Sanday, whale hunting was regarded as the most exciting form of fishing. An eye-witness wrote in the mid-nineteenth century:

> Shoals ranging from 50 to 500 in number get occasionally embayed; and upon this happening, all boats are launched, all hands active, every tool which can be converted into a weapon of offence to the strangers, from the roasting-spit of the principal tenant, to the ware (seaweed) fork of the cottar, is put into requisition. The shoal is surrounded, driven like a flock of timid sheep to shallow water on a sandy shore, and then the attack is made in earnest. The boats push in, stabbing and wounding in all directions. The tails of the wounded fish lash the sea, which is dyed red with their blood, sometimes dashing a boat to pieces. The whales in dying emit shrill and plaintive cries, accompanied with loud snorting and a humming noise easily mistaken at a distance for fifes and drums.

This description is reminiscent of the Faroe Islands, where the whole operation of driving the whales to recognized beaches, and of killing and dividing the produce, is highly organized. John Buchan captured well the lust of a Faroese whale-hunt in his novel *The Island of Sheep*.

Whale-hunting was still taking place in Orkney in the 1860s. It was noted then that they always swam upwind if they could, and if the leader was once ashore, the rest followed easily. They could be easily killed by a rifle bullet in the throat. A visitor to Stronsay described a school driven into Mill Bay in the old *Orkney Book*. Men and women from far and near assembled to kill them with harpoons, three-pronged graips and hayforks. The boat crews beat pitchers, rattled rowlocks, and shouted, as they surrounded the school in a crescent formation. A skiff that put out from the shore in front of the whales disturbed them so that they turned, but the boats followed them and eventually got them ashore at Rothesholm Bay, which the Stronsay minister described as 'the best whale-trap I know in Orkney'. On that occasion 170 whales were killed. At Sourin Bay, Rousay, 60 were slain and sold for £260. In the 1870s 300 were caught in Linga Strand, Stronsay. A dyke at Grainbank Farm, Wideford Hill, was built of the skulls of Caain' Whales driven into Kirkwall Bay. The last organized drive took place in July 1891, when 114 Pilot Whales were killed in Inganess Bay and Wideford Sands.

Figure 5.6
A Pilot Whale
stranding.
Photo: Tom Kent Collection, Orkney Library. By courtesy of the Orkney Library – Photographic Archive

A whale chase added welcome excitement and a valued addition to an islander's income. A Westray farmer, about to make a coffin for his newly-dead wife, when he heard the call 'Whales in the bay', set off immediately leaving two of his men working on the coffin, since this meant two less to share the produce. The laird who was to divide the catch was surprised to see him at such a time. The farmer's explanation was, 'I could na afford to lose baith wife and whales on the same day.'

Caain' Whales may be seen at any time of the year around Orkney, but are most often seen between May and August. Other whale species are occasionally recorded in Orkney waters. The Baleen Whales tend to migrate southwards along the continental shelf edge in late summer and autumn, and the proximity of the shelf to Orkney, together with the rich upwelling areas to the south and west of Orkney, make the region important for cetaceans. There are whale bones in Neolithic middens at Skara Brae, showing that 5,000 years ago Orcadians were using whales for house building and kitchen utensils, as well as (presumably) for food. At the turn of the century there were approximately twenty whaling stations in Iceland and Faroe. In North Norway, whaling was banned as a result of disputes with the Cod fishermen and, as the Greenland whaling began to collapse, Norwegian whalers set up three stations in Shetland (at Ronas Voe, Olnafirth and Collafirth), as well as in the Hebrides and the west of Ireland. The Shetland stations were always the most important of these, and over 3,400 Fin and 1,800 Right Whales (together with other species) were caught before the stations closed in 1929.

Before the First World War there was no evidence of over-exploitation, but afterwards it became obvious that the stocks of whales passing through the waters around Orkney and Shetland, particularly the Blue, Humpback and Right Whales, were not enough to withstand the hunting pressure.

There have been no recent sightings of Sei (*Balaenoptera borealis*) or Blue Whales (*B. musculus*) off Orkney, but Fin Whales (*B. physalus*) are sometimes seen, usually in autumn to the west of Orkney, while its smaller relative the Minke Whale (*B. acutorostrata*) seems to be not uncommon in the vicinity of upwelling areas around headlands, small islands or shallow banks. These Baleen Whales are usually seen singly or in pairs, and there is some evidence from studies elsewhere that they return year after year to the same areas to feed and defend a home range from which other Whales are excluded. Comparable in size with some of the larger Baleen Whales, is the Sperm Whale (*Physeter macrocephalus*). This species occurs in deep water off the edge of the continental shelf where it feeds on large squid. Lone males are the most commonly recorded in British and Irish waters, females and their calves tending to remain in equatorial waters throughout the year. In recent years there have been a number of sightings of Sperm Whales in Orkney waters, particularly in Scapa Flow between September and January. Included amongst these was a pod of six or seven individuals, juveniles probably accompanied by females, seen in October 1976, a pod of six present in February and March 1993, and seven that stayed for a week in April 1998. Eleven stranded on Sanday in December 1994 (p. 260).

During the nineteenth century one of the Beaked Whales, the Northern Bottlenose Whale (*Hyperoodon ampullatus*) was thought to be common in Orkney waters, although its specific identity cannot be confirmed. However, it has since been recorded in the seas west of Orkney, usually in late summer. In the north-east Atlantic concentrations occur in the Norwegian Sea, from which it migrates south in late summer and early autumn. Other Beaked Whales are rare visitors to British waters, occurring generally further south in warm temperate seas. Two species, Cuvier's Whale (*Ziphius cavirostris*) and Sowerby's Whale (*Mesoplodon bidens*) have been recorded stranded on Orkney coasts in summer, though only very rarely (the former stranded at Rackwick, Hoy in January and again in September 1963, and on the East Mainland, October 1920; and the latter at Burwick, South Ronaldsay in July 1933, North Ronaldsay, April 1954, and two females on Birsay in June 1961).

Orkney also receives visitors from colder waters. Two Arctic species, the Beluga or White Whale (*Delphinapterus leucas*) and Narwhal (*Monodon monoceros*), have both occurred in summer or autumn in Orkney waters. The White Whale has been the most frequently observed, with strandings of single animals in October 1845, August 1964 and a probable one in October 1981, and a single individual seen in October 1960. There is only one record of a Narwhal in Orkney, when two were seen off Gairsay in June 1949. In recent years White Whales have been seen relatively frequently in sub-Arctic waters off the Norwegian coast.

The Killer Whale (*Orcinus orca*) is often confused with the adult Risso's Dolphin (*Grampus griseus*) since the latter is larger than most people expect and has a relatively tall dorsal fin. The term 'grampus' has been commonly applied to both species, and past descriptions of their abundance in Orkney waters may confuse the two. Small herds of the former (usually three to six individuals) may be seen most years, usually between July and September, although it has also been recorded in Orkney waters in midwinter. Most sightings come from north-west and west Orkney, or to the south from Scapa Flow and the Pentland Firth. It is possible that the species is preying at this time upon Seal pups in inshore waters.

Other cetaceans

The Harbour Porpoise (*Phocoena phocoena*) is the most commonly observed small cetacean in Orkney waters, albeit in relatively small numbers. It occurs mainly in sheltered bays where it is probably feeding on small shoaling fish such as Sand Eels (*Ammodytes* spp.) and sprats (*Clupea sprattus*). It may be seen at any time, although most sightings occur in July to September with fewer recorded from winter months when it is possible that much of the population moves offshore. Young individuals have been seen in late summer, and breeding probably takes place around May to June not far from Orkney.

The White-beaked Dolphin (*Lagenorhynchus albirostris*) is probably the most abundant dolphin in Orkney waters during the summer and autumn, occurring in herds of between five and twenty individuals. Sightings peak in the August to October period, at the same time as large numbers are regularly seen off the North Sutherland coast, in the north Minches and off the east coast of Shetland. Most herds in Orkney appear to occur off the west coast and near Sule Skerry, although this may be because Sule Skerry is visited fairly often by naturalists, and occurrences are more likely to be sighted and reported.

The Atlantic White-sided Dolphin (*L. acutus*) is a more pelagic species than the White-beaked Dolphin. It is also observed mainly west of Orkney and in the vicinity of North Rona, Sule Skerry and Sule Stack. Herd size, though commonly between five and twenty individuals, may sometimes be up to 100, particularly during apparent long-distance movements. Sightings also peak between August and October. White-beaked Dolphins give birth in late summer and autumn, whereas the young of White-sided Dolphins are born slightly earlier, around mid-summer. Their occurrence in the vicinity of

Orkney at this time may indicate that they both breed not far from the islands.

The overall situation is of large whales passing through Orkney waters during summer and autumn on their way south to more equatorial regions, while the dolphin species (such as White-beaked and White-sided Dolphins and the Harbour Porpoise) appear to be more resident in Orkney waters, although offshore movements may occur at particular times of the year. This also seems to be the case for Risso's Dolphin, which is very rarely seen during winter or spring in Orkney waters.

Risso's Dolphin is frequently observed, in numbers ranging from four to fifteen individuals, between July and October west of Orkney, and often seen in the vicinity of Sule Skerry. Two dolphin species, though not uncommon elsewhere in Britain, are rarely observed in Orkney waters. There have been only five records of the Bottlenosed Dolphin (*Tursiops truncatus*), which occurs primarily in coastal waters, shallow bays and estuaries of the British mainland, and the Common Dolphin (*Delphinus delphis*) is rare in Orkney too, though commonly seen offshore of south-west Britain and Ireland. Stranding records over the last half-century suggest that these species were formerly amongst the commonest of dolphin species in UK waters. However, the former has almost certainly declined in recent years and the latter rarely occurs in coastal waters as far north as Orkney.

Before leaving whales, mention must be made of Orcadian involvement in polar whaling, which used to be an important source of hard cash to many families. Whalers heading from Greenland and the Davis Straits used to call in to Orkney and Shetland for crews. In 1816, 34 whaling ships were recorded at Stromness, of which 25 came from Hull. Fifty men from Stromness alone were at the Straits in 1821. Stromness merchants acted as agents for shipowners elsewhere. Arctic whaling came to an end a few years before the First World War, and (apart from the East Atlantic whaling mentioned earlier), attention shifted to the Antarctic with the establishment of bases in South Georgia after 1904 and in the Falkland Islands in 1908. Many men from the North Isles were involved in this whaling, but it was much less important to Orkney than the Arctic phase had been.

Otters

The *Orkneyinga Saga* says of Otters (*Lutra lutra*) that they 'often lay among the rocks,' and describes Otter-hunting a thousand years ago on Rousay: 'The Earl had risen early, and he and nineteen men had gone to the south end of the island to hunt the otters that lay on the rocks under the headland.' This persecution extended down the centuries, and the export of Otter skins from Orkney is on record from the seventeenth century onwards. They were rarely

Figure 5.7
Otter.
Photo: Hans Kruuk

shot, but knocked down with sticks. The skin of a winter-killed otter with plenty of fur was worth about ten shillings in the early 1880s.

Otters were commonly caught in stone traps known as otter-houses. Traces of these can still be found in some parts, more commonly in Shetland than Orkney. They were built across the tracks of Otters, and roofed with heavy flat stones, with a sliding door which slipped into place when the Otter displaced a stone inside.

Otters are highly specialized carnivores. They will take poultry (even raiding hen houses), and eat birds such as Shags, Fulmars and others, especially in late winter and early spring. However, their main food is fish. Observations of foraging Otters in Shetland showed that most of their prey (over 80 per cent) consists of small, bottom-living species such as Eelpout, Rocklings, Butterfish, Sea Scorpion and others, and they also take a few crabs. They are not very good at catching fast-swimming, mid-water fish. Interestingly, most of the prey fish are active at night and during high tides, and in daytime they hide under stones and weeds. It means that Otters can catch fish most easily during the day, which is the main reason why in Orkney and Shetland Otters can be seen active during the day, especially during falling, low or rising tides.

The distribution of Otters along sea coasts is highly dependent on the presence of fresh water, of small pools and burns, or of peat in which fresh

Figure 5.8
Otters sprainting.
Photo: Hans Kruuk

water collects underground. Otters cannot do without this, because they have to wash the salt out of their fur; they have no blubber, and for thermo-isolation are entirely dependent on their thick and very efficient fur. If they cannot wash regularly, the fur gets matted and does not keep out the water; the animals become hypothermic and die. This dependence on fresh water is the reason why there are fewer Otters in Orkney than in Shetland: there is much more well-drained agricultural land in Orkney, and more permeable rock formations than in Shetland.

Numbers of Otters are difficult to assess. Their faeces or 'spraints' may often be found along shores and river banks, but there is no clear relationship between otter numbers and spraint numbers. In Shetland, Otter distribution has been assessed by counting and mapping Otter dens (called 'holts'); each resident female uses about three different holts. Shetland appears to have just under 1,000 adult Otters, the best areas having about one animal per kilometre of coast.

Social organization is complicated: Otter females live in group-ranges of up to five, usually closely related animals with their cubs. Within the group range each female has her own 'core area'. Core areas are exclusive of each other, but all females can use the whole range of five to fourteen kilometres of coast, and defend this against other females. Males have much larger ranges, overlapping with several female group ranges. Mating in the Northern Isles takes place in spring, but the males visit the females at all times of year, for brief encounters, and the animals appear to know each other well.

Otters have up to four cubs, but the average litter size in Shetland is only 1.8. Natal holts tend to be far from the shore, sometimes as much as 1 kilometre; they are extremely difficult to find, and the cubs do not leave them until they are about two months old. All the 'active' holts have fresh water inside them ('bath-rooms'). The mother looks after the cubs for up to a year (sometimes even longer); the cubs are dependent for a long time, because fishing is a very difficult skill.

There is no way of knowing how the Otter population compares with, say, a century ago, when Buckley and Harvie-Brown could say in their *Vertebrate Fauna* (1891) that 'Otters are yet abundant in most of the islands'. There is a suspicion that the population has declined in the past decade or two. However, it is not particularly difficult to catch a glimpse of an Otter, particularly at dawn or dusk, and many Orcadians have anecdotes about meeting them unexpectedly (including the one which walked up Stromness Pier on New Year's Day 1964, and went to sleep in the Harbourmaster's Office), or of people who have reared orphan pups. In view of the near extinction of the species in southern England, it is encouraging to find that Otters, although very susceptible to oil pollution (at least ten Otters were killed in a notorious incident at Sullom Voe), can tolerate a surprising amount of disturbance. Recently an Otter family was raised in a holt below one of the main jetties at the Sullom Voe oil terminal. Although hunting and pollution must be elements in the decline of the Otter in England, a major factor is the decrease in suitable breeding sites which have been removed in the south as river banks have been tidied and straightened. At least this last is not a problem for Orkney Otters.

Further reading

GENERAL
Barne, Robson, Kaznowska, Doody, Davidson and Buck, 1997; Booth and Booth, 1998; Buckley and Harvie-Brown, 1891; Corbet and Harris, 1991; Groundwater, 1974; Hewer, 1974; Lockley, 1966.

SEALS
Berry, 1969; Bonner, 1972, 1976, 1978; Bonner, Vaughan and Johnston, 1973; Boyd, 1963; Consultative Committee, 1963; Davis and Anderson, 1976; Duck, 1997; Flint, 1979; Hammond, Hall and Prime, 1994; Harwood, 1978; Harwood and Prime, 1978; Hewer, 1964; Hiby *et al.*, 1996; McConnell, 1985; Marwick, 1975; Sea Mammal Research Unit, 1984; Smith, 1966; Summers, 1978; Summers, Bonner and Van Haaften, 1978; Tickell, 1970; Vaughan, 1969, 1975, 1977.

WHALES
Brown, 1976; De Cock, 1956; Evans, 1976a, 1976b, 1980, 1997; Reynolds and Booth, 1985; Sheldrick, 1976; West, 1972.

OTTERS
Baker *et al.*, 1981; Green and Green, 1980; Kruuk, 1995; Kruuk and Hewson, 1978; Watson, 1978.

Chapter 6

Freshwater Habitats

They have no Rivers, no place of the Land being above 2 or 3 miles distant from the Sea, therefore they draw water out of wells for their Cattel, or drive them to Lochs or Lakes, some whereof they have, or to some small brooks which run from these Lochs: Which Lochs likewise cause their Mills to go.

Thus Reverend John Brand wrote of Orkney in 1701. He says nothing about the abundant sea and brown trout of the lochs and streams which provide excellent eating. They were an important food source, in particular for the people of Harray, which is the only parish in Orkney with no sea coast, and was traditionally, therefore, a poor one. However he did write about the abundance of sea fish, which

is pleasant to taste, and also they say very wholesome, which seems to be confirmed by this that in the years of great scarcity, the poorer People lived upon them, almost as their only food, they often not enjoying a crum of Bread for many Weeks. So our good God, on the shutting of one door, opened another in his holy and wise Providence for the relief of the poor.

Table 6.1 shows the small number of lochs and streams in Orkney compared with other areas in the north. Orkney possesses few burns and these are now mainly in straight deep channels, though locally they are important as spawning and nursery grounds for trout, growth areas for eels

Table 6.1   Freshwater bodies of the North of Scotland

	Orkney	Shetland	Western Isles	Caithness
Number of burns	131	298	287	120
Number of lochs and lochans	48	195	1,094	73
Number of lochs with an area greater than 0.25km²	17	28	176	25
Mean area of standing waters (km²)	0.78	0.17	no figure available	0.33

and, as Brand pointed out, in former years for milling. Likewise the numbers of large lochs is also comparatively low, although the main lochs are very large; this is due largely to the underlying geology (see Chapter 2). A survey by the Nature Conservancy Council in 1986 of freshwater lochs in Orkney recorded the ecology of 148 water bodies, but many were smaller than one hectare (Figure 6.1). However, some of the smallest proved to be the richest in aquatic plant species, which was the main focus of the survey (Charter and van Houten, unpublished report to NCC).

Orkney is not unlike Shetland in lacking rivers and having few burns, but the Orkney waters are less diverse than the Shetland ones, because of the less varied nature of the underlying rocks. Consequently, there has been little interest in Orkney lochs and streams in the past (except among trout fishermen), and the significance of the open waters within the Orkney environment has been underestimated from the times of John Brand onwards. Since the mid-1980s they have been better recorded.

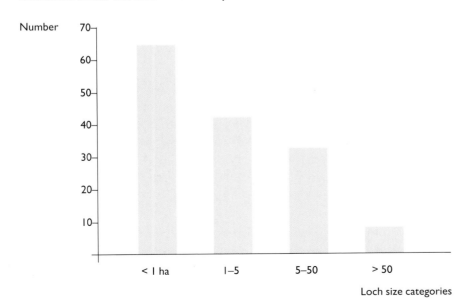

Figure 6.1
Loch size categories.

Loch types

Orkney lochs are very variable, reflecting the character of their catchments. In comparison with lochs and lakes in lowland parts of Britain, most of Orkney's lochs support a comparatively narrow variety of animal and plant species. This is a consequence of the island situation. In general the lochs are of a lowland type and as such are richer than the upland lochs of mainland Scotland although comparable to those on similar geology in Caithness. They can be grouped according to their nutrient status and productivity: 'oligotrophic', 'mesotrophic' or 'eutrophic'. Both vegetation and water chemistry may be used to classify loch status. Figure 6.2 shows the numbers of lochs in each type recorded by a survey in 1986.

The more intensively farmed lowland catchments have more varied and more productive lochs. The productivity has become even more pronounced with modern agriculture, but the variety has declined.

Figure 6.2
Proportions of Orkney lochs in each trophic type.

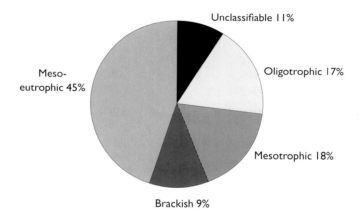

Peat lochs
The hill lochs, with their staining from peat, are limited by the meagre nutrients falling in rainfall or deposited by resting birds, mainly gulls and Arctic Skuas. Consequently the waters are unproductive and little vegetated. Such lochs are classed as oligotrophic (that is, having few plant nutrients). Hoy moorland possesses two notable lochs of this type, set in narrow valleys. They are among the deepest lochs in Orkney: Hoglinns is 55 feet (17.4 metres) deep and Heldale Water is similar. Arctic Charr (*Salvelius alpinus*) used to be found in the latter, but seems to be extinct. The Hoy lochs and lochans are some of the few places where dragonflies are commonly seen. Rousay is similar and has two 'highland' lochs – Peerie Water and Muckle Water (each 19 feet (6 metres) deep). In the hills (and occasionally in old peat workings) are smaller dark brown pools – frequented by Red-throated

Figure 6.3
Hill lochs, Rousay.
Photo: Richard Welsby

Divers (and hence called 'loomashuns'). These lochans have peaty edges while the larger lochs have more stony shores.

The water of both the larger and smaller oligotrophic lochs is similar: it is a rich brown colour with pH 4–5 (i.e. fairly acid); the oxygen content is low and the basal substrate almost always a muddy peat deposit; vegetation includes rushes and a small variety of surface plants, including the Floating Club-rush and Bulbous Rush. The nitrogen content of the oligotrophic lochs is low. The bladderwort family cope with this deficiency by catching small animals in their bladders. During the early 1990s, yellow flowers of bladderwort were found for the first time in Orkney among the reeds at Loch Watten on Egilsay.

The main problem faced by animals in such pools is lack of oxygen. For that reason pool-dwellers have special adaptations. For example, bloodworms (*Chironomid* larvae) have haemoglobin in their body fluids. Water beetles are common, including a species of the Great Diving Beetle (*Dytiscus*) which come to the water surface to obtain oxygen in the form of air bubbles which are then taken down under their elytra. When the oxygen is used up, the beetle returns to the surface to replenish the supply. Other water insects such as Pond-skaters and Whirligig beetles avoid the problem of oxygen lack by living on the water surface. The food supply for animals like these is not as poor as one might think, since most surface insects eat terrestrial insects blown onto the water, and there is an abundance of water fleas and planktonic organisms of various kinds, particularly in summer. Carnivorous phantom midge larvae (*Chaoborus*) are also found in these interesting, wild and lonely habitats.

Lowland lochs

Swannay is the deepest mainland loch, 16 feet (5 metres) deep, whilst at the other extreme, Isbister and Sabiston Lochs at 3 feet (1 metre) are shallow enough for the growth of submerged plants. Otherwise shore vegetation is rather sparse in the larger lochs. Some of the larger lochs have partly moorland and partly farmland catchments which leads to increased nutrient levels. 'Mesotrophic' is the term used for these moderately rich waters. They support a wider range of plant and animal life than the upland peaty lochs. Stony edges are more or less bare except for Spike Rush (*Eleocharis* spp.), where the fetch across the loch produces stormy waves. Only where there are bays or an inflow delta is there a stable bed of silt supporting a reed bed or thick belt of other long-leaved species, including Yellow Iris, Bur-reed and

Figure 6.4
Hill lochan, Hoy.
Photo: Richard Welsby

Bulrush. Graemeshall has one of the largest reed beds on the mainland and this provides a refuge for Otters which are rarely seen but whose fresh spraint is often found at the brig. Lochs of this type occur in Sanday, Stronsay, Westray and Papa Westray, and some of these are quite strongly influenced by shell sand which leads to lime deposits on the vegetation. Some are used as water supplies by the islanders and are carefully monitored.

The lochs which are surrounded by fertile farmland support a greater quantity, if not a greater variety of life. These lochs would probably have been less densely vegetated in the past. Their bottom sediments were known to have been carpeted in stoneworts, lime-encrusted branched algae, which are the favourite habitat for the invertebrates (particularly *Gammarus,* the Freshwater Shrimp, and *Daphnia,* the Water Flea) on which Brown Trout feed. Orkney has a particularly rich stonewort flora, with more species (fourteen) recorded than in any other part of Scotland (Stewart, unpublished report). They include seven species which are rare in Scotland and six Red Data Book species (defined as occurring in fewer than fifteen 10-kilometre squares). However, in a 1995 survey only eleven species were refound. Stewart noted that while most lochs looked clean and unpolluted, some lochs, particularly in the West Mainland, showed signs of pollution, including heavy algal growth. Plants can be more reliable indicators of long-term changes in water quality than chemical measures, many of which follow annual cycles.

There has been a trend in recent years towards denser growth of pondweeds (*Potamogeton,* water milfoil and water crowfoots) growing on the rich silt. They have relatively little emergent or floating vegetation, the main species being Marsh Spike Rush, with occasional areas of reed and pockets of true Bulrush. Floating leaved plants are restricted to pondweeds and water crowfoots, and increasingly in small pools, Common Duckweed. The scarcer species include bladderworts, Holy Grass (a Red Data Book species which may have come from Scandinavia with the Norse travellers), and Spiral Tasselweed, a plant of brackish water.

In general, the lowland lochs range from mesotrophic to eutrophic and occur mainly on the Mainland and in intensively farmed catchments on the outer islands.

Brackish lagoons

Water bodies which actually border onto the seashore are the lagoons, or as some people in the north call them, 'oyces'. Typical lagoons are shown in Figure 6.8, the average area being two to four hectares. Table 6.2 gives salinity figures for eight Orkney lagoons.

Nearness to the sea is an obvious factor influencing the sodium and chloride content of the fresh waters, but recent analyses show that gross salinity (measured as 'chlorinity') varies from loch to loch; recorded values range from only 0/15‰ (= parts per thousand) to 0.5‰, the average being 0.26‰. The lagoons have the highest salinities.

Clearly all these lagoons are more salty than the truly freshwater lochs, but their salinity is not very high, bearing in mind their proximity to the sea. All the oyces are similar in structure: they are divided from the sea by a shingle bank or 'ayre', and the outflow is through the shingle bank or a narrow channel which allows the entry of seawater at high spring tides, particularly during gales. But the water flow in and out of these lagoons fluctuates. It would be useful to sample them throughout the year to establish salinity patterns more accurately.

All of the lagoons have muddy bottoms, with occasional stones embedded in them. The quantity of vegetation is very variable: Vastray, Yinstay and

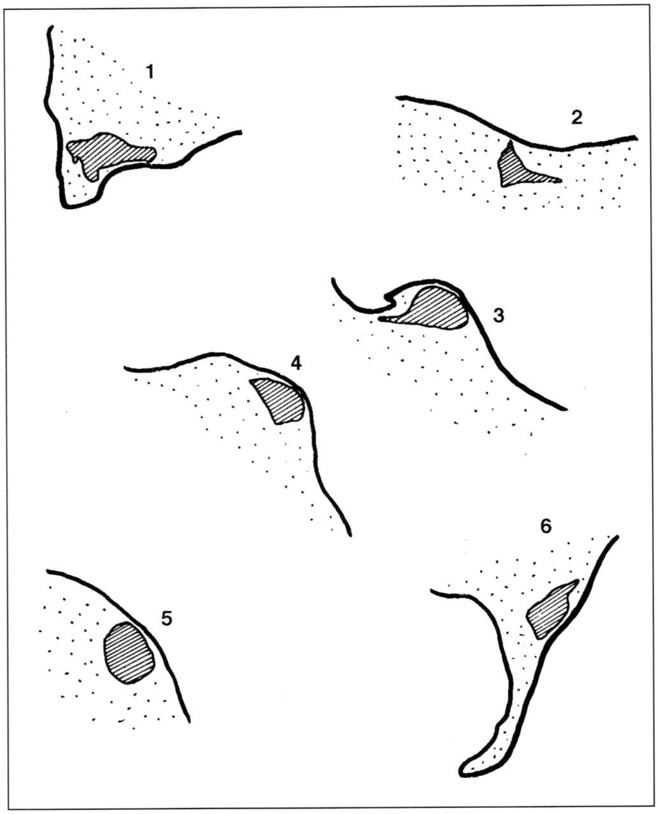

Figure 6.8
Coastal lagoons in Orkney:
1 Braebuster, Deerness.
2 Mirkady, Deerness.
3 Messigate, Tankerness.
4 Vastray, Evie.
5 Yinstay, Tankerness.
6 Lakequoy, Tankerness.

Table 6.2   Salinity of eight Orkney Mainland lagoons

Lagoon	Parish	Salinity (‰)
St Mary's Loch	Holm	7.05
Yinstay	Tankerness	3.50
Lakequoy	Tankerness	2.00
Messigate	Tankerness	14.10
Braebuster	Deerness	0.80
Mirkady	Deerness	3.90
Carness	St Ola	5.40
Loch of Vastray	Evie	0.60
(Seawater		35.40)

Figure 6.9a (opposite, top)
Shingle ayre, Shapinsay.

Figure 6.9 b (opposite, bottom)
North Sand, Rousay.

Photos: Richard Welsby

Mirkady have abundant bottom-rooted rushes (*Eleocharis* sp.) providing food and shelter for a wider variety of invertebrates than in other lagoons; but apart from these, most lagoons are characterized by a lack of plants with emergent leafy and flowering shoots. The rather scarce Brackish Bulrush, *Scheonoplectus tabernaemontani*, has been recorded at several. Floating-leaved plants are uncommon, being replaced by wholly submerged pondweeds (*Potamogeton* spp.), some of them grass-like such as the Slender Pondweed, *Potamogeton filiformis*, and the Fennel-leaved Pondweed, *P. pectinatus*. Another finely leafed species, the Brackish Water Crowfoot (*Ranunculus baudotti*) is a local specialty. The reason for the fine leaves may be connected with the relatively high salinity of the lagoons which dehydrates cells, especially if large surface areas of leaf are exposed.

Typical brackish-water invertebrates have been recorded in at least four of the seven lochs sampled: Jenkins' Pond-snail, Brackish-water Shrimp, Mysid Shrimp, Sea-slater. Typical freshwater species are also present: cased-caddis larvae are particularly abundant in vegetation, Water-boatmen (Corixids) are common, together with sticklebacks and pond-snails, such as *Lymnaea pereger*. Other species recorded are Lake Shrimps (*Gammarus lacustris*), Diving Beetles and midge larvae. Many of the lagoons have large populations of planktonic organisms.

These lagoons have received little attention in the past. A survey of lagoons by R. S. K. Barnes (1980) suggested that Orcadian lagoons are fairly typical as regards salinity and fauna; his book is worth consulting. The 1986 loch surveyors visited almost all these water bodies and found that some contained Common Ischnuras and Blue-tailed Damselflies and a variety of freshwater molluscs.

Water quality

In recent years it has been realized that the purity and naturalness of Orkney's freshwater bodies cannot be taken for granted and considerable research has centred on certain important lochs. The significance of the open waters within the Orkney environment may have been underestimated in the past, but since the mid-1980s they have been better recorded.

As concerns about water quality have grown, monitoring of water chemistry has become more frequent. Water was the responsibility of the Orkney Islands Council before 1996; then the Scottish Environment Protection Agency and the North of Scotland Water Authority were made the designated regulator and privatized water company respectively. Most attention has been paid to drinking-water sources, but analysis for conservation objectives has also been undertaken by the conservation and countryside agency, Scottish Natural Heritage. Freshwater biologists are interested in a different

Table 6.3   Water chemistry 1995 (Orkney Island Council data)

	pH	alkalinity mg/l HCO₃	conductivity µS/cm at 20°C	chloride mg/l	nitrate mg/l	calcium mg/l
Kirkbister	7.5	97	365	42.5	1.3	39.9
Boardhouse	7.7	93.5	365	46	1.2	41.8
Heldale and Hoglinns Water (Hoy)	7.0	15.4	214	58	<0.4	9.8
Saintear and Burness, Westray	7.0	205.5	664	110.5	2	73.9
Bea Loch, Sanday	7.2	144.5	547	96.5	0.7	39.2
Ancum Loch, N Ronaldsay	7.0	358	938	151	9.8	101
Sandy Loch, N Hoy	7.22	21.8	155.8	34.5	10	11

range of chemicals, particularly the phosphate level which indicates the extent of enrichment by nutrients.

A number of lochs provide the water supply on the outer islands and large parts of the Mainland. The analysis of these lochs gives a good indication of the variety of water chemistry (Table 6.3).

The sandstone of which Orkney is largely composed contributes calcium to water from the cement between the sand grains. This lime is deposited as 'tufa' where lime-rich springs arise. Such springs are typified by beds of the distinctive Black Bogrush (*Scheonus nigricans*) and are a priority habitat in the national Biodiversity Action Plan. Shell sand contributes to the high calcium figures at Ancum, Sainteer and Burness.

Although in other parts of the UK there has been evidence of loch acidification, Orkney lochs show little sign of raised pH, presumably because they are well buffered by their moderate calcium levels.

Some of the clearest and most natural waters now are the remaining undisturbed quarries. In the deeper ones it is possible to view the diverse delicate strands of pondweeds rising up from the depths. In these clear waters damselflies may be seen, such as the blue *Ischnura elegans*.

Lochs Harray and Stenness

These two lochs deserve separate discussion as together they form an important conservation site (SSSI), popular with anglers and birdwatchers. They are the two largest lochs in Orkney (989 hectares and 760 hectares respectively) and have a total drainage area of about 64 square miles (160 square kilometres). Although shallow by mainland Scotland standards (because of the flat sedimentary rock and glacial drift underlying them), they are nevertheless among the six deepest lochs in the islands. It is for these reasons that they have received particular attention over the past half-century.

Harray Loch drains a shallow basin in the centre of the West Mainland and pours its contents out into Loch Stenness through a narrow channel at Brodgar, across which there now passes a major county road. Ducts under the roadway allow the flow of fresh water into the second loch (Stenness), which in turn opens to the sea at the much wider channel at the Brig O'Waithe. Stenness has therefore always been regarded as a salt-water loch which receives at its eastern end a great volume of fresh water from Harray (2.5 square miles or 6.5 square kilometres in area). But when the tide flows in at the Brig O'Waithe, Stenness receives salt water to such an extent that the direction of water flow at Brodgar is reversed and brackish water moves back into Harray.

Brackish lagoons are identified in the EC Habitats Directive as a priority habitat for conservation, and Stenness is the largest such water body in the UK by far. Through this Directive the loch has been proposed as a Special Area for Conservation (SAC).

For years it was believed that these two lochs formed a salinity continuum from Waithe to the north end of Harray. As such it seemed to be a brackish-water ecosystem unique to Britain, even without the vast numbers of wildfowl that gather there. An early study was based on salinity differences at a few sites. In 1936, however, Edith Nicol carried out a thorough analysis of the lochs, their water, and flora and fauna. She found that Stenness water had a fairly uniform salinity (about half to three-quarters that of sea water), and that Harray water was very low in salt.

The next development came some 25 years later when local anglers became concerned about algal blooms of *Prymnesium parvum* on Harray. They associated these with saline influence from Stenness, and in 1968 one-way sluice valves were inserted in the channel ducts under the Brodgar road, permitting fresh water to flow out of Harray, but preventing salt water entering Harray from Stenness. These halved the salinity of Harray water (north end) from around 0.19–0.72‰ to 0.08–0.35‰. Since that time there has been no reoccurrence of this particular algal bloom. More recently algal blooms have been linked with the nutrient status of the lochs.

In 1978 Kirkwall Grammar School carried out a project to see how the two lochs had changed since Nicol's study of the 1930s. They found that over the 42 years between the surveys the salinities had changed little: Stenness had increased from 15‰ to 18‰ on average and Harray decreased from 1.3‰ to 0.7‰. Since the time the sluices had been constructed, they have become progressively less efficient and some salt water moves from Stenness into Harray at high tide. In 1994 the old sluices were replaced with more effective ones.

The School found that the animals were similar to those in the 1942 survey. *Gammarus duebeni* (Brackish Water Shrimp) was abundant in both lochs; it was found in Harray at salinities as low as 0.33‰. Jenkins' Pond-snail (*Potamopyrgus jenkinsi*) was locally very abundant and seems to thrive equally well in brackish and fresh water. This snail has spread its range and habitat tolerance dramatically over the last 50 years and in Orkney is found in lochs, streams, brackish lagoons and ditches. However, Stenness Loch was evidently too saline for it and laboratory experiments with Orcadian-collected specimens confirmed that they do not survive for long in water that is more than 50 per cent sea water. The invertebrate diversity of these lochs seems to be typical of similar freshwater bodies elsewhere, each loch possessing about 35 known kinds of bottom-dwelling invertebrates.

However, Harray and Stenness are remarkable lochs, unique in other biota. By the Brig of Brodgar the green alga, *Cladophora aegagropila*, occurs, forming small balls on the loch bottom; it is only known in Britain from two other localities. A mollusc of note is *Theodoxus fluviatile*, found locally abundant in Harray, the only Scottish locality for this calcium-loving animal.

The vegetation of Harray loch is certainly characteristic of eutrophic freshwaters.

In 1987 and 1988 a Canadian Pondweed (*Elodea canadensis*) explosion occurred giving trout fishermen especially cause for concern. The species was only thought to have been in the loch three to four years when it had increased so as to dominate the northern bays. In 1987 it was estimated that *E. canadensis* accounted for 52 per cent of the biomass in the loch. This was recognized as a symptom of nutrient enrichment and agriculture was the prime suspect. Research by the Scottish Agricultural College and Aberdeen University between 1989 and 1991 noted that cattle numbers had more than doubled in the catchment since 1960. Nitrogen fertilizer application per farmed hectare ranged from 62 kg to 194 kg, and phospherous 7 kg to 121 kg/ha. Leaching of nitrate from land in the catchment ranged from 1.61 kg to 35.6 kg/ha. and for phosphate ranged from 0.09 kg to 0.8 kg/ha. These figures are more typical of lowland Britain than the Highlands and Islands.

In 1996/97 Thomson (unpublished report) recorded salinities in Loch Stenness of 21‰ in summer and 8–9‰ in winter, with similar salinity values throughout the loch at any one time. He noted also that the surface, fresher, waters of Stenness appear to be increasing in nutrient status compared with 1994 and 1995, with maximum levels of nitrate 1.6 mg/lNO$_3$-N and phosphate 2.5 mg/lPO$_4$-P. Clearly further monitoring is required.

Burns

Orkney's geology is responsible for there being relatively few burns. Those that are present can be classified into either moorland or farmland streams.

The few truly moorland streams today are presumably close to the original type of Orkney stream, relatively unaffected by man. But farming has changed the landscape and in modern times, most watercourses have been straightened and deepened. Only in very few places does a stream still flow in its natural meanders at the same level as the surrounding meadows. One of the few remaining places is in the wetlands near Dounby. In addition fertilizer run-off, farm effluent and septic tank outflows affect streams throughout the county. Studies on Orkney streams affected by farming operations show that (as in other parts of the UK) the deprivation of oxygen due to the pinkish growth of bacteria or 'sewage fungus' (which thrive on the organic materials entering the water) has had the greatest effect. Only those species which can tolerate low oxygen concentrations are able to survive, such as chironomid (midge) larvae (bloodworms), etc. The enrichment effect which must presumably exist where phosphate and nitrate from fertilizers and manure drain into the streams has not yet been adequately studied. In general the farming community is aware of the problems, and legislation to control, for example, silage effluent leakage has reduced the incidence of severe pollution.

The natural stream environment is most easily studied in moorland streams. The most abundant animals are those typical of hill streams elsewhere – stonefly and mayfly nymphs, cased and case-less caddis larvae. The River Limpet, *Ancylus fluviatile,* is also found, especially in faster-flowing regions. Shrimps are scarce, but noteworthy is the presence of *Gammarus pulex* in Swartaback Burn; this species has only recently been discovered in Orkney, although it is common further south in Britain.

Many of Orkney's main hill streams have a particular charm: from the point where they emerge from peat seepage into a recognizable flow, they pass their brown peat-stained burden through some most attractive scenery with, in spring, primroses along the banks, pond-skaters darting over the pools, and Curlew and Lapwing calling round about. Where burns come tumbling down natural courses between natural rockeries of Thyme and Creeping Willow, the sunny, sheltered gullies attract Common Blue and Meadow Brown butterflies.

The fast flow of such reaches was harnessed as mill-streams in days gone by. In many parts mill-houses still remain, with recognizable mill-races and often mill-wheels. The need for water power led to the use of a variety of different water sources. Large lochs were the most reliable for such large parish mills as Boardhouse, Tankerness and Trenaby Mill in Westray which ground grain into meal. Burns with modest and often seasonal flows were harnessed for smaller threshing mills such as Finstown, Sebay and the Mill of Eyreland. Where there was not much drop in level, vertical axis mills, called 'click mills' were constructed. A working example can be seen above Dounby. Water flow was ensured by the construction of a mill-dam with sluice-type controls which allowed the required water to pass along the mill-race when grinding or threshing needed to be done. There are a host of places in Orkney today with names like Milldam and Millhouse. The wheels are now still and the dams empty, but the burns continue, although in places it is difficult to believe there was ever enough water for a mill to operate. Many other threshing mills were wind powered.

Burns provide local trout fishers with annual tasks when spawn is collected each autumn from adult fish. This spawn is transferred to a hatchery where the young are reared until they are about three months old and just over an inch (3 cm) long; the fry are then released into the lochs.

About three-quarters of the burns feed into lochs, the others flowing direct into the sea, occasionally forming mini-estuary conditions and some salt marshes (notably at Toab, East Mainland and at the Ouse in Finstown).

Invertebrates

There is little variation between lochs as far as the invertebrate fauna is concerned. Commonest species include the Freshwater Shrimp *Gammarus lacustris*, water boatmen (various species), the wandering Pond-snail (*Lymnaea pereger*), and sticklebacks. Jenkin's Pond-snail is common in Orkney. Other species found frequently include leeches and caddis-fly larvae; a number of case-building species of the latter are very common in lochs where there is plenty of vegetation available for manufacturing cases, such as Tankerness, Brockan and Echnaloch.

At the base of the food chain are, of course, green plants, in the form of algal plankton, rooted vegetation or attached algae. Plankton surveys have not been a priority for Orkney limnologists but their study could throw light on the changes taking place in the lochs. Algae seem to be the most abundant group of primary producers in the lochs, often covering the surface of flat rocks and stones, making it difficult to pick them up. The most comprehensive survey of these algae and others living on mud and other plants was conducted at the beginning of this century. It showed that Orkney and Shetland had many species in common, although some species occurred in only one or the other island groups.

In general the lochs with the richest flora also have the richest fauna. Echnaloch on Burray has a particularly varied spectrum of animal species and is an example of a loch with considerable shore and submerged vegetation and a good faunal community associated with it.

Angling

Orkney lochs have great attractions for wildfowl and ornithologists (see Chapter 8), but they are also a mecca for anglers offering some of the best Brown Trout (*Salmo trutta*) fishing in the UK. Fishing is free in Orkney's lochs. The natural stocks are augmented each year by introductions from local eggs hatched in a small hatchery near Kirkwall, under the auspices of the Orkney Trout Fishing Association. Of the major lochs, Harray is considered to offer the best fishing. The loch has a very long, indented shore-line and a large area of off-shore shallows. The trout here form a self-sustaining population which requires no stocking. The annual catch from Harray is reckoned in hundreds of thousands of fish, mainly caught from boats rather than by shore wading. The sister loch to Harray – Stenness – is much more saline and has less good fishing; the variety of species caught is, however, greater and includes Sea Trout.

In the past two decades water quality problems have affected the trout. The Harray loch underwent dramatic changes in vegetation, with the Canadian Pondweed explosion and subsequent algal blooms. The trout are now largely zooplankton feeders taking advantage of the large numbers of Water Flea, *Daphnia*, which occur in the deeper part of the loch each summer. In the past they fed mainly in the shallows on *Gammarus*, the Freshwater Shrimp. There is no indication that trout populations are in serious decline, although individual lochs vary from year to year. Only the Loch of Stenness gives cause for concern as it may not be self-sustaining through its spawning burns as it was in the past, with the burns having their own water quality problems.

Every loch has its devotees, but perhaps Swannay can be singled out as being rather special for the angler. Deepest of all the mainland lochs, it has a shallow southern half, but with skerries and troughs, provides the best (boat) fishing; shore wading conditions are notoriously treacherous and have caused many an upset. Swannay has a reputation for fickleness, but its trout are said to be wild and strong, considered by some to be amongst the best-quality wild Brown Trout in the country.

This is not the place to discuss the best fly to use in which loch and under which circumstances. Suffice it to say that local anglers have adapted well-tried flies to suit local conditions and it is remarkable how close to the natural invertebrate prey a fisherman can get when constructing a fly. For example there are many who fish with shrimp-like flies and sedges (caddis mimics); analysis of stomach contents of Orkney Brown Trout show that these two invertebrates are the most abundant prey – at least during the summer months.

Amphibians

Both Barry (1805) and Low (1813) claim the Common Frog (*Rana temporaria*) and the Common Toad (*Bufo bufo*) as present, the latter being sometimes found in gardens in the evening. Frogs were patchy in distribution. Buckley and Harvie-Brown (1891) however, only mention the toad ('common'); frogs had presumably been wiped out by the end of the nineteenth century. Toads are now rare except on Hoy and the West Mainland and are decreasing there. There have been numerous releases of frogs over the past 30 years or so, and they seem to be established on Egilsay and Rousay. Spawn has been found on Burray, Mainland, Sanday and South Ronaldsay but it is not known where there are permanent populations on these islands. Attempts to introduce newts seem to have been unsuccessful.

The future of Orkney's fresh waters

Running and standing water can be regarded as indicators of the sustainability of the land-use in their catchments. Waste will show up in water quality as well as the life in the loch or stream. With increased loads of waste products the diversity of organisms generally decreases and many beautiful and delicate species are lost.

Some small lochs are gradually being choked by vegetation. This is partly due to agricultural enrichment which increases the speed of succession towards marsh and eventually dry land. This is especially apparent at Hooking Loch, North Ronaldsay.

The most severe damage to Orkney lochs has been through drainage. In recent years a number of smaller lochs throughout the islands have been drained and there are likely to be other marshy areas (and perhaps shallow lochs) considered for reclamation in the foreseeable future. It is difficult to predict what will happen in the farming/conservation conflict, but it is essential that each and every drainage application should be examined most carefully; wetlands are part of Orkney's most precious heritage, and their destruction or alteration in any way would detract from the islands considerably, to say nothing of the moral responsibility which Orcadians have for their own habitats.

Further reading

Balfour-Browne, 1949; Barnes, 1980; Barry, 1805; Britton, 1974; Buckley and Harvie-Brown, 1891; Bullard, 1972, 1975; Bullard and Goode, 1975; Dunn, 1973; Heppleston, 1972, 1983a, 1983b, 1983c, 1984; Kellock and Maitland, 1969; Low, 1813; Maitland, 1979; Maitland and Kellock, 1971; Murray and Pullar, 1908; Nicol, 1938; Sutcliffe, 1974; Swan, 1997; Trowbridge and Heppleston, 1984; West and West, 1905.

Chapter 7

Terrestrial Animals

The land animals of Orkney are not, in general, well known. There are few mammals, of which the Orkney Vole and the seaweed-eating sheep of North Ronaldsay are the most distinctive. The Lepidoptera have been studied in some detail, largely through the labours of a London businessman, Ian Lorimer, who married an Orcadian, spent many holidays in the islands, and then retired there. His work has been carried on by his local collaborator, Sydney Gauld of St Ola. The Mollusca were lovingly collected for many years by Robert Rendall, poet, theologian, and local businessman; his labours have been continued by Alan Skene of Stromness and Mrs Nora McMillan of the Merseyside Museum. All other groups are very patchily known.

Mammals

Orkney Vole
Arguments over the origin of the Orkney Vole have already been presented (Chapter 1). It was first recognized as distinct from the Common Vole (*Microtus agrestis*) of mainland Britain by J. G. Millais in 1904. His original specimens came from Stenness. The discovery caused great excitement (p. 231), and Millais was prompted to collect voles from other islands. A year after his original description, Millais added a sub-species from Sanday, *Microtus orcadensis sandayensis*, on the grounds of a lighter colour than the Mainland form ('hair-brown rather than mummy-brown' above; cream-buff ventrally) and a shallow 'first outer re-entrant angle of the first molar'. In the next few years further sub-species were added from Westray, Rousay and South Ronaldsay. The Westray voles were said to be slighter, smaller and darker than the Sanday ones; the other two races could not be distinguished

from the Mainland form on external appearances but were differentiated on trivial cranial traits.

It was pointed out as early as 1905 that the Orkney Vole was very similar to the widespread Continental Vole, *Microtus arvalis*, but it was not until the 1950s that it was shown that *arvalis* and *orcadensis* had apparently identical chromosomes, and could in fact hybridize freely and produce fertile young. The various Orkney races are now regarded as sub-species of *M. arvalis*. It is doubtful if the inter-island distinctions are worth even sub-specific recognition. The Westray animals are the most distinct.

Some years ago, Fred Rose, the then biology teacher at Kirkwall Grammar School, and I carried out a detailed examination of the relationships of the different Orkney races to each other, and to different continental populations. We were led to do this by a remark of Dr Gordon Corbet of the Natural History Museum in London, that Orkney Voles seemed to be more like *M. arvalis* from southern Europe than from Germany. My flippant response to this was that it suggested voles were originally introduced to Orkney from ships of the Spanish Armada which were wrecked on the islands. Fred Rose and I then set out to determine the relationships between as many population samples as we could obtain. We used the frequency of non-metrical skull traits in our work. (These are characters such as extra bones in sutures, missing foramina, etc.) These traits are known to be inherited, and their incidences in different populations can be used as a measure of the genetic difference between the populations in question. When a large number of such measures are combined, a single multivariate statistic can be obtained which is a measure of genetic distinctiveness or distance: the larger the distance, the less closely are the populations related.

Figure 7.1
Orkney Vole.
Photo: F. Rose

Figure 7.2
Orkney Vole as painted by Archibald Thorburn for J. G. Millais's *Mammals of Great Britain & Ireland*.

It was clear from our work that the Orkney races were markedly different from all other populations to which they were compared, whilst most of the continental samples were apparently closely related to each other. The only place where *Microtus arvalis* occurs in the British Isles outside Orkney, is in Guernsey. The Guernsey Voles were very similar to north German animals on the characters we used (Figure 7.3).

Now if the Orkney Voles are a relict of a previously widespread north-west European population, they should resemble most closely their geographical neighbours. Most differences would be assumed to have arisen following isolation. If, on the other hand, the voles colonized Orkney after the islands were cut off from mainland Scotland, they might be expected to show much greater differences: although their closest affinities will obviously be with the population from which they came, the alleles fortuitously carried by the founding animals will mean that the 'genetic distance' between the two may be quite large from the start, never mind any subsequent adaptation as they establish themselves in their new habitat. Consequently, the existence of large and apparently random differences between geographically close (but isolated) populations indicate that the populations have been founded by introduction rather than surviving as relicts. On these criteria, Orkney Voles are clearly not relicts.

We know that voles have been in the islands 4,000 years or more, because their remains have been found in the lower layers of buildings excavated at Skara Brae. It seems reasonable to assume that they were introduced by some of the first human colonists to the islands, presumably inadvertently. It is possible that these colonizers came from the eastern Mediterranean, where

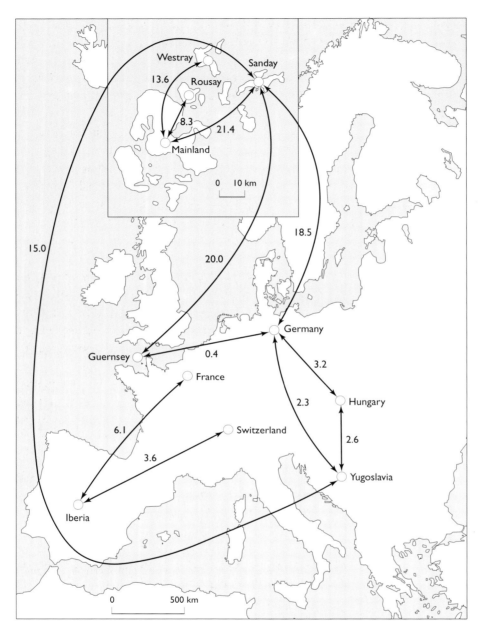

Figure 7.3
Measures of genetic distance based on non-metrical skull characters between samples from *Microtus arvalis* populations. The closest relatives of the Orkney Vole (inset at top) are in Yugoslavia; the Continental forms are much more homogenous than the introduced Orkney races; and the four Orkney races can be most easily derived from an original colonization on Sanday, thence to Mainland and from there independently to Westray and Rousay.
Based on Berry and Rose, 1975

the Orkney Voles have their apparent closest relatives; but that is rather a long way to stretch the argument.

The Sanday voles are the ones most like any continental sample, followed by Mainland, Rousay, and Westray, in that order. From comparisons with other populations, it is likely that the Rousay population was founded from the Mainland, which makes geographical sense.

The Mainland population could have been an off-shoot of the Sanday race, or may have been a completely different introduction; the Westray population is rather nearer Mainland than Sanday, but the Westray and Sanday voles are now regarded as indistinguishable in traditional taxonomic traits (despite their separation by early workers). Hence it seems reasonable to suggest that the Westray race originated from Sanday. There is no case for arguing that the sandy colour of the Sanday voles is a cryptic adaptation to the widespread exposed sand on that island, since Westray is topographically very different from Sanday and not at all sandy – but on average the voles are the same colour. Voles on the South Isles (South Ronaldsay and Burray; there are no voles on Hoy) are probably indistinguishable from Mainland ones. There are now no voles on Shapinsay; they were last recorded there in 1906. Voles were introduced into Eday from Westray in 1987 and 1988, allegedly by birdwatchers to encourage raptors to nest on Eday.

A number of colour forms have been reported; in his book, Groundwater notes black, white, russet, and grey. Most of these are probably recent mutants. However, black animals occur not infrequently in (particularly) the Stenness area. Although some of these may be true melanics, others seem to be 'slow moulters' which lose their black colouration after several weeks. This is a phenomenon which needs more investigation.

The Orkney Vole occupies a wide range of habitats, including marsh, heather, grass and growing crops. It is found up to about 700 feet (200 metres) in the hills. Unlike the continental form, it does not seem to inhabit short pasture or arable land. It makes long runways, with subterranean nests if the ground permits. The runways extend up to 20 feet (6 metres) from the nest. In captivity, the animals are docile, and readily live in groups as long as only one mature male is present. They are the main prey of Hen Harriers and Short-eared Owls.

North Ronaldsay sheep

The North Ronaldsay sheep are small and short-tailed, related to the Soay sheep of St Kilda, and the primitive sheep of Shetland and Iceland. They were formerly found on Flotta, as well as on North Ronaldsay, but they are now confined almost entirely to the latter island (plus Linga Holm off Stronsay, where the Rare Breeds Survival Trust established a flock in 1974 to ensure their survival if anything happened to the animals on North Ronaldsay; a small flock was also introduced to Auskerry in the mid 1990s).

On North Ronaldsay, the sheep are kept away from the cultivated land by a 6-foot (2-metres) high, 12-mile (19-kilometres) long wall, which runs right round the island. Since there is little grass outside the wall, the sheep feed almost entirely on seaweed.

The date of the wall is unknown; its earliest mention is in the *Statistical Account* of 1832. It was associated with strip cultivation and corresponds to

Figure 7.4
North Ronaldsay
sheep.
Photo: Richard Welsby

the boundary wall of common hill grazing, to which the shore on North
Ronaldsay is equivalent. Strip cultivation was abolished on the island in the
1880s, but communal sheep husbandry continued apparently unchanged,
regulated by an island Court of twelve elected 'sheep men' acting on regulations laid down by the landlord. The regulations state that the tenants of
each of 71 holdings were allowed to keep between ten and 60 sheep on the
shore, with the sheep men being permitted an extra ten sheep for their
trouble. From the earliest records in 1790 until comparatively recently there
were about 2,000 sheep on the island; there are now at least twice as many,
largely because of inadequate manpower to organize effective management.
Each tenant was responsible for the repair of a length of the perimeter wall,
so that it remained 'above leaping height'. The decline in the island human
population means that the wall is not now kept in as good repair as it should
be, and it is not infrequently breached.

Although the sheep are free to wander over all the shore, they behave like
hill sheep and keep to their own area or *clowgang*, a term that is elsewhere
given to the sheep pasture of a crofting township. The only time the sheep
come within the wall is after lambing, when the ewes are tethered on grass.

The North Ronaldsay sheep are small, the carcass weight of a mature ewe
being only about 30 lbs (13.5 kg). The lambs are also small at birth, around
three to four pounds (1.4 to 1.8 kg); lambing takes place in late April to early
May. Traditional management involves one lamb of any twin pair being
killed, so that each ewe has a single lamb to feed. On average, one in four
ewes and their lambs are returned to the shore in August. One ram lamb to
every twenty ewes is left uncastrated. This is a high proportion of rams, even
by pre-modern standards. This may be to allow for deaths on the shore;

despite their adaptation to exposed conditions, mortality is relatively high.

The original North Atlantic sheep were very variable in colour. Iceland and Shetland sheep still contain many brown and black individuals. In 1730 on Sanday, there were 57 per cent white, 24 per cent black, 18 per cent grey, and 1 per cent 'tanay'. However, the North Ronaldsay crofters select lighter-coloured rams for breeding: some use grey animals in the belief that they are the most vigorous, others preferring white males because white wool fetches the highest prices. The commonest colour nowadays is grey, often with a black line along the backbone.

As in Soay sheep, there is a hairy and a woolly type of coat. Both black and white fleeces can be hairy, but because hairy fibres tend to be dark, black and grey fleeces are usually more hairy than white ones. In fact, grey fleeces are the hairiest, because they consist of mainly white wool mixed with black hairs. White hairs are typically woolly, and as fine as the best Shetland wool. In his *Tour*, Low described the annual 'rooing' or plucking of fleece in mid-summer, which enabled the wool to be obtained unmixed with hair. 'Rooing' still takes place, although more often in Shetland than Orkney.

Well-meaning animal-lovers have sometimes been offended at the rather scruffy appearance of North Ronaldsay sheep, and taken animals away to good pasture. Invariably many animals die if this is done. This used to be thought to be because they in some way needed seaweed in their diet. It is now known that the deaths are due to copper poisoning: there is only a small amount of available copper in seaweed, and Orkney sheep have an inherited ability for high efficiency in absorbing copper; when they feed on grass containing more copper than they are used to, they absorb it in often toxic quantities.

Other mammals

The other land mammals of Orkney are largely unremarkable (Booth and Booth, 1994). There are only a few species present, and many of them reflect nothing more than the interests and endeavours of past generations of naturalists. The best evidence of this is the Hedgehog (*Erinaceus europaeus*). Writing in 1848, Baikie and Heddle do not list the Hedgehog as being present in Orkney. Buckley and Harvie-Brown (whose book was published in 1891) state that a few Hedgehogs brought from Dirleton, near Edinburgh, were released around 1870. However, they were not abundant on mainland Orkney until the 1950s. The known later introductions are:

1930s   The cargo boats *Cormorant* and *Busy Bee* came each summer to Orkney with fencing stabs from Loch Eriboll in Sutherland. The crews gave out Hedgehogs to small boys who played about the pier at Kirkwall.

1946   Four Hedgehogs from Shetland were released at Holm in

	the Mainland. In exchange, a box of Cabbage White butterflies was taken from Orkney and released in Shetland.
Late 1940s	Hedgehogs from Netherbutton, Holm were released in Westray.
1949	Twelve Hedgehogs from Stroma were released in Hoy.
1958	Four Hedgehogs from mainland Orkney were released in Egilsay.
1965	Hedgehogs from mainland Orkney were released at Melsetter in Longhope.
1965	Hedgehogs from Egilsay were released in Wyre.
1972	A pair were released in a greenhouse on North Ronaldsay to help control slugs, but they escaped.
1972	Four were brought to Eday in October and released in April 1973; one had a litter that year.
1976	Hedgehogs were noted on Sanday, where there had probably been an introduction a year or two earlier.
1980	Several were released on Gairsay, but some were later found dead and the introduction was unsuccessful.
1980	About this time, Hedgehogs were released on Stronsay, where they are now well established.

Apart from the islands mentioned above, Hedgehogs are present on Burray, Flotta, Graemsay and South Ronaldsay, but details of when they were introduced are not known.

Hedgehogs feed mainly on invertebrates, but they will eat eggs and young of ground-nesting birds. On North Ronaldsay they increased rapidly following their introduction in 1972. As there had been a decline in the breeding success of the ground-nesting birds on the island, it was thought that this might be due to predation by Hedgehogs.

In 1986 it was estimated that there were 514 Hedgehogs on the island (and that they were longer lived and slightly heavier than Hedgehogs from elsewhere). Two hundred animals were airlifted from the island and released on mainland Scotland. In 1991, there were estimated to be 105 Hedgehogs on North Ronaldsay. Unfortunately there was no improvement in the breeding success of ground-nesting birds

Both British hares occur on Orkney, the Mountain Hare (*Lepus timidus*) on Hoy and the Brown Hare (*L. europaeus*) on the Mainland. Earl Harald is recorded in the *Orkneyinga Saga* as 'hunting hares', but we are not told where and which species.

Mountain Hares were certainly present on Hoy at the beginning of the sixteenth century as there is a reference by John Bellenden in 1529 to white hares being hunted there with dogs. Barry (1805) notes: 'There are no foxes nor hares, only I was informed that about eighty years ago there were

Figure 7.5
Mountain Hare on
Hoy.
Photo: Richard Welsby

several, either white or black hares, on the two great mountains of Choye' (Hoy).

Low, in the eighteenth century, does not specifically mention the Mountain Hare, but noted that a Mr Moodie of Melsetter had tried to introduce Hares. He also made reference to the fact that Rabbits which 'continually keep to the mountains, are in the winter hoary', but it is unlikely he would have mistaken the Rabbit for the Mountain Hare. Baikie and Heddle stated that the 'Alpine Hare was extinct' and this was reiterated by Buckley and Harvie-Brown in 1891, but they also said that mountain hares were introduced into Gairsay about 1875 and were still present there in 1884. They are now extinct on the island and there is no record of when they were last seen. It would seem therefore that the Mountain Hare became extinct on Hoy about 1620, and a re-introduction made after 1891, probably between 1898 and 1914. Mountain Hares were introduced into Shetland in 1900 and also in 1907.

The species is now fairly common above the hundred-metre contour with a population of 300 to 400, a higher density than on other Scottish islands and much of mainland Scotland.

The Brown Hare is widely distributed on the Mainland, although numbers have decreased considerably over the past few decades, as they have also in mainland Britain. Before this it was very common. In December 1955, the *Orcadian* recorded the export of three tons of hares (about 800 animals) to Germany.

Brown Hares were introduced into both Orkney and Shetland about 1830 by the then Member of Parliament, Samuel Laing. A number of individuals were released on the Mainland, near Kirkwall. Buckley and Harvie-Brown record that hares were present in good numbers on Hoy, Eday, Rousay, Shapinsay and South Ronaldsay, and that they had been taken to Papa Westray by the Traill family. However, after the Traills left, the hares were rapidly exterminated by the local tenants. Nowadays they are found only on the Mainland; they were last recorded on Rousay in 1977.

Rabbits (*Oryctolagus cuniculus*) are abundant on the larger islands, and are mentioned by all the early naturalists. Wallace in 1693 noted that there were warrens in almost every isle, well stocked with rabbits. Thirty-six thousand skins were exported in 1792, and 25,890 in 1819. Myxomatosis arrived in 1954, being first seen on Burray in August of that year. It spread rapidly in the 1960s and reduced populations for a time. Outbreaks still occur, but many individuals do not show symptoms and others recover; rabbits seem more abundant than ever in some places.

Among rodents, the Orkney Vole has been discussed. No other voles occur. The Long-tailed Field Mouse (it is meaningless to call it by its English and continental name of 'wood mouse' since in Northern Scotland it is much more an animal of the hills and moors) (*Apodemus sylvaticus*) was described by Low in the 1770s. It is probably under-recorded (Table 7.1); as recently as 1984 it was reported from Sanday for the first time (although it may, of course, be a new introduction there). Shetland and Hebridean Field Mice are more closely related to the Norwegian population than to that of the Scottish mainland; they were probably brought to the islands as commensals by the Vikings. Nothing is known about the relationships of the Orkney animals.

House Mice (*Mus domesticus*) were recorded by Baikie and Heddle as being common everywhere except on a few of the smaller isles; Buckley and Harvie-Brown note they were abundant everywhere 'including Stronsay'. Numbers have decreased in recent years as the main reservoir of the species in winter stacks of corn has declined, and with it the availability of secure refuge habitats.

A study of the population on North Faray, which has had no permanent human inhabitants since 1946, showed that numbers regularly fall below 50 during the winter. It seems likely that the species will become extinct here soon. The populations on three islands (Eday, Westray and Faray) are unusual in having fewer chromosomes than usual, as a result of fusion (or Robertsonian translocation) between different chromosomes. The normal diploid chromosome number in House Mice is 40. On Eday, the mice have 34 chromosomes, on Westray and Faray 36, although the fusions on Faray are different from those on Westray. A similar but more complicated situation occurs in Caithness. Fusions of this nature have been reported also in Switzerland, Germany and Italy, but the Caithness and Orkney fusions are the only ones known in Britain (Scriven and Brooker, 1990; Searle, 1991). The reason for this variation is unknown. Eday mice introduced into an existing population on the Isle of May in the Firth of Forth bred successfully with the native animals, and the Eday fused chromosomes spread (Scriven, 1992).

In the 1770s, Low stated that the Black (or Ship) Rat (*Rattus rattus*) was 'still present in South Ronaldsay where there were no Brown Rats', but numbers appeared to be declining on other islands as Brown Rats (*Rattus norvegicus*) increased. However, Black Rats persisted on South Ronaldsay at least until the 1930s when it was recorded on three separate occasions. The last Black Rats in Orkney were in Westray. They came from a German grain boat which ran aground in 1939 below the farm of Skaill at the south end of the island. Rats spread rapidly over the southern half of the island, but then apparently retreated again and were last recorded in 1968. The *Old Statistical Account* of 1795–98 recorded both Black and Brown Rats in Kirkwall and St Ola, but no rats of either species on Eynhallow, Rousay or Egilsay.

Figure 7.6
Cattle are now feral on Swona, left when the last human inhabitants moved away from the island.
Photo: Richard Welsby

Buckley and Harvie-Brown reported Brown Rats on Stronsay in 1868 and Sanday in 1888. Among the larger islands they are still absent from Westray and North Ronaldsay. The species occurs on some of the smaller islands, including Eynhallow where it was first recorded in 1998, probably introduced with sheep feed during the preceding winter. Strenuous attempts to exterminate the rats were immediately taken before too many birds were killed.

In common with many of the other Scottish islands, the only shrew is the Pygmy Shrew (*Sorex minutus*). Low stated it to be rare in the 1770s although it was recorded from Birsay in the *Old Statistical Account*. It is now fairly widely distributed and common. Water Shrews (*Neomys fodiens*) are said to occur on Hoy, but the records are doubtful.

There are no native deer in Orkney, although bones of Red Deer (*Cervus elaphus*) have been found in peat, notably on Hoy and Westray. A Westray farmer experimented with Red Deer farming in the early 1980s.

Bats
Early naturalists regarded bats as only occasional visitors to Orkney and there are many Orcadians who have never seen a bat in the islands. However, small colonies of Pipistrelle (*Pipistrellus pipistrellus*) do occur. There were regular sightings of Pipistrelles in Stromness from the 1940s to 1991, with up to five having been seen together at any one time. The roost was probably in the Old Academy, but following repairs and other building work carried out there about 1990 when two were found dead, this roost appears to have been abandoned and there have been no recent reports from the town.

Table 7.1 Mammals recorded in Orkney. The year is the last record for each species (up to the end of 1995). *(Data provided by Mrs Sheila Spence.)*

	Brown Hare	Mountain Hare	Hedgehog	House Mouse	Wood Mouse	Otter	Rabbit	Black Rat	Brown Rat	Common Seal	Grey Seal	Pygmy Shrew	Water Shrew	Orkney Vole	Noctule Bat	Pipistrelle Bat	Bearded Seal	Walrus	Ringed Seal
Mainland	1995		1995	1994	1994	1995	1995		1995	1993	1993	1995		1995		1990	1988		1992
Shapinsay			1987	1968	1968	1968	1968		1972	1971		1968					1988		
Gairsay						1960	1994		1993		1971								
Wyre			1971	1971		1971			1971	1968	1968								
Egilsay			1994	1971		1994	1994		1971	1971	1971	1994							
Rousay	1977			1993		1994	1994		1993	1971	1971	1993		1993				1986	
Eynhallow						1960				1971	1971								
North Faray				1971							1971								
Westray			1994	1971		1994	1994	1968		1971		1994		1994					
Papa Westray			1986	1986	1986		1994		1993	1975	1976								
Eday			1984	1982	1965	1994	1994		1993					1993					
Stronsay			1995	1995	1995	1995	1995		1995	1971	1971	1995							
Sanday			1984	1971	1991	1994	1994		1968	1971	1971			1991		1994			
North Ronaldsay			1994	1994	1994	1994	1994				1971				1976				
Burray			1995	1991		1994	1994		1995	1961									
Lamb Holm						1993	1994												
Glims Holm						1994	1994					1994			1988				
South Ronaldsay			1994	1994		1994	1994		1994	1974	1971	1994		1995					
Hoy		1994	1993	1971	1972	1994	1995		1990	1974	1971	1995							
Longhope				1971		1994	1994			1974		1995							
Graemsay			1978	1971	1973	1995	1973			1974		1994							
Flotta			1974	1974		1972			1973	1974		1973							
Cava						1972			1974	1974		1966							
Copinsay				1972	1972	1973	1994				1975	1972							
Swona				1994			1995			1974	1971	1994							
Holm of Grimbister				1972								1972							
Damsay									1972										
Switha						1973				1974	1971								
Holm of Aikerness										1971									
Auskerry											1971								
Linga Holm					1977	1994	1994			1977	1968	1994							

Table 7.1 continued.

	Brown Hare	Mountain Hare	Hedgehog	House Mouse	Wood Mouse	Otter	Rabbit	Black Rat	Brown Rat	Common Seal	Grey Seal	Pygmy Shrew	Water Shrew	Orkney Vole	Noctule Bat	Pipistrelle Bat	Beared Seal	Walrus	Ringed Seal
Muckle Green Holm									1994										
Little Green Holm											1971								
Holm of Faray											1971								
Wart Holm											1971								
Rusk Holm											1971								
Sweyn Holm											1971								
Holm of Boray											1971								
Grass Holm											1971								
Little Skerry											1971								
South Fara						1970	1993		1987	1974									
Long Holm Harray Loch														1989					
Ling Holm Harray Loch														1989					
Baa Holm Harry Loch														1989					
Glass Holm														1989					
Holm of Huip							1993		1993			1993							
Hunda							1972												
Calf of Copinsay										1975									
Barrel of Butter										1974									
Holm of Papa Westray						1994	1994			1975									

Another site from which there have been reports as long ago as the nineteenth century is Melsetter, Hoy. In 1994, this was confirmed as a colony of Pipistrelles, probably fewer than ten animals, of the type that calls at 45kHz.

At present this is the most northerly known colony, not only of Pipistrelles but of any bat species in Britain. Colonies of Pipistrelles do move the location of their roosts and it is possible that there are sometimes roosts elsewhere in the islands. There have been reports in the past of bats from Rousay and Shapinsay during the summer months, and also the finding of a pregnant female Pipistrelle in Kirkwall at the end of June 1995.

Four other species of bats have been recorded in Orkney, including a Hoary Bat (*Lasiurus cinereus*) in South Ronaldsay in 1847. This is a large North American bat which makes long-distance migrations and is quite capable of accomplishing the journey to Orkney unaided. There have been records of single Noctule (*Nyctalus noctula*) bats in 1976, 1978 and 1988 and of Brown Long-eared Bats (*Plecotus auritus*) in 1931, 1948 and 1987. These may have come from colonies further south in Britain, but a Continental origin is almost certain for a Nathusius' Pipistrelle (*P. nathusii*) found in South Ronaldsay in June 1995.

There have been a number of sightings of unidentified bats away from any of the possible roost locations, most frequently between July and October with a peak in October, often at times when numbers of migrant birds, usually from the Continent, are passing through the islands.

Invertebrates

Although many people have collected or incidentally recorded invertebrates in Orkney, the only fairly well-known group is the Lepidoptera, largely as the result of the work of Ian Lorimer of Orphir, who has summarized his own and other people's records in the *Lepidoptera of the Orkney Islands* (1983), updated posthumously as *Unfinished Business* (1998). Other groups with more than fortuitous records are listed in the Appendix. Orkney is no better or worse off than other British islands in invertebrate knowledge, as can be seen by comparing the publication lists for different groups in Ken and Vera Smith's *Bibliography of the Entomology of the Smaller British Offshore Islands* (1983).

As far as Lepidoptera are concerned, 424 species have been recorded, almost half of them since the early 1960s. This list is apparently very slight when compared with over 2,500 species for Great Britain as a whole. Notwithstanding, and recognizing that species will continue to be added to the Orkney total, it probably represents fairly the depauperate nature of the fauna of a north temperate, windswept archipelago. It is difficult to compare the Orkney list with those for Caithness or Shetland, because of the neglect of microlepidoptera in

Figure 7.7
Common Blue
butterflies.
Photo: Richard Welsby

those counties (only partial as far as Shetland is concerned). However, there is no doubt that the Orkney Lepidoptera are much more closely related to Caithness than Shetland, because of the proximity of the former and the fact that insect flight virtually ceases in northerly winds. With the possible exception of the Yellow-ringed Carpet (*Entepheria falvicinctata*), Orkney has no resident species which are absent from Caithness. In contrast, most of the endemic Shetland forms (e.g. Netted Pug, *Eupithecia venosata*; Red Carpet, *Xanthorhoe munitata*; Grass Rivulet, *Perizoma albulata*; etc.) are absent, and in the few cases where a similar local form exists in Orkney and Shetland, it extends also into Caithness (e.g. Dark Marbled Carpet, *Chloroclysta citrata*, and Autumnal Rustic, *Paradiarsia (Amathes) glareosa*). In a few cases (mostly robust and fast-flying noctuids, such as *Diarsia mendica* and *Hadena confusa*), an Orkney series bridges the gap between Caithness and Shetland specimens; among the more fragile and less mobile geomtrids (e.g. *Perizoma albulata*), there is a great difference from the Shetland form.

The Orkney Lepidoptera can be regarded as being divided into 'natives', immigrants, colonists, and imported. This is a rather arbitrary classification, because it is often impossible to know where a particular species should belong, and in particular when a colonist becomes a 'native'. However, there are 31 species (including five with wingless females) which are found only in the sheltered Berriedale to Burn of Segal area of Hoy, which are likely to have been resident for a very long time, perhaps from the times at the end of the Pleistocene when a land connection with Caithness may have still existed (see pp. 19–21).

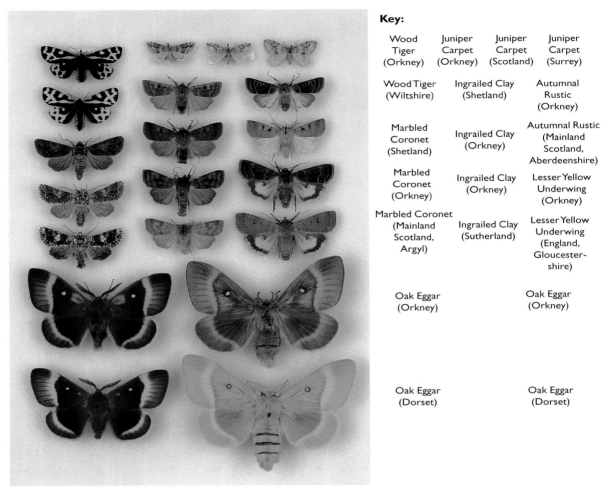

Key:

| Wood Tiger (Orkney) | Juniper Carpet (Orkney) | Juniper Carpet (Scotland) | Juniper Carpet (Surrey) |

| Wood Tiger (Wiltshire) | Ingrailed Clay (Shetland) | Autumnal Rustic (Orkney) |

| Marbled Coronet (Shetland) | Ingrailed Clay (Orkney) | Autumnal Rustic (Mainland Scotland, Aberdeenshire) |

| Marbled Coronet (Orkney) | Ingrailed Clay (Orkney) | Lesser Yellow Underwing (Orkney) |

| Marbled Coronet (Mainland Scotland, Argyl) | Ingrailed Clay (Sutherland) | Lesser Yellow Underwing (England, Gloucester-shire) |

| Oak Eggar (Orkney) | Oak Eggar (Orkney) |

| Oak Eggar (Dorset) | Oak Eggar (Dorset) |

Comparison of the species recorded in the nineteenth century and those currently present show that some species that are now so common and conspicuous that they could not be missed by competent observers are missing from the earlier lists. It seems likely that *Scotopteryx chenopodiata*, *Diachrysia chrysitis* and *Hypena proboscidalis* come into this category; there is good evidence that *Pieris napi* first appeared in Orkney in the mid-1930s. To 'natural' colonists must be added some species introduced inadvertently on food plants. Such species are found particularly around Binscarth on the Mainland. *Hofmannophila pseudospretella* was recorded in Orkney (on Hoy) only 45 years after the probable date of its first introduction into the United Kingdom from Asia.

Immigrant species have been recorded from 1869 onwards, in every season when lepidopterists have been active. They can be divided into immigrants from the south and south west (from the UK, but also butterflies and moths such as the Red Admiral and the Gem from south Europe and the Mediterranean Basin), usually associated with depressions moving around

Figure 7.8
Local forms of many moths are common in Orkney, although not as extreme as in Shetland. The photo shows Orkney forms in comparison with Shetland and mainland Britain.
Photo: Natural History Museum

high-pressure areas well to the south of Orkney; and those from the east and south east such as the Great Brocade and the Scarce Silver Y following sustained high pressure over the Low Countries and southern Scandinavia, most commonly in early August when there is a light on-shore breeze.

Probably some hazel-feeding species still common in Caithness (e.g. *Colocasia coryli*, *Electrophaes corylata*) became extinct in Orkney centuries ago (although the Nut Bud Moth, *Epinotia tenerana*, survives locally, presumably having changed its food plant). Nevertheless, the general picture is of a gradually increasing lepidopteran fauna. The only breeding species whose future seems in doubt (and which should therefore not be collected until more information about it is available) is the Yellow-ringed Carpet, *Entephria flavicinctata*, which lost much of its food plant in a major fire on Hoy in 1984; it is distinct, being recognizably brighter than the mainland Scottish form. However, the devastation of the sand dunes on Burray and the continuing drainage of wetlands could put other species at risk. The opposite problem – over-abundance causing damage to plants – is rare in Orkney; only *Plutella xylostella* has ever been a serious agricultural pest, *Pieris brassicae* is a minor nuisance, and there is no record of the Antler Moth (*Cerapteryx graminis*) ever destroying upland pasture as it may do elsewhere. *Operophtera brumata* has shown an increase in recent years, sometimes defoliating large areas of heather in midsummer. In southern England it is a pest of orchards and forest trees. Flocks of up to 400 Common and Lesser Black-backed Gulls may be seen feeding on the species. The only other major gull predation in Orkney is on tipulids and the cocoons of *Phragmatobia fuliginosa*.

Weather affects moths in Orkney very little, the main exception being northerly winds which almost completely inhibit flying. On the other hand, butterflies are very vulnerable to rain and lack of sun. Wet summers produce a drastic collapse in butterfly populations, especially *Maniola jurtina*, *Argynnis aglaja* and *Polyommatus icarus*. Early flying species are less affected.

Early-spring moths emerge in late April, four or so weeks later than the same species in England, while late-autumn species appear relatively even earlier. The total period of breeding activity is thus reduced by about a quarter. Individual species have adapted in different ways. For example, *Aglais urticae*, the only Orkney butterfly which hibernates as an imago, goes into hibernation almost immediately on emerging in mid-August, although over most of Britain it feeds for six to eight weeks before hibernating.

There is only scattered information about other invertebrate groups. Laurence (1997) has reviewed the occurrence and relationships of the Diptera for both Orkney and Shetland. He finds that most species recorded in the islands are widely distributed on the British mainland, and suggests they have reached the islands in 'successive postglacial invasions'. However, there are species which normally are restricted to mountains which are found down to sea level. Laurence favours interpreting these as relics from early postglacial

Figure 7.9
Golden Ringed
Dragonfly on Hoy.
Photo: Richard Welsby

times; he regards other forms (particularly woodland species) as having arrived in the last 150 years. A generally similar explanation for the beetle fauna is given by Sadler and Buckland (1998).

An interesting situation in bumble bees shows how better knowledge and recording might help us to understand and interpret dynamic interactions within particular groups. By repeated collecting trips, Plowright, Plowright and Williams (1997) have shown the *Bombus muscorum*, which used to be found widely on northern coasts and islands in Britain and Ireland and which had a distinct subspecies *orcadensis* in Orkney, was largely replaced in the 1980s by its widespread conspecific *B. pascuorum*; *B. m. orcadensis* may now be extinct. The reason for this is unknown, but *B. muscorum* is larger and has denser hair than its relative, and may have been better adapted to harsher conditions in the north. *B. pascuorum* was regularly recorded as an immigrant into Orkney; it could be that climatic changes have provided it with the opportunity to out-compete the native bees.

And finally, the New Zealand flatworm (*Artioposthia triangulata*) which causes havoc in southern British swards is in gardens in Stromness and Kirkwall, but so far has not been reported as causing damage.

Mite allergy

An interesting interaction between invertebrates and the human population has emerged from an investigation into the causes of asthma and rhinitis (hay fever) among the farming population of Orkney. One of the principal factors in these conditions is the high level of mite infestation of stored hay and grain. These so-called 'stored product' or 'storage' mites feed on the fungi that grow in stored feedstuffs, and are therefore numerous in the damp and humid climate of Orkney, being particularly prevalent after a wet summer when the hay has been baled and stacked before being adequately dry. Although individuals are barely visible to the naked eye, very large numbers can often be seen as a coating of pinkish dust on the floor of the barn in which the hay is stacked. The numbers of these mites are greatest in October soon after stacking, when the fungal content is high and they have adequate food available.

In the winter of 1977–78, samples from a number of Orkney farms showed an average of over 1,000 mites per gram of stored hay in October, falling to 350 in November and eventually averaging out at about 500 mites per gram (which represents over 12 million mites in a half-hundredweight bale).

There is a wide variety of 'storage' mite species present in the hay, but those found most frequently and in the greatest numbers in Orkney hay are *Acarus farris*, *Tyrophagus longior*, and *Calvolia* sp. *hypopi*. *Glycyphagus destructor* is also found but to a lesser extent, although it appears to be one of the principal causes of allergic symptoms. These species are also important in producing allergic respiratory diseases on the Scottish mainland, but the numbers there are less than in Orkney.

The house dust mite (*Dermatophagoides pteronyssinus*) and other pyroglyphid species, which are among the commonest causes of allergic asthma generally, are as prevalent in Orkney houses as in houses elsewhere, but are not found in stored hay or grain.

Further reading

MAMMALS
Baikie and Heddle, 1848; Berry, 1977; Berry and Rose, 1975; Booth and Booth, 1994, 1998; Buckley and Harvie-Brown, 1891; Corbet and Harris, 1991; Ellison, 1906; Godfrey, 1906; Groundwater, 1974; Hewson, 1948; Hinton, 1913; Major, 1905; Millais, 1905; Miller, 1908; Rose, 1975; Ryder, 1983; Ryder, Land and Ditchburn, 1974; Scriven, 1992; Scriven and Brooker, 1990; Searle, 1991; Turner, 1965; Turtle, 1997; Zimmermann, 1959.

INVERTEBRATES
Bradley and Fletcher, 1979; Cuthbert *et al.*, 1979, 1983; Foster and Parsons, 1997; Laurence, 1997; Lorimer, 1975, 1983, 1998; Picozzi, 1981; Plowright, Plowright and Williams, 1997; Smith and Smith, 1983; South, 1888; Traill, 1869, 1888; White, 1882. See also the references given in the lists in the Appendix referring to invertebrates.

Chapter 8

Birds*

Visitors to Orkney quickly become aware of the richness of its bird life, a richness which has drawn a steady stream of ornithologists to the islands for the past 150 years. This richness is chiefly the result of the presence of several different semi-natural habitats being found within a relatively small area. From the immense sea cliffs with their teeming sea bird 'cities', one need move only a few paces inland and be standing on maritime heath, the summer home of thousands of Arctic Terns and Arctic Skuas. Then, within less than a mile or so it is possible to leave the seabirds behind entirely and be among some of the best wetlands and loch shores in the country, with up to eight breeding species of ducks and seven of waders. Climbing a little further, the visitor can be among the heather-covered ground of the hills and moors, the song of Curlews everywhere, and the chance of seeing a hunting Hen Harrier or Short-eared Owl. Even farmland, a habitat becoming increasingly desert-like in southern Britain, has retained good bird numbers, although even in Orkney agricultural intensification is beginning to take its toll.

The importance of Orkney for its breeding birds is reflected in the fact that the Royal Society for the Protection of Birds has no fewer than eleven reserves in the islands, some 8 per cent of the land area. The sea cliffs are rep-

---

* This chapter has been written by Eric Meek (see p. viii).

Figure 8.1
Seabird cliffs, a never-failing excitement for casual observer as well as experienced ornithologist.
Photo: Richard Welsby

resented by Marwick Head and Copinsay, each with around 50,000 sea birds, and the Noup Cliffs (Westray) which has in excess of 100,000. The maritime heath reserve is the North Hill of Papa Westray, a 200-hectare site which often holds the largest Arctic Tern colony in Britain, together with up to 150 pairs of Arctic Skuas. The Loons (Mainland) and the Mill Dam (Shapinsay) represent wetlands; both are overlooked by hides which give excellent views of ducks and waders. Moorland sites are the Birsay Moors and Cottascarth, and Hobbister (both Mainland), Trumland (Rousay) and the spectacular, mountainous reserve of Hoy; all are important for breeding divers, raptors and skuas.

Table 8.1

Birds breeding regularly in Caithness but not in Orkney

Black-thoated Diver	Sand Martin	Spotted Flycatcher
Common Scoter	Tree Pipit	Long-tailed Tit
Goosander	Grey Wagtail	Coal Tit
Ptarmigan	Dipper	Blue Tit
Grey Partridge	Redstart	Great Tit
Woodcock	Whinchat	Treecreeper
Greenshank	Ring Ouzel	Magpie
Wood Sandpiper	Mistle Thrush	Siskin
Cuckoo	Grasshopper Warbler	Redpoll
Tawny Owl	Whitethroat	Goldfinch
Long-eared Owl	Blackcap	Crossbill
Swift	Chiffchaff	Bullfinch

Birds breeding regularly in Orkney but not in Caithness

Manx Shearwater	Gadwall	Whimbrel
Storm Petrel	Pintail	Sandwich Tern
Gannet	Black-tailed Godwit	

Birds breeding regularly in Orkney but not in Shetland

Little Grebe	Water Rail	Song Thrush
Grey Heron	Coot	Sedge Warbler
Gadwall	Sandwich Tern	Willow Warbler
Hen Harrier	Short-eared Owl	Jackdaw
Sparrowhawk	Dunnock	Greenfinch
Buzzard	Stonechat	Linnet
Pheasant		

Birds breeding regularly in Shetland but not in Orkney

Leach's Petrel	Greenshank	Redwing
Whooper Swan	Red-necked Phalarope	

Birds breeding regularly in Orkney but not in the Western Isles

Gadwall	Pheasant	Whimbrel
Pintail	Water Rail	Sandwich Tern
Sparrowhawk	Black-tailed Godwit	House Martin
		Linnet

Birds breeding regularly in the Western Isles but not in Orkney

Black-throated Diver	Cuckoo	Wood Warbler
Leach's Petrel	Dipper	Spotted Flycatcher
Goosander	Whinchat	Coal Tit
Golden Eagle	Mistle Thrush	Blue Tit
Greenshank	Grasshopper Warbler	Great Tit
	Whitethroat	Treecreeper

Many of the RSPB reserves are in Sites of Special Scientific Interest (SSSIs), conservation areas designated (but not owned or managed) by the government conservation agency, Scottish Natural Heritage, which cover about 22 per cent of the land area. As the majority of SSSIs have been designated for their bird interest, these figures underline the national and international importance of Orkney in an ornithological context.

Orkney supports vast numbers of seabirds, but it is also close to the landbird 'reservoir' of mainland Britain. It is instructive to compare and contrast the breeding birds of Orkney with those of Shetland and with Caithness, the closest part of the Scottish mainland (Table 8.1).

Breeding birds

Divers and grebes
Red-throated Divers or Rain Geese are amongst the most characteristic birds of Orkney. Over 130 pairs nest in the islands, a population which is either stable or even slightly increasing despite their apparently poor breeding success. The Orkney birds represent some 10 per cent of the British population, only Shetland having a higher concentration. Within Orkney, most diver nesting sites are on Hoy, the most favoured waters being the small, oligotrophic lochans of the hilltops, although they also nest on islets in some of the larger, more eutrophic, lowland lochs of the Mainland such as Harray and Hundland. The small lochans are usually without fish, so the divers must fly to the sea in order to feed. The preferred food is Sand-eels, and diver breeding success is probably related, at least in part, to the availability of this particular species.

Figure 8.2
Red-throated diver
on nest.
Photo: RSPB

Divers have used some of their current sites for at least 800 years, as is evident from the Norse place name Looma Chun (literally 'lochan of the divers') which is found in both the east and west Mainland as well as on Rousay and Hoy. The densest concentration of nests anywhere in the islands is on the Mill Loch on Eday, a SSSI overlooked by a hide erected by SNH. Another good site at which to watch divers without disturbing them is at Burgar Hill, the wind generator site in Birsay where there is a RSPB hide overlooking Lowrie's Water, a lochan with one to three breeding pairs. Divers are sensitive to disturbance, eggs and small chicks being vulnerable to predators if left unprotected by the adults.

The only other species of diver or grebe to nest in the islands is the Little Grebe. This very scarce breeder is found on a few lowland lochs usually associated with beds of *Phragmites*. The loch at Graemeshall in Holm is one such.

Herons and waterfowl

Most of the Herons in Orkney are migrants from Scandinavia which may arrive as early as July. There is only a very small breeding population of ten to twelve pairs in a forestry plantation; a previously well-known colony on the west Mainland cliffs has not been occupied for over twenty years.

The Mute Swan is conspicuous on many of Orkney's larger lochs. Some 60 pairs nest, up to half of them on the Harray and Stenness Lochs. The colonization of the Harray Loch by the alien Canadian Pondweed *Elodea canadensis* in the 1980s resulted in a vastly increased food supply for the resident swans, and the breeding population quadrupled to 115 pairs by 1990. This phenomenal expansion resulted in many birds forgoing their normal territoriality and nesting colonially, especially on islands in the Harray Loch. The following winter, well over 1,000 Mute Swans were present, together with over 1,000 Whooper Swans and 10,000 Wigeon, all feeding on the burgeoning pondweed. By the spring of 1991, however, juvenile Mute Swans were beginning to die and by the end of that summer at least 250 had succumbed, those on which post-mortems were carried out suffering from gut infestations of a parasitic worm. By 1992 the breeding numbers on the two lochs had slumped to just thirteen pairs; the slow climb back to normal numbers gradually took place, although in 1998 numbers leapt to 60 pairs, an indication that pondweed might be peaking again.

A single pair of Greylag Geese were first found nesting in 1985, at the Loch of Hundland. Over the next decade, breeding numbers increased and there are now around 100 pairs, mainly on the islands in Wide Firth with others in the west Mainland and on Shapinsay, Rousay and Copinsay. It was first thought that this colonization was natural, stemming from Icelandic winterers lingering into the spring. However, it later became apparent that birds may have originated from a release scheme related to a shooting enter-

Figure 8.3a
Eiders off Stronsay.
Photo: David Wood

Figure 8.3b
Eider nesting in an old
fish box.
Photo: Eric Meek

prise on Shapinsay. It should be noted, however, that Greylags began breeding in Shetland at about the same time, and it is unlikely that these birds also had their origins in Shapinsay.

A further possibility is that the Orkney breeding population may be related to the native Greylags of north-west Scotland. This seemed remote until two colour-marked birds originally caught in Sutherland the previous summer were seen in the islands, in winter 1996/97.

No fewer than ten species of ducks breed regularly in Orkney. The Mallard is by far the commonest, nesting in a wide variety of habitats. Of the other dabbling ducks, Teal is the next most numerous, and like the somewhat less common Wigeon, is catholic in its choice of nest-site, breeding birds being found from very low-lying eutrophic waters up to the highest moorlands. In contrast, Shovelers depend solely on the nutrient-rich waters of low ground. An unusual feature of this species is its disappearance from almost all its Mainland sites during the winter months, despite remaining on its North Isles breeding waters throughout the year. Another of the dabblers is an Orkney speciality, the Pintail. A 1991 survey of the species indicated an Orkney breeding population of 22 to 26 pairs, a remarkable figure when it is considered that the total known British population is no more than 40 pairs. This species too, requires eutrophic waters in the pre-breeding period and for chick rearing, although the nests may be some distance from water. The main Orkney concentrations are in the west Mainland, on Stronsay and on Shapinsay. The scarcest dabbling duck in Orkney, although much commoner than the Pintail in the United Kingdom as a whole, is the Gadwall. Currently confined to the North Ronaldsay and Shapinsay wetlands, Gadwall number only some five to six pairs.

Tufted Ducks are the only true diving ducks nesting in the islands; they are widely scattered in small numbers. Scaup has nested occasionally in the past but does not do so at present. Pochard has recently bred on both North Ronaldsay and Shapinsay. Numbers of moulting male Red-breasted Mergansers at sites such as Echnaloch Bay in Scapa Flow indicate an isles' population of perhaps 150 pairs but nests are rarely found; the first indication of breeding is usually the appearance of a female with ducklings on some of the lochs. Eiders, as might be expected, are mainly coastal in their breeding distribution. However, nests have been found on moorland up to 3 kilometres from the sea. Uninhabited offshore islands hold most breeding pairs, with perhaps as many as 70 on the Copinsay group. Areas of maritime heath also hold good numbers, with 36 nests on the RSPB's North Hill reserve on Papa Westray.

Finally amongst the wildfowl, the Shelduck is believed to number just over 100 breeding pairs in the islands. This burrow-nester forms conspicuous gatherings on inter-tidal mudflats in the early spring, the main localities being Cumminess (Stenness), Otter's Wick (Sanday) and Widewall Bay (South Ronaldsay). The Orkney Shelduck population undertakes a moult migration in autumn, probably to the river estuaries on the north coast of Germany; returning birds can be seen in November and December, although most arrive after the New Year.

Birds of prey and owls

Six diurnal raptors are regular breeding birds. A seventh, Golden Eagle, bred on Hoy between 1966 and 1982 but the female member of the pair disappeared and breeding ceased. The species is now only a rare vagrant. White-tailed Eagles were relatively common breeders in the past but by the 1870s but had been wiped out by persecution. It is to be hoped that the re-introduction programme in the west of Scotland will eventually result in the re-appearance of this magnificent species.

All of the six current breeding species are either scarce or under threat.

Figure 8.4a
Hen Harrier.
Photo: RSPB

Figure 8.4b
Merlin on nest.
Photo: RSPB

The best-known in an Orkney context is the Hen Harrier which was the subject of a long and detailed study by native Orcadian ornithologist, Eddie Balfour, who worked with the species from 1944 to 1974. After Balfour's death, Nick Picozzi of the Institute of Terrestrial Ecology continued with an intensive study from 1976 to 1981. Since then, data on the harriers' breeding biology has been collected by RSPB staff. Protection measures during the 1930s and cessation of gamekeeping during the 1940s allowed an increase in the population (Booth *et al.*, 1984). The increase continued throughout Balfour's time and into the period of Picozzi's study with a peak in 1978 of 95 breeding females in the West Mainland. With small numbers of birds also nesting in the East Mainland, Hoy, Rousay and Eday, it is probable that the

Orkney population exceeded 110 females at that time. As the population increased, polygyny became widespread, with most males paired with either two or three females, although the record was seven. The immediate reason for the polygynous breeding arrangement was an imbalance in the sex ratio, probably due to greater mortality amongst first-winter males compared to first-winter females during their migration south out of the islands. However, it is possible that the breeding habitat could simply support no further males. Within a polygynous male's harem, one female usually receives most of his attention and the food items he brings in. This results in the other females having decidedly poorer breeding success. It is thus disadvantageous to a female to be a member of a polygynous group. However, some subordinate females do manage to rear young, so a polygynous male's breeding output is increased in such a situation.

Since Picozzi's study there has been a marked decline in the Orkney Hen Harrier population, and this has accelerated in recent years. By 1996 the West Mainland held no more than 40 females and perhaps half of these did not attempt to breed; breeding success of the remainder was poor and brood sizes very small. The reason for this change in fortune is probably food-related. Land-use changes on the margins of the moorlands may have resulted in small birds and Orkney Voles being less available at critical times during the breeding cycle. The decline in Harrier numbers is also evident in the communal winter roosts which form in reed-beds or areas of long heather; the three most regularly used sites now contain fewer than ten birds each.

The Merlin is another species which has had changing fortunes but seems, at present, to be holding its own. Up to the 1960s the species had some 25 pairs, although no systematic census was carried out. These numbers fell, possibly the result of pesticide contamination, until there were as few as six pairs in 1984–86. Thereafter, a gradual increase occurred so that by 1993 the population had returned to eighteen pairs, dropping in 1994 to twelve pairs but then rising again in 1995 to sixteen and, in 1996, to twenty. The cause for the marked decline of the mid-1980s has not been established, although the change was mirrored in Shetland. Both populations had unusually high levels of mercury in infertile eggs, but whether this was a causal factor is unproven.

Kestrels have declined greatly since the late 1960s. From being a common bird, the nesting numbers are probably now not more than fifteen pairs. Nest sites vary: sea cliffs, inland crags and deserted buildings are all used, while Orkney is unique in Britain in holding a number of ground-nesting pairs. This habit was first noted in 1945 (Balfour, 1955) and by 1955, nineteen such sites were known. However, only two ground nests were recorded in 1995. Food supply seems to be the controlling factor and, as with the Hen Harrier, it may not necessarily be limiting during the breeding season. The disappearance of oat stacks and hence a decreased availability of mice during the winter months may be the critical factor here. There was a slight upturn in breeding numbers in 1997 and 1998; it remains to be seen whether this will be sustained.

Peregrines in Orkney are mainly sea-cliff breeders, although one or two inland sites are used. Up to eighteen pairs breed annually and the population may never have been many more than this, although it apparently was as low as six in 1919 (Groundwater, 1974). As elsewhere in the country, breeding success was poor during the 1960s. In recent years, the ban on organo-chlorine chemicals has led to a burgeoning of Peregrine numbers in Britain generally, although not in Orkney where breeding success remains relatively poor. The reasons are believed to lie in the fact that much of their prey in the islands consists of seabirds which may be passing on PCBs from the marine environment. Another factor may be the increase in Fulmars on the sea cliffs. Fulmars are known to regurgitate over newly-fledged Peregrines as the latter explore the ledges around their nest-sites; such contaminated birds invariably die.

Sparrowhawks were only irregular breeders until the early 1980s. Since then up to six pairs have bred each year on five different islands. Breeding success is poor, as one might expect for a species usually dependent on an abundance of newly-fledged woodland passerines on which to feed its young. Open-country species such as Meadow Pipit are often found in the prey remains at nests, indicating that adults are hunting in what is, for them, something of an alien environment.

Another recent increase is in Buzzards which only appear to have bred in Orkney since about 1961 (Balfour, 1967). All nesting records are from Hoy where three pairs have bred in recent years. A pair displaying over a West Mainland area in 1991 raised hopes that the species might be about to increase to the levels which the abundant food would seem able to support.

The only species of owl to regularly nest in the islands is the Short-eared or Cattie-face, although a few pairs of Long-eared Owls bred in Orkney in the mid-1950s, again between 1968–71, and then in 1997. The former is mainly a bird of the extensive moorlands of the Mainland and Rousay. Although young Rabbits and Brown Rats are quite important in terms of biomass, most of the owls' prey comprises Orkney Voles. The vole is, however, absent from Hoy and, presumably for this reason, Short-eared Owls are scarce there. Eday was another island with heather moorland and no voles; it had small numbers of breeding owls in the past but birds apparently commuted to nearby Sanday to hunt. Voles have now been introduced to Eday and the owls may find sufficient food nearer to home. In the early 1980s the Mainland population was thought to be as many as 60 pairs, with up to a dozen pairs elsewhere. Fluctuations in numbers certainly occur but these are not as dramatic as in mainland Britain where the main prey is the Common Vole, a species with a markedly cyclical population. Orkney Vole numbers are much more constant, and variations in both their and the Short-eared Owl numbers may be more weather-related. These fluctuations have, however, in more recent years been superimposed on what appears to have been an overall decline, perhaps the result of increasingly intensive agriculture affecting vole distribution and numbers.

Game birds, crakes and rails

Red Grouse are present on suitable moorland but are nowhere plentiful. The wet heath communities of the Orkney hills are not nearly so conducive to the species as the dry heaths of the eastern Highlands so that the lower densities are to be expected. In addition, there is little management of moorland specifically for grouse, so that conditions are far from ideal.

Pheasants have been extensively introduced for shooting purposes and are now a common sight in many of the islands. Attempts to introduce Grey Partridges have not met with success. The only migrant British game bird, the Quail, varies in numbers from year to year. In a good year, several establish territories and breed, but in poor years there may be none at all.

Water Rails are scarce breeders. Very secretive in their reed-bed habitats, regular nesting is thought to occur at only three or four localities; they are commonest in the North Ronaldsay wetlands.

The story of the Corncrake is a sorry one. An abundant nester before and during the nineteenth century, by 1979 the species had declined to just over 100 calling males. A decade later only 30 males remained, and by 1993, only six. This massive decrease was mirrored elsewhere in the species' British range as modern farming methods resulted in the earlier and more rapid cutting of grass destroying nests and birds alike. In 1993 a concerted effort to save the Corncrake from extinction was begun. A RSPB/SNH/Scottish Crofters' Union scheme provided payments to farmers for late cutting of grass (after 1 August) and so-called 'Corncrake-friendly mowing'. The results were initially heartening: in 1994 numbers rose to twenty calling males and, in 1995, to 41. However in 1998 only thirteen calling males were located. It remains to be seen whether the efforts to conserve this species will be successful in the efficient agricultural environment of Orkney.

Moorhens are widespread but thinly distributed in wetland areas and lowland watercourses, and are a species which may have declined due to widespread agricultural drainage. Coots are more local and confined to sites with open water.

Waders

Survey work carried out in 1993 and 1994 has highlighted the importance of Orkney for the commoner wader species, the islands being second only to the Western Isles in terms of UK breeding numbers.

Oystercatchers are one of the bird success stories of the twentieth century.

Having managed to break with tradition and move inland from their original coastal haunts, they now number almost 10,000 pairs. They reach their highest densities on areas of maritime heath, but are found throughout the arable areas. Lapwings have declined as a result of agricultural changes, but more than 5,000 pairs still nest on arable land and wetland. The move away from mixed farming and the drainage of wet field corners are their greatest threat. Redshanks and Snipe are the two waders tied most tightly to wetland habitats and have declined as such areas have been drained. However, about 1,700 pairs of Redshanks and over 3,000 pairs of Snipe are still nesting in the islands, impressive populations for species which in lowland England are now almost confined to nature reserves.

The other common wader of Orkney, and one which visitors comment most upon, is the Curlew. A first impression of Orkney's fields is of almost wall-to-wall Curlews, over 4,000 pairs breeding on the lower ground alone. Taking the higher moors into account, the total Orkney population is believed to be over 5,000 pairs. Research has shown that the intricate mosaic of low-lying moorland (for nesting) and rich agricultural land (for adult feeding) together with the presence within the moorland of insect-rich flushes (for chick feeding) creates ideal conditions for this species which was decidedly scarce in the last century.

Ringed Plovers were last surveyed in 1984 when 560 pairs were recorded, mainly in coastal habitats, but with some on inland loch shores and disturbed ground. The major concentration was in the very suitable habitats in Sanday. In contrast, Golden Plovers are confined as nesters to the higher moorlands. Numbers probably do not exceed 100 pairs with most in northern Hoy and on the northern west Mainland moors. A decline in their population has coincided with the loss of moorland to agriculture. In similar localities but in different habitat are found most of the nesting Dunlins. The pools within hill-top blanket bog are the favourite resort of this species, whose nest and chicks are a real challenge to locate. A few pairs breed on lower ground especially around eutrophic wetlands in the west Mainland; but the total population is probably similar to that of Golden Plover.

In contrast to Shetland, Whimbrels are scarce breeders in Orkney. A small population on Eday, apparently established in the late 1960s, can number up to ten pairs. During the 1980s a further area in the West Mainland was colonized and now has up to thirteen pairs present. With other territories recently observed on Westray and Stronsay, hopes are high that this species will continue to expand.

Common Sandpipers are scarce. Orkney's streams do not seem to provide the required food, and the species is more or less confined to stony loch shores. Fewer than fifteen pairs nest each year. Even rarer is the Black-tailed Godwit; only ever sporadic in its appearance, a single pair has haunted a West Mainland site for several years recently, but has only occasionally been proved to breed. However, pairs are believed to have bred at two further localities in 1998. The only other wader on the islands' breeding list is the Woodcock, but there are fewer than half-a-dozen records of proved or presumed breeding, the most recent being on Hoy in 1984.

Seabirds

Two of the most characteristic species of the summer months in Orkney are the Arctic Skua and the Great Skua or Bonxie. Arctic Skuas were breeding in the islands when records began in the early nineteenth century and in the most recent survey (1992) there were 1,056 apparently occupied territories (aots) (Meek *et al.*, 1994). Territories were recorded on 27 islands with the largest colonies on the moors of Hoy (211) and Eday (106) and the maritime heaths of Papa Westray (151) and Rousay (137). This represents a marked increase since 1969 when there were only 231–3 pairs in the islands. The rate of increase has slowed considerably during the last decade, probably mainly through declines in the main food resource in the form of Sand-eels which the kleptoparasitic Arctic Skuas steal from other seabirds in spectacular aerial chases. Part of the slowing is also believed to be due to interactions with Bonxies which, in areas where the two species nest in close proximity, can cause high mortality among newly fledged young. On Hoy there was a decline to only 98 aots in 1996, with birds probably redistributing themselves to other Orkney colonies.

Bonxies were not proved to nest until 1915, and there were still only 87 pairs in 1969. Since then, however, the increase has been dramatic and the 1992 population was 2,018 aots (Meek *et al.*, 1994). Territories were occupied on seventeen islands, but by far the biggest colony was on Hoy where there were 1,900 aots, 94 per cent of the total. This colony is still

Figure 8.5
Bonxie in flight.
Photo: Charles Tait

Figure 8.6
Fulmar with chick on nest.
Photo: Richard Welsby

growing, although the increase has slowed over the last decade, albeit not as much as with the Arctic Skua. Bonxies are not well liked in Orkney: they are seen as a savage bird not averse to tearing other 'nicer' birds limb from limb. In fact, the great majority of a Bonxie's food is small fish and discards from fishing vessels, and only when this is not available do they turn to other birds as food. In conservation terms, the Orkney Bonxies are extremely important. The species totals only 12,000 pairs in total, so that with around 2,000 pairs, Orkney has almost 17 per cent of all the world's Bonxies.

Fulmars did not nest in Orkney until 1900, but when last counted in 1985–87, their numbers were a staggering 84,500 pairs. Characteristically a bird of the upper, broader, earth-covered ledges of sea cliffs, most of these sites are now occupied and birds have spilled over onto old buildings, the heads of beaches and, on some smaller islands, peat-hags. Only nine islands in the archipelago did not have breeding Fulmars during the survey, but by far the biggest colony was on Hoy and South Walls where 37,490 sites were counted. The island of Eynhallow has been a Fulmar study site for Aberdeen University since 1950 when James Fisher, Robert Carrick and George Dunnet first began work there. The last-named went on to become Regius Professor of Zoology at the University and, until his untimely death in 1995, oversaw the gathering of large amounts of data from this long-term study, especially in relation to the longevity and productivity of the birds. The birds breed for the first time between six and nineteen years of age, with most males beginning at eight and most females at twelve years. Breeding birds are very faithful to both mate and nest site and may live to over 50 years old, the survival rate of adults from one year to the next being 96 per cent. Such low mortality, together with a relatively high breeding success of over 35 per cent, helps to explain the phenomenal success of this species this century.

The Manx Shearwater is chiefly a bird of Britain's western seaboard and is not common in Orkney as a breeding species. Knowledge of Orkney's shear-waters is scanty because of their nocturnal habits, and the only currently known colony (on Hoy) holds perhaps 50–100 pairs. Other small colonies may exist on Hoy and perhaps also in the north isles where birds are often seen during the summer months, but no nests have been located in recent years.

The other nocturnal seabird, the Storm Petrel, is much commoner. Two large colonies exist, on Auskerry and Sule Skerry. Survey work on Auskerry has recently estimated the numbers there at over 3,600 pairs, while the Sule Skerry population is at least as large. Smaller colonies exist on at least six other small islands, and churring birds have been heard on several more. Leach's Petrel has only been proved to nest once, on Sule Skerry in 1933. However, considerable numbers are seen there each summer and it may well be that breeding is occurring undetected.

Orkney's only Gannetry is on Sule Stack, an inhospitable hunk of black, metamorphic rock to the south of Sule Skerry and certainly Orkney's least-visited island. Gannets have been there since at least the early seventeenth

Figure 8.7
Sule Stack, the isolated outpost of Orkney.
Photo: Richard Welsby

Figure 8.8
Shag.
Photo:Tim Dean

century and, as still occurs on Sula Sgeir (Western Isles) today, expeditions were made to collect the young. A count of the Sule Stack colony in 1994 by aerial photography revealed 4,888 apparently occupied sites. Hopes have been high in the past that another colony might be established in the islands in the same way as on Fair Isle, between Orkney and Shetland in 1975. Birds were seen ashore each summer for many years on the Horse of Copinsay. However, such records are fewer now and these hopes have come to nought.

Cormorants nest in a number of discrete colonies either on low, rocky skerries or on remote cliff tops. An aerial census in 1985 (Reynolds and Booth, 1987) located 570 apparently occupied nests in eight colonies, the largest of which (223 nests) was on the Calf of Eday. This work was repeated in 1995 when the total number had fallen to 491. The largest colony was still the Calf of Eday with, amazingly, an identical number of nests as a decade earlier.

Whereas Cormorants have decreased by 14 per cent in the last ten years, their close relative the Shag has declined even more. The Seabird Colony Register counts of the mid-1980s gave a total of 2,577 nests in the islands, a fall of some 28 per cent from the figure obtained during the Operation Seafarer survey in 1969–70. By far the largest Shag colony is on Sule Skerry where, in 1986, there were 874 nests; this declined to 701 in 1993, but had risen again to 724 in 1998. South Ronaldsay held 365 nests in 1998; and the boulder beaches at the foot of the great cliffs of Hoy had at least 280 nests.

The 1985–87 seabird counts also revealed what to many is very surprising: the Guillemot is the most numerous bird in Orkney. With 183,000 adults counted it easily outstrips any of its nearest rivals either on sea or on land. Yet there are many living in the islands who are not familiar with this species. Unless one specifically visits one of the enormous 'seabird cities' during the breeding season or stumbles on a 'wreck' of dead and dying birds in winter one may remain unaware of their presence. However, a visit to one of the large colonies like Marwick Head or Copinsay or to the largest of them all at The Noup on Westray, imposes an indelible imprint on the memory. The sight, sound and smell of one of these great colonies is one of the great ornithological experiences, with tens of thousands of birds bobbing and purring on their narrow, densely-packed ledges. Declines have occurred since the heyday of these colonies in the late 1970s and early 1980s, probably associated with declining availability of Sand-eels as food. However, in recent years breeding success appears to have been normal and certainly better than other seabirds which also depend on Sand-eels but catch their prey nearer the surface of the sea.

The Razorbill is outnumbered by the Guillemot by about 20:1, just under 10,000 adults being counted during the Seabird Colony Register surveys. All the big seabird cliffs have considerable numbers of nesting Razorbills but they are less conspicuous than other species, tending to tuck themselves away in cracks and crannies on the cliff face rather than sitting out on the open ledges. Like Guillemots the single chick fledges onto the sea at night in late June or early July and in the company of the male parent, swims out to

Figure 8.9
Auks in Orkney

(left) Razorbill.
Photo: Andrew Richford

(right) Puffins 'billing'.
Photo: Andrew Richford

(bottom) Black guillemots.
Photo: Richard Welsby

sea, generally heading eastwards until its flight feathers have fully developed.

The Black Guillemot or Tystie is one of Orkney's most evocative birds. Visitors arriving at Stromness on the ferry from the Scottish mainland will have already met them as they sail through Hoy Sound and they are to be found scattered throughout the islands. Almost 6,900 adults were counted during surveys in 1983 and 1984, the standard survey method involving walking coastlines just after dawn in April. An extended visit to a Tystie colony to watch the comings and goings of foraging birds bringing mainly bright orange butterfish to their nests is something not to be missed. The largest, albeit declining, colony is on the Holm of Papay; a most unusual one is that in a concrete pier at the old Admiralty base at Lyness on Hoy.

Most visitors to the islands want to see Puffins but, unfortunately, they are not very easy to find. These burrow nesters are present at most of the big seabird cliffs, but only in tiny numbers. The best chance of viewing them is on the South Ronaldsay cliffs or, even better, at Stanger Head in south-east Westray or on Copinsay. There is actually a colony of at least 3,000 birds in the St John's Head area of Hoy, but these enormous 1,000-feet high (360 metre) cliffs do not exactly allow for easy viewing! The biggest colony of all with an amazing 58,000 pairs is also in a virtually inaccessible location, that remote speck in the ocean, Sule Skerry. Here, the vast colony has honey-combed the peaty soil with such a complex system of burrows that it is impossible to stray from the lighthouse paths without breaking through the surface. A midsummer visit to the Sule will reveal a never-to-be-forgotten spectacle of up several thousand Puffins performing a seemingly unending flight around the island for all except the single hour or so of darkness which occurs at that time of year.

Six species of gulls nest in Orkney. The commonest by far is the cliff-nesting Kittiwake which, during the Seabird Colony Register surveys of 1985–87, was found to number 64,000 pairs. Kittiwakes are a standard resident of the 'seabird city' communities, sharing the narrowest ledges with Guillemots but, in contrast to that species, building a substantial nest for their eggs. Although some Herring Gulls nest on cliffs, the majority nest on flat ground on moors or offshore islands. Two thousand eight hundred pairs were counted during 1985–87, but declines are thought to have occurred since. The scarcest of the gulls is the closely related Lesser Black-backed Gull whose population of 1,600 pairs in 1985–87 is much more localized, with most on the east Mainland moors now sadly much reduced in area owing to recent reclamation. This species is a true migrant to the islands, with virtually no records during the winter months. In contrast, the Great Black-backed Gull has a resident population more than four times that of the Lesser. Five thousand eight hundred pairs were estimated in counts of adults during 1985–87, which probably represents at least 40 per cent of the British population and perhaps as much as 5 per cent of the world population. The

Figure 8.10
Immature Kittiwakes
on cliff ledges.
Photo: Richard Welsby

biggest colony is that on the Calf of Eday but other very substantial ones are found on Copinsay, on Stronsay and on Hoy. Perhaps a quarter of all Britain's Common Gulls nest in Orkney, the estimated 7,900 pairs being scattered in many colonies across the islands' moors and heaths. Declines have certainly occurred in the decade since the mid-1980s survey so it will be of interest to gauge the extent of the loss when the Seabird Colony Register is updated. The last of the gulls is the Black-headed. Very much a bird of Orkney's wetlands, around 2,700 pairs were breeding in the mid-1980s although some decline may have occurred since then due to drainage. The largest and most spectacular of the colonies is that at the RSPB's Mill Dam reserve on Shapinsay where 711 nests were counted in 1994.

The arrival of the Arctic Terns, usually in the second week of May, is always a cause for comment, especially in Orkney's north isles. There, the appearance of the 'pickies' at the end of their 8,000-mile journey from the Southern Ocean is often one of the first real signs of spring. The maritime heaths of Westray, Papa Westray and Rousay and the moors of Flotta hold the largest colonies, together with the offshore islands of Auskerry, Swona and the Pentland Skerries. A comprehensive survey in 1980 revealed a total of over 33,000 pairs at a time when most seabirds were doing well. Further surveys in 1989 and 1994 have indicated a decline of some 60 per cent, not unexpected following poor breeding success in the intervening years, believed to be correlated with a marked decrease in the availability of the terns' main prey species, the Sand-eel. A similar decline has been recorded in Shetland where the presence of a commercial Sand-eel fishery has exacerbated the problem even further.

Common Terns are rather scarce in the islands, the 1994 survey recording only 374 adults in seventeen colonies. Breeding birds are usually associated with Arctic Terns; the most important sites are the Pentland Skerries, the Holm of Rendall and islands in the Stenness Loch. Similarly, Sandwich Terns are also outnumbered by Arctics: 566 adults were present in five colonies in 1994. Two of the main Common Tern colonies, Holm of Rendall and Pentland Skerries, are also regular haunts of Sandwich Terns, but other important sites are North Ronaldsay, Westray, Sanday and South Ronaldsay. An interesting feature of this species has been the overwintering of one or two birds off Stronsay in recent years. A fourth tern species, Little Tern, was recorded as nesting only once (on Sanday in 1984), but up to five pairs have nested each year since 1997, so it may be becoming a regular breeder.

Doves and Cuckoos

Pure-bred Rock Doves are still a common sight in Orkney, although their numbers may be decreasing due to inter-breeding with domesticated stock. The nests are chiefly on cliffs and in derelict buildings. Wood Pigeons were scarce in the islands up until the mid-nineteenth century but thereafter spread rapidly. They are now relatively common in all the plantations and, in addition, are nesting on the ground amongst heather (*Calluna*), rushes (*Juncus*) and reeds (*Phragmites*). The spread of the Collared Dove across Europe and northwards through Britain has been well documented. A bird

Figure 8.11
Arctic Terns on
North Ronaldsay.
Photo: Richard Welsby

was first noted in 1962 and the first nest with eggs was found at Binscarth in 1964. Today they are quite widespread in areas of wooded gardens and in the vicinity of farms with grain supplies.

The Cuckoo is a somewhat enigmatic species in Orkney, proof of breeding being difficult to obtain. However, birds call every spring, and eggs are undoubtedly laid in some years. Hoy has been a favourite location for singing birds in recent times.

Passerines

The typical passerines of woodland are either absent or present in only very small numbers in the islands, the obvious result of the lack of this particular type of habitat. Blackbirds are quite widespread, using buildings for nesting almost as often as shrubs, but Robins and Song Thrushes are scarce, the former having their stronghold in the small, conifer plantations on Hoy. The Dunnock has a very similar distribution to the Robin but is less numerous in the Hoy plantations, concentrating its small population in the wooded gardens of the Mainland and Rousay. Of the woodland warblers, only the Willow Warbler is a regular breeder, but neither it nor the Goldcrest, both of which find the Hoy plantations to their liking, usually exceed fifteen pairs in any one year. Greenfinches are currently on the increase and, from being a very scarce breeder, have now become relatively common in areas with large gardens such as Kirkwall and Finstown.

Chaffinches are found in small numbers in most of the main woodland areas. The relative isolation of the main nesting sites formed the basis, in the late 1970s, for a study of their song by Peter Slater, then of the University of Sussex. Chaffinch song varies from place to place, rather like human speech dialects, and the use of sonograms allows small variations between songs to be detected and analysed. Birds in the same wood tend to share a song type because young birds learn their songs from singing adults and usually copy them very exactly. However, the copying is not always accurate and, as a result, each wood contains a spectrum of different song types. Some of these are similar to each other and probably result from inaccurate copying; others are more distinct and are likely to have been introduced by birds moving from other woods. Sixteen song types were recorded during the study, some sung by only single birds, some more widespread and one which was sung by several birds at each of the three main woods of Binscarth, Balfour and Trumland.

The only truly woodland-nesting corvid is the Rook. Numbers of this species increased from 957 nests in 1975 to 1,419 in 1987 and to 1,898 in 1996. Sixteen colonies were located during the 1996 survey, varying in size from one nest to 363 at Woodwick House in Evie. The Kirkwall area had the greatest concentration of Rooks, with 639 nests in three separate colonies in the town itself, and another of 338 nests at nearby Berstane Wood. Other large rookeries are located at Binscarth Wood (216 nests) and Grindally in Orphir (144 nests). Unusual nest sites located during the survey included one on a buttress of St Magnus Cathedral and another on the strandline of a shingle beach in Tankerness! Rooks are not everyone's favourite species; they are accused of damaging potato crops and oat stooks, as well as simply making a mess on Kirkwall's pavements. The undoubted good that they do in controlling certain insect pests goes largely unacknowledged. A number of other woodland nesting species are either past or occasional breeders. The two northern thrushes, Redwing and Fieldfare, have both bred but have failed to establish themselves. Spotted Flycatchers nested regularly until a few years ago but no longer do so while, amongst the warblers, Garden Warbler, Blackcap, Whitethroat, Lesser Whitethroat and Chiffchaff have all at least attempted to breed on occasion. Three other finch species have also bred, Siskin, Redpoll and Brambling all having tried to colonize Hoy in recent years.

The more open-country passerines make up the bulk of Orkney's small birds. Skylarks are common breeders on moorland, less so on farmland. They tend to prefer shorter vegetation than the Meadow Pipit. The latter is certainly the most numerous of this group and is common in all moorland habitats as well as many other areas. Meadow Pipits are migratory in Orkney and the hills are deserted by them during the winter months. Strangely, the pipit found in the hills in winter, albeit in very small numbers, is the Rock Pipit. Confined to the coast during summer (when an estimated 700 pairs breed) and still common there in winter, a small number of birds also frequent open moorland and peat tracks during the colder months. What makes these birds leave the apparently food-rich littoral zone? Are they not Orkney birds at all but visitors of the Scandinavian race, *littoralis*, which is indistinguishable in winter? Pied Wagtails are another migrant species like the Meadow Pipit, only a tiny number managing to overwinter in the islands often, for some reason, associated with schools! In summer they are characteristic of those parts of the county retaining dry-stone dykes which provide ideal nest sites. Yellow Wagtail is a scarce migrant which has only nested on a couple of occasions in the north isles. The Grey Wagtail nests more regularly, albeit in very small numbers. A single pair was regular on Hoy during the 1980s but has not been seen for some years; occasional sites are used on the Mainland, the most recent being one in Firth. Many Orkney burns look ideal for Grey Wagtails and one can only assume that food is in short supply. The same must hold for their closely associated species, the Dipper. The great majority of Dipper records are from Hoy, but breeding has only been confirmed on a handful of occasions, most recently in 1994. The numbers of two other species are strongly affected by the winter weather: a hard winter reduces the Stonechat population to a few pairs on Hoy and usually on the Hobbister RSPB reserve in Orphir; after a run of mild winters such as occurred in the late 1980s and early 1990s, numbers can rise to over 100 pairs with nesting on Eday, Rousay and South Ronaldsay as well as on Hoy and the Mainland. Wrens follow a very similar pattern although they do not completely disappear from certain areas, despite severely reduced numbers. Wheatears are the first of the truly long-distance migrants to arrive back in Orkney in spring, the first record being expected in the last few days of March each year. They are primarily birds of stony heathland so are not particularly common on the blanket bogs of the Mainland hills. Rather, they are commonest on the west coast maritime heaths or on the rockier moorland areas of Hoy. Ring Ouzels, often associated with Wheatears further south, are a very scarce, sporadic breeder in the islands, most recently on Hoy. Both Linnets and Twites breed in Orkney. The Linnet tends to be a bird of scrubby vegetation on the moorland fringe and is predominantly a summer visitor. The Twite, on the other hand, is a bird of open moorland or vegetated sea cliffs and tends to be resident, considerable flocks occurring in food-rich areas in winter. Such areas do seem, however, to be fewer in number nowadays as modern farming methods leave little seed available, and Twite flock sizes have decreased.

Two passerines, the Sedge Warbler and the Reed Bunting, are particularly associated with wetland or wetland margin habitats. The former is a trans-Saharan migrant which does not arrive in the islands until well into May. Its main concentrations are in *Phragmites* beds such as that at Graemeshall Loch or in willow scrub as in the Durkadale valley. Reed Buntings are common in such habitats too but are also found quite commonly in the tall-herb communities of the dales in the West Mainland hills. This is another seed-eating species, numbers of which appear to have decreased in the same way as the Twite.

The only other bunting which still breeds in Orkney – but only just – is the Corn Bunting. Formerly common and widespread, this is another casualty of modern farming methods. Its decline over the last 50 years resulted in only a tiny number still surviving on the islands of Sanday and Stronsay in the 1980s, and it now appears to be extinct as a breeder. It seems that this species has followed another bunting, the Yellowhammer, into extinction within the islands.

Ravens, which have declined greatly in mainland Britain in the face of blanket forestry, are still numerous in Orkney. The islands' population is probably about 90 pairs, the great majority being sea-cliff nesters but with a few inland in trees and on derelict buildings. The well-monitored Mainland population reached a peak of 35 pairs in 1995, 21 of them successfully rearing young. Orkney birds are unusual in their dependence upon Rabbit as their major food source (Booth and Marquiss, 1986).

The other corvid largely dependent on sea cliffs for nesting is the Jackdaw. Booth (1995) estimated the Orkney population at 275–325 pairs and, although up to five pairs still nest in Kirkwall chimneys plus one or two in trees at Berstane, all the rest are on cliffs, with the largest colony of some 50 pairs at Costa Head. The final Orkney crow is the Hooded Crow and it too utilizes the sea cliffs for nesting, although not to the same extent as the previous two species. A higher proportion nest inland in bushes, trees, on old buildings and even, in many moorland sites, on the ground. In areas where neither twigs nor dried seaweed are available for nest-building, both the Hooded Crow and the Raven will commonly use wire fragments gleaned from rusted fences; this habit seems especially frequent on Westray. Rooks and Jackdaws have occasionally been known to do the same.

The four remaining breeding passerines in the islands are all dependent, to a large extent, on man-made structures for nesting. Swallows have increased astonishingly in recent years, in contrast to the trend elsewhere; the Orkney population in 1997 was 270 pairs. They are especially fond of farm buildings and, particularly, old air-raid shelters for their nest sites. Breeding success is very weather-dependent but, in good summers, it is not unknown for occasional pairs to rear three broods. House Martins are much scarcer and do not usually exceed ten pairs; as elsewhere in Britain, their favourite nest site is beneath the eaves of modern bungalows. The House Sparrow is a seed-eating species which seems to be undergoing a decline like the Corn Bunting and Twite. Large flocks are no longer a feature of the more intensively farmed areas, although they still occur where more traditional methods prevail, for example on North Ronaldsay. The Tree Sparrow which once nested on Eday has been extinct there for almost 30 years and the species is now no more than a very scarce migrant, although a single bird recently hybridized with a House Sparrow on North Ronaldsay. The Starling nests in buildings, but is perhaps even commoner in dry-stone walls. In addition, a proportion of the population breeds colonially on moorland, building nests in rabbit burrows or desiccation cracks in the peat. A peculiarly Orcadian habit is the Starling's liking for post office letterboxes, a habit annoying enough to often necessitate the provision of a large stone to block the entrance or even, in some cases, a bright red nest box erected nearby!

Birds in winter

Despite its reputation for stormy weather, Orkney is a winter haven for large numbers of birds. Windy it often is, but hard frosts and snow are comparatively rare, the warming effect of the sea together with the salt-laden air resulting in few long freezing spells.

Many thousands of waterfowl arrive from Arctic breeding grounds in the autumn and congregate on both salt and fresh water. Great Northern Divers winter most commonly in Scapa Flow; in 1998/99 there were up to 780, almost certainly the largest concentration in Europe. The sounds around Wyre are another key area, usually holding about 100 birds. Great Northerns moult and become flightless in the period immediately before their northward migration in spring. At that time the Scapa Flow birds gather in the Bring Deeps, and their wild calls echoing over the sea on a calm morning is a memorable experience. Black-throated Divers are much scarcer, but up to 60 can occur in the Flow in winter, moving between Echnaloch and Waulkmill Bays. Slavonian Grebes number about 100 in the Flow, Echnaloch Bay again being an important site. However, the freshwater Harray Loch can also hold a concentration of up to 40.

Long-tailed Ducks are the commonest wintering sea-duck and, like the Slavonian Grebes, may be from either the Icelandic or Scandinavian populations. Over 1,000 may be present in the Flow between October and April while, again, the sounds around Wyre hold another important concentration which may exceed 2,000. The Orkney name 'Calloo' seems very apt as their calls mingle with those of the Great Northerns on a still day. Although Eiders and Red-breasted Mergansers are common, other purely wintering sea-ducks are fairly scarce. Common Scoters, for example, are not often seen, although small numbers of Velvet Scoters are found, especially in the favourite areas of other wintering sea-fowl.

Icelandic Whooper Swans both pass through and winter in the islands. On arrival in October their main food source is spilt grain on stubble fields, but in a normal year this is soon devoured and many birds move on to mainland Scotland. The Canadian Pondweed explosion in the Harray Loch totally altered the Whoopers' habits for a few years in the late 1980s and early 1990s when up to 1,000 remained throughout each winter. They are much scarcer now, but parties of up to about 70 can be found in favoured areas on the Mainland, Shapinsay and Sanday.

Also from Iceland come growing numbers of Greylag Geese. A census in autumn 1998 indicated that the wintering population is now almost 18,000, a vast increase on the few hundreds which wintered in the 1980s. Like the Whoopers, they are initially stubble-feeders but soon move onto grass, a habit which earns them a bad reputation with farmers. Although Pink-footed Geese pass over the islands in considerable numbers in October, very few remain. However, three discrete flocks of Greenland White-fronted Geese are found. The largest is centred on Birsay and can number 150, while smaller parties occur on Stronsay and the Hurtiso area of the east Mainland. Also of Greenland origin is a flock of up to 1,100 Barnacle Geese which feeds on South Walls and roosts on the uninhabited island of Switha. Like the Greylags, the Barnacles have been causing some problems for local farmers especially because of their liking for the 'early bite', the flush of new grass growth in the early spring. As a result, Scottish Natural Heritage have established a system of refuges where farmers are paid to fertilize the land and bring on good grass specifically for the geese while a 'goose-scarer' is employed on non-refuge areas.

The Wigeon is the commonest wintering duck in the islands. The Canadian Pondweed era on the Harray Loch saw up to 10,000 scavenging weed fragments in the wake of the swans which were pulling the plants up from the loch bed. Numbers have returned to more normal levels now, with up to 3,000 on Harray and up to 1,000 at a few other sites, typically grazing on fields adjacent to the lochs. Considerable numbers also winter on the coast. Mallard and Teal winter in smaller numbers with numbers in excess of 300 of either species at any one site being of special note.

Amongst the diving ducks, Pochard favour the Lochs of Harray and Boardhouse. Four and a half thousand were recorded on Harray in February 1983 and 2,720 on Boardhouse in November 1974; a more typical maximum on each loch is about 1,000. The Harray Loch is also a favourite resort of Tufted Ducks with, again, about 1,000 being a typical midwinter count. The neighbouring, brackish Stenness Loch can also hold large numbers, especially if Harray is frozen. Scaup are increasing in numbers, up to 360 being counted in the last year or two on the Stenness–Harray complex. Goldeneyes are found in small numbers on most lochs and a flock of 50 or more frequent the Kirkwall harbour–Peedie Sea area, but again it is the Harray and Stenness Lochs which hold the largest numbers with some 400, especially on the latter.

A complete survey of waders wintering on the Orkney shoreline was carried out in 1982/83 and 1983/84, with counts on the best stretches being repeated in subsequent years. The overall total of 51,000 waders amazed even those with a thorough knowledge of Orkney's birds, and the concentrations of several species are of international significance. The 18,000 Curlews represent almost 20 per cent of all those wintering in Britain, while the 6,000 Turnstones represents 9 per cent. However, it was the count of 5,600 Purple Sandpipers which raised most eyebrows; it represents some 27 per cent of the British population. Other well-represented species were Redshank (6,900), Ringed Plover (1,600), Dunlin (2,055), Bar-tailed Godwit (770) and Sanderling (860), although the last two have their populations centred in the north isles and are relatively scarce on the Mainland. The most important area for wintering waders is eastern Sanday, and the already impressive winter concentrations there are swollen even further by spring passage in April and May. Away from the shore, Lapwings and Golden Plovers occur in considerable flocks on farmland unless a spell of frost and snow causes them to escape further south-westwards into Scotland and sometimes even as far as Ireland.

Resident gulls are joined by others from further north during winter. The darker (nominate) race of Herring Gull from Scandinavia is frequent amongst the paler local birds while Glaucous Gulls from Iceland and Iceland

Gulls from Greenland(!) are quite often seen too. The lumbering Glaucous is most often encountered on the open shoreline, while harbours are favoured by the more delicate Iceland. Both have been decidedly scarcer in recent years, perhaps parallelling the decline of fishing in the islands.

A frequent feature of recent winters has been an auk wreck. In January or February, especially after prolonged periods of easterly winds, large numbers of Guillemots often accompanied by Razorbills and, on occasions, by Puffins and Little Auks too, are forced into Scapa Flow. There, in the absence of any substantial food source, they die and are swept ashore, sometimes in their hundreds. To what extent this is a purely natural phenomenon or to what extent it is as a result of over-fishing is open to debate.

Wintering passerines are not as conspicuous as they often are further south. The Redwings which may arrive in enormous numbers in autumn tend to move on further south-west and leave only only a few to over-winter. Fieldfares, which used also to be October birds, have tended to arrive later in recent years and may not come until after the turn of the year. An enormous arrival of this sort occurred in the third week of January in 1996. The numbers of wintering Blackbirds and Robins probably depend largely on weather conditions in the previous autumn, westerly weather preventing large arrivals. Starlings seem always to be present in large flocks. Ringing has shown that the local population is augmented not only, as expected, by birds from the Baltic region but also by birds from southern Scotland and northern England, a phenomenon as yet unexplained.

Migration

Students of migration once believed that Orkney and Shetland acted like stepping stones for birds moving north in spring and south in autumn. While this is true to an extent, more recently it has become apparent that the majority of the migrants which reach Orkney's shores, other than those destined to breed or winter in the islands, do so because their journey has been affected by weather patterns.

The largest seabird movements usually occur as the strong north-westerly winds following a depression begin to abate. Birds apparently forced into the North Sea then begin to make their way back into the Atlantic, passing close to Orkney's northernmost points as they do so.

Thousands of Fulmars, Kittiwakes and auks together with considerable numbers of petrels, shearwaters and skuas may be recorded passing west-wards off North Ronaldsay and would doubtless be noted too off Mull Head (Papa Westray) and the Noup (Westray) if these sites were more regularly watched. Off the Brough of Birsay (north-west Mainland) recorded move-ments are smaller, perhaps the result of birds veering off towards Cape

Wrath and thus occurring further out to sea. Passage through the Pentland Firth appears to be relatively light. During large autumn movements, the rarer shearwaters such as Cory's, Great and Mediterranean have been seen, as have Pomarine and Long-tailed Skuas, although the spring passage of the last, which is now well documented for the Western Isles and, more recently, for Shetland, has not been witnessed in Orkney.

The classic weather pattern for a 'fall' of passerine migrants in autumn has two components: an anticyclone over Scandinavia allowing birds to set off on their journey, and a depression advancing into the southern North Sea which produces inclement weather, disorienting the birds. The birds are then either drifted eastwards by the anti-clockwise circulation around the northern perimeter of the low pressure area or, perhaps, actively fly downwind along the line of the front. Whichever mechanism prevails, the result is the same – the eastern seaboard of Britain may be inundated with a host of migrants which should never have passed this way at all! Just such a scenario developed on 8/9 September 1995 with the result that Orkney's eastern north isles (North Ronaldsay, Sanday and Stronsay) together with the east Mainland and South Ronaldsay experienced an arrival of hundreds of chats, warblers and flycatchers from north and east Europe.

Similar, though smaller, 'falls' may occur in spring too. Fewer birds are involved at that time because there are no large numbers of newly-fledged young. However, an arrival at that time of year tends to be particularly spectacular because the birds involved are in their breeding finery.

Whenever migration is under way, there is the chance of vagrants from anywhere in the world. In spring such vagrants are most often of southern origin, birds making their way north from Africa into the Mediterranean area but 'overshooting' their destination and making landfall in Orkney or Shetland. Species such as Short-toed Lark, Bee-eater, Hoopoe and Subalpine Warbler all come into this category. In autumn, wanderers tend to be from the east as birds from central and eastern Siberia, moving within the intense anti-cyclone which often develops there in late September/October, get caught up in our weather systems in the way described above. This can be the most exciting time of all for the migrant searcher as thrushes such as White's, Black-throated, Eye-browed and Siberian; warblers such as Paddyfield, Dusky, Radde's and Pallas's Grasshopper; and buntings such as Pine, Yellow-browed, Yellow-breasted and Rustic may be found. Even rarer are birds which manage to make it all the way across the Atlantic from North America. Obviously aided by strong westerly winds but unpredictable in their occurrence, species such as Yellow-billed Cuckoo, Swainson's and Grey-cheeked Thrushes, Yellow, Yellow-rumped and Tennessee Warblers have all landed in Orkney in recent years.

One form of migration which generates much comment among the public is the irruption. Irruptive migrants do not have an annual north–south pattern. In years of plentiful food they are birds which have had a very

Figure 8.12
Fowling was tradi-
tionally part of
Orkney life, although
never as important as
on St Kilda or Faroe.
This photo from the
Tom Kent collection
shows a man lowered
onto a ledge to
collect eggs.
*Photo: Tom Kent Collec-
tion, Orkney Library. By
courtesy of the Orkney
Library – Photographic
Archive*

successful breeding season and build up a high population level in their
normal range. If the food supply then fails they must move to avoid starva-
tion. Species affected include Waxwings, Crossbills, Mealy and Arctic
Redpolls and even, on a smaller scale, Great Spotted Woodpeckers. An
addition to this list of irrupive migrants in the autumn of 1994 was the
Bullfinch, until then a scarce visitor with only a handful of records each year.
In 1994 several hundred birds of the larger, more colourful northern race of
this species descended on the islands, convincing the public that there had
been a mass escape of exotic cage-birds! Four species of titmice (Great, Blue,
Coal and Long-tailed) also occasionally occur in Orkney and may also arrive

as a result of irruptions. The scarcity value of titmice in the islands may be gauged from the fact that journeys of up to 70 miles have been made by Orkney birders keen to see their first island Blue Tit!

The future

Being in a relatively remote, offshore-island situation, Orkney's birds and their habitats have escaped the worst ravages of 'development' as seen further south in Britain. Urbanization and road building have not been a problem, whilst the difficulty of establishing and growing trees on a commercial scale has prevented the devastation of important moorland ecosystems which has occurred as close as Caithness. The oil industry does present threats but, to date, has a good record in the islands and no declines in seabird numbers can be attributed to this source. Development of the new oilfields to the west does, however, require to be carefully monitored to ensure that this situation is maintained. Similarly, pressure from tourism, now the most important source of income in Orkney, requires monitoring, although the numbers of visitors are not currently a problem.

Undoubtedly the greatest threat to Orkney's land birds comes from modern agricultural methods. Despite the fact that government grant aid is no longer available for the drainage and reclamation of moorlands and wetlands, such rich habitats continue to be lost to the seemingly inexorable process of 'improvement', a challenge which is part of the pioneering psychology of the Orcadian farmer. The islands are still renowned for the ornithological richness of their 'wider countryside', outside the protected areas of reserves or SSSIs. However, that richness is continually being whittled away while the search goes on for a grant system which will reward the farmer for retaining these important habitats. Such a system whereby agricultural income is maintained or improved whilst, at the same time, rich habitats are protected, is essential to the retention of biodiversity in the islands.

Appendix: the ornithological importance of Orkney

The Orkney Islands archipelago has a land area of just 974 square kilometres. This represents only 0.4 per cent of the land area of Britain and less than 0.01 per cent of that of Europe. These figures should be borne in mind when considering the significance of the bird populations of Orkney in comparison to the British and European totals. For inclusion in the '% Biogeographical population' column, the criterion chosen is that the Orkney population must reach 1 per cent of the biogeographic population, of which the Orkney population forms a part.

Ninety-two species breed regularly in the islands while a further fifteen have bred occasionally in recent years. Orkney supports more than 1 per cent of the British breeding population of 46 species, the most important species groups being seabirds, wildfowl, birds of prey and waders. In winter, the islands retain their importance with 34 species reaching the 1 per cent of British population level. Twenty-one of the important wintering species are not breeders so that, in all, no fewer than 67 species achieve nationally important levels in the islands. Twenty breeding species and thirteen winterers reach the internationally important level. Eleven are not common to both, giving a total of 31 species of international importance.

Table 8.2

BREEDING BIRDS

Species	Orkney population	% British population	Biogeographical area	% Biogeographical population
Seabirds				
Red-throated Diver	135	11		
Fulmar	84,500	16	WE	1
Storm Petrel	(10,000)	7–50	W	7+
Gannet	5,000	3	WE	2
Cormorant	500	7	WC	1
Shag	2,600	7	WE	2
Arctic Skua	1,056	33	WE	6
Great Skua	2,018	24	WE	15
Black-headed Gull	2,700	2		
Common Gull	7,900	12	WC	2
Lesser Black-backed Gull	1,600	2	WC	1
Herring Gull	2,800	2		
Greater Black-backed Gull	5,800	30	WE	7
Kittiwake	64,000	13	WE	3
Sandwich Tern	377	3	WE	1
Common Tern	250	2		
Arctic Tern	10,700	24	WC	4
Guillemot	183,000*	17	WE	5
Razorbill	9,900*	7	WE	1
Black Guillemot	6,900*	19	WE	3
Puffin	60,000	7		
Wildfowl				
Mute Swan	350*	1		
Shelduck	150	1		
Wigeon	(70)	18		
Teal	(100)	3		
Mallard	(1,000)	1		
Pintail	24	57		
Shoveler	(70)	6		
Tufted Duck	(100)	1		
Eider	(1,000)	3		
Red-breasted Merganser	(150)	7		

Species	Orkney population	% British population	Biogeographical area	% Biogeographical population
Raptors and Owls				
Hen Harrier	40	6		
Merlin	20	2		
Peregrine	15	1		
Short-eared Owl	50	3		
Waders				
Oystercatcher	9,850	26		
Ringed Plover	570	7		
Lapwing	5,370	3		
Dunlin (schinzii)	100	1		
Snipe	3,125	6		
Whimbrel	20	4		
Curlew	5,000	14		
Redshank	1,725	5		
Miscellaneous				
Corncrake	15	3		
Rock Pipit	(700)	2		
Raven	75	1		
WINTERING BIRDS				
Black-throated Diver	60	9		
Great Northern Diver	780	26	WE	8
Slavonian Grebe	100	25		
Mute Swan	450	2		
Whooper Swan	300	2	W	2
Greenland White-fronted Goose	220	2	W	1
Greylag Goose	18,000	18	W	5
Barnacle Goose (Gld)	1,100	4	W	3
Wigeon	20,000	7	NW	3
Teal	3,500	2	NW	1
Mallard	5,000	1		
Pochard	4,600	11	NW	1
Tufted Duck	2,750	5		
Scaup	370	3		
Eider	5,000	7		
Long-tailed Duck	3,500	15		
Velvet Scoter	80	3		
Goldeneye	850	5		
Red-breasted Merganser	650	7		
Coot	1,350	1		
Ringed Plover	1,600	6	EAF	3
Golden Plover	(5,000)	2		
Sanderling	850	4		
Purple Sandpiper	5,700	27	EAF	11
Snipe	(>2,000)	2		
Bar-tailed Godwit	770	2		
Curlew	20,000	17	EAF	6

Species	Orkney population	% British population	Biogeographical area	% Biogeographical population
Redshank	7,000	6	EAF	6
Turnstone	6,000	9	EAF	9
Common Gull	(20,000)	2		
G.B-b. Gull	2,700	7		
Long-eared Owl	20	1		
Twite	(2,000)	2		
Snow Bunting	(1,000)	8		

Note 1: The biogeographical Areas referred to are: NW – north-west Europe; NW + C – north-west and central Europe; WE – western Europe; WC – western and central Europe; EAF – East Atlantic Flyway; W – World.

Note 2: All population given as pairs except those marked with an asterisk which are individual adults. The Orkney Hen Harrier population is given as females present on territory.

Note 3: Orkney populations are given on the basis of surveys or partial surveys except those in brackets which are best estimates.

Further reading

GENERAL

Arthur, 1950; Baikie and Heddle, 1848; Balfour, 1968, 1972; Booth and Booth, 1998; Booth, Cuthbert and Reynolds, 1984; Buckley and Harvie-Brown, 1891; Cunningham *et al.*, 1995; Groundwater, 1974; Lack, 1942, 1943; Lloyd *et al.*, 1991; Low, 1813; Omond, 1925; Lea and Bourne, 1975; Meek, 1995; Watson, 1977; Williamson, 1965.

SPECIFIC

Adam, 1998; Avery *et al.*, 1989; Balfour, 1955, 1962, 1967, 1970; Balfour, Anderson and Dunnet, 1967; Balfour and Cadbury, 1975, 1979; Balfour and Macdonald, 1970; Birkhead, 1984; Booth, 1979, 1982, 1995; Booth *et al.*, 1981 onwards; Booth and Marquiss, 1986; Bourne, 1983; Bullock and Gomershall, 1981; Cadbury, 1980; Corse and Adam, 1997; Dunnet, 1992; Dunnet, Ollason and Anderson, 1978; Duffey, 1955; Heppleston, 1981; Hope-Jones, 1979; Hudson, 1965; Lea and Bourne, 1975; Marler, 1952; Meek, 1993a, 1993b; Meek *et al.*, 1994, 1998; Ollason and Dunnet, 1983; Picozzi, 1980, 1981a, b, 1983a, 1983b, 1984; Picozzi and Cuthbert, 1982; Ratcliffe, 1984; Reynolds and Booth, 1987; Robertson, 1934; Robinson, 1934; Scharf and Balfour, 1970; Slater and Ince, 1979; Tay and Orkney Ringing Groups, 1984; Tomison, 1904; Wood, 1997.

Chapter 9

Orcadians

First the aborigines
That houked Skara Brae from the sand.
Then the Picts,
Those small dark cunning men
Who scrawled their history in stone . . .
And then the tigers from east over sea,
The blond butchering Vikings,
Whose last worry on sea or land
Was purity of race, as they staggered couchwards
After a fill of ale.
Finally, to make the mixture thick and slab,
The off-scourings of Scotland,
The lowest sleaziest pimps from Lothian and the Mearns
Fawning in the train of Black Pat,
And robbing and raping ad lib.
But that's not all.
For many a hundred ships have ripped their flanks
On Rora Head, or the Noup,
And Basque sailor lads and bearded skippers from Brittany
Left off their briny ways to cleave a furrow
Through Orkney crofts and lasses.
Not to speak of two world wars
And hordes of English and Yanks and Italians and Poles
Who took up their stations here:
By day the guns, by night the ancestral box-bed.

Only this morning I delivered a bairn
At Maggie O'Corsland's
With a subtle silk-selling Krishna smile.
A fine mixter-maxter!

(George Mackay Brown,
What is an Orcadian, from *The Storm*, Kirkwall, 1954)

Orkney lies at a cross-road of seaways, and seafarers have called in at the islands briefly or permanently for as long as they have had boats able to cross the North Sea or the Pentland Firth. There have been suggestions that there were Mesolithic settlers in Orkney, based on flint tools found in various places. However, the most northerly good evidence of Mesolithic activity is at Freswick Bay in Caithness; the first certain human occupants of Orkney were Neolithic farmers. The earliest radiocarbon dates from human dwellings and pollen from peat cores show that food-producing communities were well established in the islands by about 3500 BC. The earliest settlements that have been excavated are Skara Brae on Orkney Mainland, Rinyo on Rousay, Links of Noltland on Westray, and Knap of Howar on Papa Westray. These are sites of established farming communities; it seems unlikely that they include the homes of the first pioneering colonists. We know effectively nothing about the first Orcadians.

Figure 9.1
The neolithic village of Skara Brae.
Photo: R. J. Berry

Two different sorts of pots have been found in the four well-known Neolithic sites. The inhabitants of Knap of Howar had 'Unstan ware', while the other three villages used 'Grooved ware'. There are other differences in the artefacts and house-plans between the villages, showing that there were at least two cultural traditions present in Orkney, characterized by the different pottery types. The later radiocarbon dates from Knap of Howar are contemporary with the earlier ones from Skara Brae; these two cultures existed alongside each other. It has been suggested that Grooved ware is a development of Unstan ware; this is uncertain. We have to admit that we do not know if the two cultures were ethnically the same or whether they derived from different areas in Britain or even continental Europe.

A large tomb at Isbister on South Ronaldsay (the 'Tomb of the Eagles') dated at around 3000 BC contained skeletons of people physically very similar to modern Orcadians, albeit slightly shorter. A sobering reflection is that very few adults among the 340 individuals excavated had survived beyond their twenties.

The Neolithic villagers brought with them cattle, sheep, goats, pigs, dogs and seed corn. They lived in compact villages, and built complex chambered tombs. Skara Brae is the best known of the early settlements. Radiocarbon dates have shown that it was inhabited from a little before 3100 BC to around 2500 BC.

Most of the houses we can see today belong to the later phase of occupation, and then, as now, they would have appeared subterranean; they were built into previous midden deposits, and then had more rubbish piled round them. The dwelling rooms are all remarkably similar in size and shape. They have a central fireplace, up to four stone box beds, sometimes a dresser, small stone boxes in the floor, and cupboards in the wall. Each building would house a family; probably half-a-dozen houses would have been in occupation at any one time.

Contemporary with the Neolithic villages are chambered tombs, of which there are two main types: 'Maes Howe' (Maeshowe itself; Quoyness; Cuween Hill, Firth; Wideford Hill and Quanterness, Kirkwall), and 'stalled' (Isbister in South Ronaldsay; Unstan in Stenness; Midhowe on Rousay); pottery from them suggests that the former was linked with the Grooved ware culture, and the latter with the Unstan ware. The Maes Howe chambers are entered by a relatively long, low passage which opens into a central room with several smaller side cells. The passage in stalled tombs leads into an elongated chamber which is partially divided by shelves at the end. Apparently the dead were first reduced to skeletons (perhaps by being left exposed to the elements), and then a selection of bones was taken into the chamber, together with food offerings, broken burnt pottery, bone pins and flints.

The Ring of Brodgar and the Stones of Stenness are ceremonial complexes apparently belonging to the latter part of the Neolithic period.

'Burnt mounds' at Beaquoy, Harray, and Liddle, South Ronaldsay, are Bronze Age remains, formed largely from rubbish piled round a building. In contrast to the preceding Neolithic, the Bronze Age buildings were alongside small streams and not confined to the coast. No classical crouched burials, which typify the Beaker folk, have been found in Orkney, although Beaker sherds occur at Rinyo in Rousay.

Figure 9.2
The Ring of Brodgar, probably dating from late Neolithic times.
Photo: Richard Welsby

Picts and brochs

Some of the most spectacular archaeological remains in Orkney (and in north Britain generally) are isolated round towers, built without mortar and 40–80 feet (10–25 metres) in diameter. There are 102 known in Orkney alone. These are brochs. There have been many theories about their inhabitants and purpose, but their real nature has been shown from Orkney excavations. Traditionally, they were dated to the first and second centuries AD by Roman artefacts. However, similar structures occurring much earlier than this are now dated from the Iron Age. A number of brochs in Orkney were still sufficiently recognizable when the Vikings arrived in the late first millennium for them to be called *borgs* (defences), transformed later into the word 'broch' by which they are known today. It is now almost certain that they were a development from round houses, which appeared in Orkney at the beginning of the Iron Age, as early as 700 BC. The possibility of making these into defensive keeps was recognized, and brochs are found contemporaneous with surrounding buildings, ramparts and ditches (as at Gurness in Evie, and Midhowe on Rousay). The internal layout of both round houses and brochs is very similar, with a central hearth and perhaps a cooking box, surrounded by a service area which had several large storage cupboards and a series of interconnecting rooms. This plan differs from that in non-round houses of the early Iron Age (and from the previous Neolithic and Bronze Age structures) and, to a lesser extent, from that in buildings around the later brochs.

Figure 9.3
Main archaeological sites on Orkney.

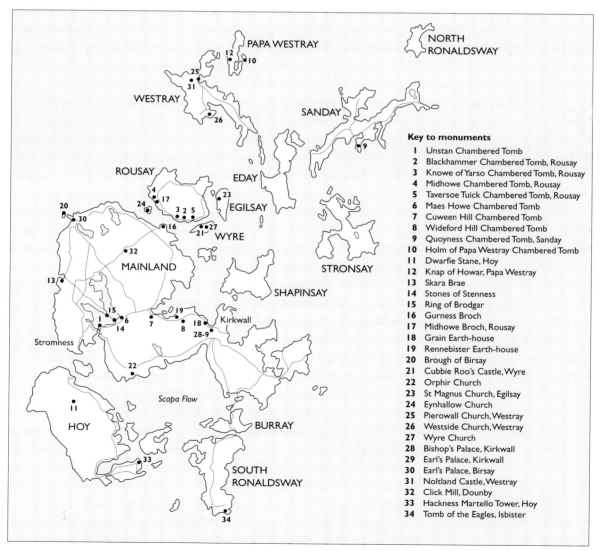

Key to monuments

1 Unstan Chambered Tomb
2 Blackhammer Chambered Tomb, Rousay
3 Knowe of Yarso Chambered Tomb, Rousay
4 Midhowe Chambered Tomb, Rousay
5 Taversoe Tuick Chambered Tomb, Rousay
6 Maes Howe Chambered Tomb
7 Cuween Hill Chambered Tomb
8 Wideford Hill Chambered Tomb
9 Quoyness Chambered Tomb, Sanday
10 Holm of Papa Westray Chambered Tomb
11 Dwarfie Stane, Hoy
12 Knap of Howar, Papa Westray
13 Skara Brae
14 Stones of Stenness
15 Ring of Brodgar
16 Gurness Broch
17 Midhowe Broch, Rousay
18 Grain Earth-house
19 Rennebister Earth-house
20 Brough of Birsay
21 Cubbie Roo's Castle, Wyre
22 Orphir Church
23 St Magnus Church, Egilsay
24 Eynhallow Church
25 Pierowall Church, Westray
26 Westside Church, Westray
27 Wyre Church
28 Bishop's Palace, Kirkwall
29 Earl's Palace, Kirkwall
30 Earl's Palace, Birsay
31 Noltland Castle, Westray
32 Click Mill, Dounby
33 Hackness Martello Tower, Hoy
34 Tomb of the Eagles, Isbister

Figure 9.4
Remains of the Broch
of Gurness, from the
air.
Photo: Richard Welsby

The brochs were inhabited by Picts. The twelfth-century *Historia Norve-giae* placed these shadowy people firmly in legend: 'they little exceeded pigmies in stature; they did marvels in the morning and the evening in building towns, but at midday they entirely lost their strength, and lurked through fear in little underground houses . . . Whence they came there we are entirely ignorant.'

There has long been mystery about the Picts. Orkney was described as Pictish in AD 46, in a fourth-century document which was known to Bede. Their kingdom came to an end when it was united with that of the Scots under Kenneth Mac Alpin in AD 843. The clearest glimpse of the relationship between Orkney and mainland Pictland comes from about AD 561, when St Colomba visited King Bridei mac Maelchon near Inverness and found the Orkney king present at Bridei's court. According to Adomnan, Colomba's biographer, the saint was concerned for the safety of Christian missionaries sailing in northern waters, and he persuaded Bridei to issue instructions which subsequently saved then from sudden death when they arrived in Orkney: 'Some of our peope have gone forth seeking a remote place across the unsailed seas; should they, after long travel, reach the islands of Orkney, command this *regulus* (sub-king) whose hostages you hold, that no evil will befall them within his territory.'

This passage implies that Pictish rule extended to the islands and that King Bridei could expect to be obeyed, yet the King of Orkney seems likely to have been capable of a good deal of independent action and was not necessarily much inferior in status. Bridei was well disposed to Christianity, if not himself a convert, yet this apparently did not automatically ensure a friendly reception for missionaries in Orkney. It is significant that hostages were being held to secure the Orkney king's obedience, and while this was a standard Dark Age precaution, it is an indication of a potentially hostile relationship.

A century later the relationship with Pictland is further illuminated by entries in Irish annals, which record that Orkney was devastated by King Bridei mac Bile *about* AD 682. There is no information about the events which had provoked the wrath of the Pictish king, but the entries imply a major expedition against the isles. One possible reconstruction links this with the siege of Dunottar in the previous year; it has been suggested on no grounds other than the dates (and these are somewhat uncertain) that Dunottar may have been attacked by the Orkneymen and that Bridei's expedition was a reprisal. It is also possible that the king was subduing rebellious northern areas before turning his attention to southern Pictland, where three years later in AD 685 he ended 27 years of Northumbrian occupation by his great victory at Nechtansmere.

There is limited place-name evidence about the Picts in Orkney (for example, the Pentland or Pightland Firth); there are carved symbol stones and inscriptions using the Ogam (Pictish) alphabet, and a few pieces of metalwork, most dateable to the seventh and eighth centuries. Perhaps the best

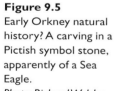

Figure 9.5
Early Orkney natural history? A carving in a Pictish symbol stone, apparently of a Sea Eagle.
Photo: Richard Welsby

way of thinking about the Picts is to regard anything and anywhere in Orkney and northern Scotland as Pictish from early Iron Age to Viking times.

Christianity was brought to Orkney in the seventh century; there was said to be an Early Christian monastery on the Brough of Birsay. During the pagan Pictish period there is some evidence that the dead were cremated and put in short cists. The introduction of Christianity led to simple burial in cemeteries, probably in long cists; there is an example on the Brough of Birsay.

The Vikings

The saga accounts imply that the Viking settlement of Orkney began only a little before the reign of King Harald Fairhair (*d.* 945), but in fact it must have been much earlier. The years 790–800 saw the beginning of Viking raids not only in the Hebrides and Ireland, but also on the east and south coasts of England. Clearly such a flood could not have bypassed Orkney, which lay on the main route to the west and south.

There is a well-entrenched tradition that the Vikings came to a virtually empty land when they crossed the North Sea at the end of the eighth century. A Shetlander, Gilbert Goudie, writing in 1904, believed that the Picts 'and their Christianity alike' appear to have vanished before the arrival of the Scandinavians. A generation later another writer claimed that 'the Pictish inhabitants, numerous as they must have been, had been wiped cleanly off the page of history in some unexplained fashion . . . an entire people disappears in silence'.

The fullest exposition of this point of view is in a book by Professor A. W. Brøgger, published in 1929:

The Norsemen did not destroy a numerous Celtic population in the Shetlands and Orkneys. They did not wage a war of extermination against such a population or drive it into the sea and seize its possessions, its farms, and its civilization. It seems clear that a race which possessed the great brochs for defence and real fleets of ships, would not have allowed itself to be destroyed by the Norsemen even if the craftmanship of the latter in the shaping of weapons was superior and their art in shipbuilding of a very high order. Perhaps the broch-people, small in numbers, a warlike aristocracy, had gradually drifted away from the islands into the Scottish mainland, leaving the poorer classes of Celts in possession. The Norse settlers came sailing to a land in which there were few people. On all sides they saw traces of old houses and farms, ruins and foundations of houses and outhouses. The greatest impression they received was that created by the sight of old brochs. All their imagination was fired. Did they not step ashore into a veritable museum?

This is vivid but almost certainly not true. The *Historia Norvegiae*, written around 1200, described islands inhabited by 'Picts and Papae'.

At that time the islands were not called Orchades, but Pictland; whence still the Pictland Sea is so named by inhabitants, because it divides the Orkney islands from Scotland; and there is the greatest of all whirlpools, which draws in and swallows down in the ebb the strongest ships, and vomits and casts up their fragments in the flood. Whence the people came there we are entirely ignorant.

And the Papae have been named for their white robes, which they wore like priests; whence priests are all called papae in the Teutonic tongue. An island is still called after them, Papey. But, as is observed from their habit and the writings of their books abandoned there, they were Africans (sic) adhering to Judaism.

The idea that modern Orkney was founded by a pure Viking race rested upon a debatable lack of evidence (of place names). For example, Jakob Jakobsen (1897), the doyen of place-name researchers, began by believing that no pre-Scandinavian place names had survived in Orkney or Shetland, but then changed his mind and produced a list of over 40 Celtic place-name elements in Shetland; while the Orcadian Hugh Marwick (1951) strengthened the argument by listing nearly 30 Celtic elements in Orkney place names.

If we add the positive evidence of Pictish symbol stones and Ogam inscriptions which can be dated confidently to Viking times in the islands, and the continuity of Christian traditions in places like Birsay, Deerness, Papa Westray, and probably Eynhallow, we are forced to the conclusion that the pre-Viking inhabitants of Orkney were, in Hugh Marwick's words, not so much exterminated as expropriated, or as John Hedges (1984) has put it, the 'archaeological record indicates integration rather than continued violent conflict'. A good description of the probable state of Orkney in the first millenium AD is given by the late F. T. Wainwright in a collection of essays he edited under the title *The Northern Isles* (1962). He summarizes the arguments of Brøgger and others, then goes on:

During the historic Pictish period (AD 300–850) the inhabitants of Orkney and Shetland became part of the historical Pictish kingdom and were included within the all-embracing collective name Picti. Long before the Scandinavians arrived they were being subjected to intrusive

Scottish influence from the Gaelic west, represented most clearly in missionary activity and Ogam inscriptions and commemorated in the Papae of history and place-names. It is not surprising that the sagas do not mention the Picts. The sagas are concerned chiefly with the deeds of great men and the feuds of great families, and they were composed at a time when, in England at least, the Picts were less than a memory and no more than a fable. There is no reason why the Picts should appear in the sagas, and their failure to do so certainly cannot be used as evidence that they did not exist or were too few to merit notice. The Scandinavian settlement was the result of a mass-migration, and its impact on the Picts must have been overwhelming.'

The Scandinavian settlement of Orkney was a major event, perhaps the most important event in the human history of the islands after they were first colonized. But it was not a hiatus; it did not represent a complete end to the old order, followed by a brand-new beginning. Despite the changes that must have taken place, there was a continuity of occupation and at least some traditions, from Pictish to Viking times.

There are at least two lines of positive evidence for continuity, apart from the traditional arguments about the survival of Pictish place-name elements

Figure 9.6
The Viking settlement on the tidal islet of the Brough of Birsay. *Photo: Richard Welsby*

and the emerging conclusions from archaeology. Firstly the Vikings did not suddenly appear and take over around AD 800. For at least two centuries before this, trading contacts had existed between people on both sides of the North Sea.

Secondly, place names, burials and inscribed stones all suggest that Christianity (traditionally brought to Orkney in the sixth century by followers of Kentigern) survived the Viking settlement, and fairly rapidly drew the incomers into its embrace (almost certainly much earlier than the threat recorded in the *Orkneyinga Saga* of Olaf Tryggvason to kill Sigurd the Stout and devastate his followers unless they all accepted the true faith).

The continuity of Orkney life from Pictish to Viking times needs emphasizing because almost all histories divide the occupation of the islands into three or four periods: the early settlers, often linking these with the Picts (up to about AD 800); the Viking period; and the period of Scottish influence, beginning in 1471 when James III 'annexed and united the earldom of Orkney and the lordship of Shetland to the Crown, not to be given away in times to come to any person or persons except to one of the king's sons got of lawful bed'. The coming of the Vikings is then described in great detail, usually relying on the doubtful historicity of the saga accounts. (It is worth recalling that the *Orkneyinga Saga* is not equivalent to the Icelandic *Landnamobok*; rather it is an Earls' saga treating of individual people and their relationships in life or death with little concern for history or geography.) The effect is that each phase of history has been treated as a separate unit, with a beginning and an end. Although it is clearly necessary to identify the dominant influences of different eras, too often the giving of names to a period isolates it from the ongoing interactions of history, and thus distorts our understanding of the whole process. This distortion tends to be magnified by the attention that is given to the Pict–Viking divide.

A cross-roads of history

Orkney history is a continuum. We know that now. It is an ongoing story with high and low points, triumphs and tragedies, incomers and outmigrants, but with no absolute interruptions. Despite Goudie, Brøgger, and the like, it is wrong to think of Orkney being occupied at different times by different peoples. A present-day Orcadian is a person moulded by something like 6,000 years of life in the islands, although we can distinguish five major immigration episodes:

Episode 1. The original two groups of Neolithic incomers (the 'aborigines', of George Mackay Brown), who were largely contemporary with each other and had more in common than they had differences.

Episode 2. Around 700 BC, the Bronze Age came to Orkney. Archaeologically, it is often difficult to distinguish overt invasion from imported influence, but the fairly sudden appearance together of metal artefacts, horses, rotary querns, round houses and long-headed combs implies a new wave of immigrants. These are the people we call the Picts. Perhaps in time the archaeologists and anthropologists will be able to tell us more about them. Pictish times are still very mysterious. They may be nothing more than a simple evolution of the 'aboriginal' culture through an intensification of contacts which were taking place all the time.

Episode 3. Beginning in the early seventh century, Scandinavians began to make their presence felt, culminating in a massive population movement into Orkney at the end of the eighth century, when they 'arrived in numbers sufficient to overwhelm the earlier inhabitants politically, socially, culturally and linguistically'.

Episode 4. During mediaeval times there was a considerable influx of Lowland Scots, originally merchants and bureaucrats, but increasingly followers of the land-owners. However, we have virtually no idea of the numbers who contributed genetically to the population.

Episode 5. Finally, we have recent immigration – soldiers and sailors in two world wars, but even more recently a massive influx of (mainly) English people who have halted and reversed the population decline which had been continuous in Orkney for more than a century.

Life in ancient Orkney

It has been said that Orkney stayed in the Stone Age until the seventeenth or eighteenth centuries. This is clearly a gross exaggeration, but for a long time technological developments had less impact in Orkney than elsewhere. There are no cultural differences to enable archaeologists to date artefacts and this caused major problems in distinguishing one period from another until the introduction of radiocarbon and other methods of independent dating. The dietary staple in Orkney must always have been grain, albeit mixed with weed seeds. In Neolithic times, mortars and pestles seem to have been a favoured means of reducing this to flour, but in the Bronze Age saddle querns appear; these are long stones, with a central shallow trough along which a 'rubbing' stone was pushed backwards and forwards. At some time in the Iron Age, rotary querns made an appearance. They consisted of an upper circular stone, rotated on a similar lower one while grain was fed down a central hole. This principle is still used to a limited extent in Orkney, although it is now mechanized. Quernstones need to have their grinding faces periodically roughened and this could well be the function of some of the beach pebbles found in the sites of all periods. Other pebbles could have been grinders and pounders used with different sorts of devices designed to reduce hard foodstuffs to powder; mortars, for instance, continued in use and there were 'trough querns' in the Iron Age.

In the Neolithic, most meat came from sheep and cattle, which were kept in almost equal numbers. Both were smaller than Neolithic ones elsewhere, and the sheep were rather like the modern North Ronaldsay animals. Pigs were kept, but were few in number. Most animals were killed when young, presumably because of the difficulty of providing food for them in winter. The meat would have had to be skinned and jointed, and up to the Iron Age this was probably accomplished with tools of flint and chert or split stone. Thereafter iron knives were probably used.

Large saithe, cod and similar fish were eaten, as well as inshore fish, suggesting that catches were made several miles off shore. Seal and whale-bone found in excavations may have been carrion, but show that early Orkney man exploited his environment to the full. Crab shells occur at Isbister. Hens appear by late Pictish times; domestic geese, oats and flax occur by Viking times. Red Deer were eaten during Neolithic times (notably at Noltland); it is unknown whether they were farmed or were wild.

Neither the potter's wheel nor the kiln seem to have been significant in Orkney, and during two periods, the Bronze Age and the Viking, the art of potting was neglected. There are other materials from which vessels can be made and there are alternative methods of cooking. Judging from the amount of debris found, the most popular means in the Bronze Age was to drop hot stones into a trough of water; this may have been a local equivalent to the cauldrons used elsewhere. This method remained popular into the Iron Age, although by Pictish times it seems to have fallen out of favour. In the Viking period the main vessels used were of steatite (soapstone); this does not occur in Orkney and must have been imported from Shetland or Scandinavia. From the high period of the brochs throughout the Pictish period, socket holes are commonly found on either side of hearths; these probably housed a superstructure from which pots were suspended.

Bones (and wood) can be split and shaped with stone blades, as can pumice (grooved pieces which are known for all periods), but bone items from the Iron Age have been found in Orkney which could only have been made with the use of saws, gravers, and even some sort of auger. The main implement for shaping stone implements and furnishings was probably a hammerstone, which can be picked up on most beaches in every shape and size. Metalwork, both bronze and iron, was introduced slowly and in only limited roles. Since the moulds found are made of steatite, it may be that visiting itinerant metalworkers, rather than the resident population, were responsible for casting Bronze Age objects.

It is very difficult to detect the manufacture of perishable items such as leather, woodwork and textiles, but one large group of implements which are probably relevant are the numerous bone 'awls', 'gouges', etc. These decrease in number with time, being comparatively rare by later Pictish and Viking times when iron was fully integrated into use. Although finds of spindle whorls and needles only start in Orkney with the Iron Age, there is a good probability that people spun (and wore clothes of textiles) at least by the Bronze Age.

Necklaces seem to have been in vogue in the Neolithic. In his account of the excavations at Skara Brae, Gordon Childe (1931) painted an imaginative picture of a woman losing her beads as she ran along a passageway being inundated by sand. Similar beads of bone, shell and antler were found (together with a polished dog's tooth) in the tomb at Isbister.

There have been many finds of Bronze Age jewellery in the British Isles, particularly from the earlier part of the period: gold and copper neckrings or diadems, lunulae, torcs, bracelets, rings and pins as well as necklaces of amber and jet, and toggles and buttons of jet and bone. Such articles do not seem to have been at all common in Orkney, but a cist in one of the Knowes of Trotty, Harray, which contained a cremation, yielded an amber spacer-plate necklace and four gold discs (of unknown use).

Mediaeval and modern Orkney

Historians have tended to regard Viking times as a Golden Age in Orkney, and later events as indicative of decadence. The islands came under the Scottish crown in 1468, but this was only one stage in a process which had been continuing for centuries. From the days when Earl Thorfinn, one of the major figures of the *Orkneyinga Saga*, held nine earldoms in Scotland, and when St Magnus (of the Cathedral) was intruded on Orkney as a Scottish-backed candidate for a divided earldom, links with Scotland were both frequent and important. The Earls of Orkney owed allegiance to Norway, but they were also Earls of Caithness owing allegiance to Scotland. Ties of kinship extended into the Celtic frontier lands of Sutherland, to the Hebrides, the Isle of Man and Ireland, as well as throughout Orkney. From the twelfth century onwards, marriages of earls were more likely to be made in Scotland than in Norway. In the last century of Scandinavian rule, the names of those in the earls' entourage are predominantly Scots.

Despite these indications of considerable Scottish influence in the upper strata of society at a time when Orkney was still politically part of Scandinavia, it is impossible to be sure what degree of immigration it implied, or to what extent such influence spread downwards into Orkney society as a whole. The last official document written in Norse is dated 1425, 43 years before the transfer of sovereignty to Scotland, but Orkney Norn, the local language, was still being spoken at the end of the seventeenth century.

The Reformation period and the end of the Stewart earldom in 1615 was undoubtedly a period of major Scottish immigration. Nevertheless 'continuity' is a word which can be appropriately applied to Orkney history. Genetic comparisons between the present-day Orkney population and other North Atlantic populations, based on blood groups and other inherited traits, show that the biological affinities of the Orcadians are not particularly clear cut. They are more or less equally related to the Scots and Irish on the one hand, and Scandinavian and Scandinavian-derived populations (Iceland, Faroe, etc.) on the other. Despite being at the cross-roads of sea-ways for over a thousand years, there is still such a person as a real Orcadian. At the 1991 census there were 19,328 people in Orkney, 172 of them visitors. Of the 19,156 residents, 90 per cent are recorded as having been born in Scotland; most, of course, within Orkney itself.

Further reading

BOOKS
Anderson, 1982; Bailey, 1971; Berry, 1985; Berry and Firth, 1986; Brøgger, 1929; Capper, 1937; Childe, 1931; Childe and Clarke, 1983; Clouston, 1932; Coleman and Wheeler, 1980; Fenton, 1978; Forsythe, 1982; Goudie, 1904; Gunn, 1909; Hedges, 1984; Jakobsen, 1897; Laing, 1974; Linklater, 1965; Marwick, 1951; Miller, 1976; Renfrew, 1979, 1985; Ritchie and Ritchie, 1978; Shaw, 1980; Shearer, Groundwater and Mackay, 1966; Shetelig, 1940; Sutherland, 1966; Thomson, 1981, 1983; Wainwright, 1955, 1962.

ARTICLES: ARCHAEOLOGY AND ANTHROPOLOGY
Barclay, 1965; Berry and Muir, 1975; Boyce, Holdsworth and Brothwell, 1973; Brothwell, Tills and Muir, 1986; Davidson, 1979; Davidson, Jones and Renfrew, 1976; Harvey, Suter and Tills, 1986; Hedges, 1975, 1986; Jakobsen, 1901; Marwick, 1930; Ralegh Radford, 1983; Renfrew, Harkness and Switsur, 1976; Ritchie, A., 1983; Ritchie, A. and Ritchie, G., 1974; Ritchie, J., 1978; Roberts, 1986; Roberts, Roberts and Poskanzer, 1979; Small, 1968; Thomas, 1884; Thomson, 1986.

Chapter 10

Life in Orkney

Survival has always been a battle in Orkney, with sometimes the humans, sometimes the elements in the ascendancy. When the first inhabitants arrived, the presumed absence of grazing mammals and the unlikelihood of lightning-induced fires in summer, make it likely that scrub formed a low but almost complete cover from the shores of sea, lochs and fens to around 500 feet (about 150 metres) up the hills. With a reasonably unbroken cover, trees, however small and scrubby, could have survived; the widespread discoveries of hazelnuts show that mature hazels were common. This cover would have allowed the development of a rich understory of herbs, grasses, sedges and ferns, extremely vulnerable to fire and all very tempting to domestic animals introduced in Neolithic times around 3500 BC. Above the tree line, the hills probably retained their post-glacial tundra-type vegetation which still persists in parts of Hoy, perhaps with a higher proportion of lime-loving plants (such as *Dryas*) which are scarce today.

As we have seen (p. 53), the role of human activity in causing the birch–hazel scrub to decline is uncertain. Some pollen studies indicate a largely treeless landscape since at least 4,300 years ago. The dating of a settlement at the Knap of Howar to 4800 BP puts the erection of these earliest known domestic buildings in Orkney very close indeed to the decline of the birch–hazel scrub around 5000 BP, as shown from samples taken in the west Mainland. Possibly the transition from birch–hazel scrub occurred in two phases, with woody species disappearing first by grazing and the change to pasture vegetation. Certainly it all took place over a relatively short period of time. The presence of tree remains found preserved in peat below sea level in Otterswick Bay (Sanday) shows the complexity of interacting biological and geological factors. The birch–hazel scrub declined less rapidly in more sheltered sites and sufficient relics survived throughout the Neolithic period to permit some regeneration in the early part of the Bronze Age; one pocket still survives in Berriedale in north Hoy (p. 53).

Barley (in its primitive six-rowed form as bere) and wheat were grown by the early inhabitants of both Knap of Howar and Skara Brae. They kept cattle, which were smaller than Neolithic ones elsewhere; almost equal numbers of sheep, which were probably not unlike the seaweed-eating rac still living on North Ronaldsay; and a few pigs. Animals were slaughtered young, presumably because it was difficult to provide winter feed. Birds and littoral molluscs were eaten. In the Skara Brae houses there are water-tight boxes made from stone flags which may have been used for keeping shell-fish until they cleared themselves of grit. The bones of large saithe and cod imply that the early Orcadians had boats good enough to fish some distance off-shore.

Neolithic Orkney had no blanket peat. C14 dates show that this began to form between 3,000 and 3,400 years ago. Thus there were nearly 2,000 years between the disappearance of the birch–hazel scrub and the appearance of the now familiar 'grim and inhospitable' dark moorlands. Unfortunately, pollen analyses on this period are few in number. They indicate considerable differences from place to place and are generally unhelpful since a number of species of tall-herb and fern communities occur in the relics of the scrub understory, as well as in fen and pasture. It is therefore not easy to distinguish between these vegetation types from the pollen evidence. Weeds of cultivation were present. There is an indication that heather tended to replace the lost scrub for a time, but was in turn replaced by grasses until just before the onset of peat, when the heather expanded rapidly again.

At the beginning of this 'open' period there was a decline in ferns which are readily damaged by grazing. Towards the end of the period there was a short period of increase of such plants as Ribwort (*Plantago lanceolata*), Buttercups and some of the rosette-forming Compositae which are an indication of an increase in grazing pressure. Between about 3900 and 2900 BP the human population seems to have been relatively small. There are also indications of burnings in the earliest blanket peat. Fire and animals cleared the land of its earlier cover, and the more open landscape removed shelter and made for a harsher climate. It is not clear how much this contributed to peat formation following the inevitable waterlogging of treeless soils, nor why the human population apparently declined. It is interesting to note that recent studies on relict woodland in Hoy show a normal growth rate. The present-day lack of trees in Orkney cannot be due to climate alone.

The Orkney landscape has been intimately influenced by humans ever since their first arrival. Nearly half the land area is now improved pasture or agricultural land. But even the 'unimproved' land has been much modified by human activity: cliff-face vegetation is grazed wherever sheep can gain access; the blanket of Wood-rush on some of the highest Hoy cliffs has increased in thickness within living memory, apparently as a result of sheep being taken off the hills. In the nineteenth century especially, labour was so plentiful that cattle could be herded all day, and food carried to pigs penned a mile or more from the steading. Heather-dominated moorland, which may seem natural vegetation *par excellence*, is in fact a human creation maintained by man-made fire. It can now maintain itself where there are no regenerating trees to shade the heather.

The earliest farming was carried out on the lighter soils. The growth of bere and oats as the only arable crops did little to stabilize such soils. Erosion was recorded as early as 1492 – and much further back if one counts the inundation of Skara Brae by blown sand! Draining of wetlands had, and still has, a marked influence on wildlife habitats. The introduction of wild white clover in the 1920s allowed animals to be taken from the hills to the clover-improved pastures (p. 208) around farms. In the 1970s and 1980s technology enabled improved pastures to be extended into moorland areas. The numbers of horses has increased since the mid-1980s and they are now a major factor in grazing on more acidic pastures and heaths.

Since 1949 the arable area has increased by some 25,000 acres (10,000 hectares), almost as much as the total land under cultivation in 1833. Areas classed as rough grazing seem to have declined, although some hills are heavily grazed by sheep. A considerable proportion of moorland is now owned by the RSPB, and tall heather growth is encouraged for breeding birds. Accidental fires are a major factor. Burning is rarely carried out for grouse management. Some inland gull colonies are very large; their manuring has a local enriching effect on the vegetation. However there is no doubt that grazing by non-commensal herbivores is a significant factor affecting habitats in Orkney today. The Blue (or Mountain) Hare is confined to Hoy; numbers of Brown Hares elsewhere are too small to have much influence on vegetation. It is the rabbit, which declined but subsequently increased enormously following myxomatosis, which has had the greatest impact, particularly where sandy soils allow extensive burrowing. For example, *Poa alpina* was recorded from the Hoy hills for the first time in 1963, and a few years later the reduced Rabbit population allowed it to reach astonishing abundance; it is now becoming quite rare again. Although its runs are often conspicuous, the Orkney Vole seems to have a minor effect. There are no wild deer. Attempts at farming or introducing 'free' Red Deer

have been unsuccessful. The breeding sites of the large Grey Seal colonies
show negligible erosion and practically no permanent damage to vegetation.

Orcadians and their land

Arable land, in spite of modern methods of weed control, still provides
ruithe (Old Norse *hrooi*) – the small seeds of weeds such as Wild Mustard
and Corn Spurrey. These were once used by the very poor to make bread and
provide pickings for small mammals and a large number of birds, notably
flocks of waders and geese. Birds also make good use of improved pasture,

especially in winter. Rough pasture is extremely variable in character. It is extensive on the many (mainly small) uninhabited islands in Orkney, most of which carry sheep at the present time. Although reclamation of hill and wetland continues quite rapidly there are some large areas, sometimes even alongside new reclamation schemes, which were once under cultivation but have fallen into disuse or neglect. Dry pasture may revert to grass heath, while one-time machair becomes dominated by coarse herbs and the False Oat-grass (*Arrhenatherum elatius*); wetland becomes infested with rushes and eventually poor fen, with very tussocky Tufted Hair-grass (*Deschampsia cespitosa*) often common (p. 54). In a country where trees and hedgerows are scarce, these rough pastures provide considerable shelter in addition to feed. They are rich in invertebrates and are frequented by birds of prey and the smaller gulls. As with old peat cuttings, they may develop into fen, but are often colonized by Willow (*Salix* spp.) to become patchy carr. These provide Hen Harrier winter roosts, and wind shelter for herons.

Water-filled quarries and old mill-dams are fed by unpolluted water and are often richer in plant life than natural sources of open water. They are diminishing in number as they are often used as rubbish tips.

Although there are now no areas of natural woodland in the agricultural parts of Orkney, several plantations exist, and Sycamore (*Acer pseudoplan-*

Figure 10.2
Orkney farmers use all the good land on the farms, improving pasture right to the cliff edge.
Photo: Richard Welsby

tanus) is widely grown around farms and in the towns and settlements. Gardening is a popular hobby, and a wide variety of shrubs are planted, some of the most successful coming from the South Island of New Zealand where the daisy bushes (*Olearia* spp.), Hebe and New Zealand flax (*Phormlum tenax*) grow in a similar climate. Many tree and shrub species can be grown, including Ash (*Fraxinus excelsior*), Beech (*Fagus sylvatica*), Whitebeam (*Sorbus intermedia*), Wych Elm (*Ulmus glabra*) and Alder (*Alnus* spp.). Some of these can produce viable seed. One of the more interesting plantations is at Carrick in Eday where long-established Larch trees (*Larix decidua*) grow almost horizontally due to exposure.

The two most successful conifer plantations in Hoy are, after a slow start, now making apparently normal growth. Alaskan sources of *Pinus contorta* have so far proved the most succesful conifer on poor soils.

These introduced trees and shrubs add to the range of habitats available naturally. They provide breeding sites for a few woodland birds which might not otherwise become resident in Orkney, shelter and food for migrants, and probably widen the range of invertebrates, fungi, etc. There is some evidence that tree planting improves the structure and drainage of soils.

Several plants on the Orkney list are known only from roadsides (e.g. the Bedstraw (*Galium album*) and the Greater Stichwort (*Stellaria holostea*)); often verges are the sole indication of the natural vegetation prior to cultivation. They form a refuge for species normally occurring in grass heath and unimproved grassland such as Bell Heather (*Erica cinerea*), Birdsfoot Trefoil (*Lotus corniculatus*), Sea Plantain (*Plantago maritima*) and *Carex* spp. Some of the wetter roadsides have relics of fen vegetation with Ragged Robin (*Lychnis floscuculi*), Lady's Smock (*Cardamine pratensis*), Yellow Flag (*Iris pseudacorus*) and Meadowsweet (*Filipendula ulmaria*). The Primrose (*Primula vulgaris*) is particularly abundant, and orchid species (Northern Marsh and Northern Spotted) delight and surprise visitors later in the season. As in most rural counties, the Islands Council owns a large acreage of wildlife habitat alongside roads. They are managed by frequent cutting, leaving the cut material to rot. This results in a dominance of coarse grasses to the detriment of flowering plants. Coxfoot and Hogweed are becoming more abundant, helped by fertilizer spreading from the adjacent fields.

It is only in the past few years that modern technology has given weapons and protection to enable the people to win their battles over the climate more often than not. Although it is never really cold in Orkney, the wind and damp mean that adequate supplies of fuel are essential. For most of this century, imported coal, and now electricity or oil, have been available for heating; but in earlier centuries, the population depended on the availability of peat.

Most people used to have access to peat from neighbouring mosses, but in places where there was little peat, or where the banks were exhausted, alternative sources had to be sought. As a result, there was quite a movement and

Figure 10.3
Old-style farming methods may still be seen in Orkney, particularly on some of the North Isles.

(top) Bringing home the harvest.

(bottom) Threshing by hand. Note the flagstones used as roofing material.

Photos: Tom Kent Collection, Orkney Library. By courtesy of the Orkney Library – Photographic Archive

trade in peat throughout the islands. Horses with 'mezzies' (straw baskets) transported peats throughout the Mainland. After the roads were improved, this movement was greatly facilitated; up to 40 or 50 oxcarts at a time made a dramatic sight as they moved loads of peat from the moorlands of Birsay and Harray to parishes less fortunate in their fuel resources.

Some of the islands were extremely badly placed in relation to adequate winter fuel supplies. South Ronaldsay had virtually no peat and had to ship

Figure 10.4
Changes in farming
methods.

(top) Cutting corn
with a binder in
Deerness.

(middle) Threshing
with a tractor-
powered mill.

(bottom) Most
farms now make
silage, rather than
stacking grain and
threshing.

Photos: Richard Welsby

in fuel from Burray; Graemsay had to import from Hoy and Walls; Sanday and North Ronaldsay had to send boats to Eday. Some of the larger Sanday farms needed up to 80 tons of peat every year, for which the proprietor had to be paid, while the poorer folk dried tangles (*Laminaria* spp.) and cow-dung as cheaper sources. By the end of the eighteenth century, those who could afford it were burning imported coal, although increasing fuel costs and the development of commercial peat extraction are once again making peat burning a worthwhile economic practice.

The moorland commons had other uses besides livestock grazing and peat cutting. Heather was gathered for thatching, and the tough wiry stems of Crowberry (*Empetrum nigrum*) provided material for thatching ropes. Tethers and bridle reins for livestock were made out of long moorland grasses. The fish-oil cruisie lamps had wicks made from the pithy stems of rushes. In Firth Parish this was done at Lammastime, and by the light of a full moon.

The state of unimproved Orkney was described by Murdoch Mackenzie in 1750:

> The soil of the Islands is various, and not unfertile if rightly improved; but the Inhabitants have not yet acquired a competent knowledge of Agriculture. Bear (*sic*) and Oats are the only Grain they produce; of which, however, they have a Deal more than supplies their own Neces-sities. Cabbages, Gardengreens, and most Kinds of Kitchin-roots, grow to as great Perfection as in other Parts of Scotland; which, with Geese, Fowls, and other Provisions they afford, are a great Refreshment to Shipping that pass this way.

Agricultural improvements

The agricultural improvements of the early nineteenth century brought sweeping changes to the human landscape of Orkney. Although grass and clover seeds and turnips were introduced about 1770, the big change in agri-cultural practice came with the enclosures of the commons and the abolition of run-rig strip cultivation soon after 1830. The division of common land brought particular problems for squatters who had carved out smallholdings for themselves beyond the hill dykes. They had no legal right to the land they farmed. In practice, holdings broken in for 40 or more years were held to belong to those who had improved them.

By 1845 extensive drainage programmes were being discussed, partly to employ fishermen and whalers during the winter months, with an additional bonus that the sub-soil from the drains was valued as manure. The use of artificial manures was introduced and although the practice of flaying or

Figure 10.5
Slicing turnips – old style.
Photo: Richard Welsby

paring was stopped, the impact of agriculture on the environment quickly increased. Far more stock could be carried as increased crop yields meant that more winter feed became available, although animals were still herded on the 'hill' during the summer months, except for a few tethered milk cows and perhaps ewes with lambs. The impact of large numbers of animals on the uncultivated countryside must have been considerable. One writer describes a population of about 5,800 pigs in the 1870s, when 'one was liable to encounter droves of angular, black, hairy apparitions among the peat bogs'. Reclamation was accelerated. There was an increase from 25,000 acres (10,000 hectares) under cultivation in 1833, to 70,000 (30,000 hectares) by 1870, and another increase of a further 19,483 acres (8,120 hectares) between 1872 and 1936. Much of this reclamation was of 'brecks' – mineral soils or thin peat which carries a more or less natural vegetation of grass-heath rich in herbs.

A major step in reclamation of hill land came in 1848 when the Government allotted a first grant of £20,000 to Orkney. This was principally spent by the large landowners, major grants going to S. Balfour of Trenabie (£6,000), J. G. Heddle of Melsetter (£3,000), G. W. Traill of Wyre (£3,000), the Earl of Zetland (£2,000), and A. Fortescue of Swanbister (£1,000). These five owned about 56 per cent of the total agricultural area; their tenants were very poor. *A Guide to the Highlands and Islands of Scotland* (1850), recorded,

Their cottages are, in general, miserable looking abodes, with peat stacks in front, and the intervening space sadly cut up by the feet of the cattle. The door, which is in many cases common to the cot and the cow-house, is sometimes less than five feet high – the cows turning into one end of the building and the people to the other; and often a favourite or delicate cow, or a few calves, are kept in the fore-house or but, along with the family.

By the mid-nineteenth century, the previously ubiquitous run-rig was being replaced by a five-shift rotation:

1. Oats after ley land.
2. Turnips, potatoes, and a few marigolds.
3. Bere and oats with grass.
4. Grass cut for hay.
5. Grass pastured by cattle.

Farmers who had an abundance of seaweed for manure often increased this to a six-shift rotation, growing oats for two years. The intensification of cereal production was marked by increased mechanization. Between 1869 and 1872, an astonishing 300 threshing machines were imported.

Some time in the early part of the twentieth century another substantial transformation in agricultural practice took place which seems to have had almost as much effect as the earlier destruction of trees and shrubs. Today it seems difficult to appreciate the importance of this and why the low-growing, perennial variety of *Trifolium repens* introduced then was so vitally 'better' than the old White Dutch Clover. However a chat with any older Orcadian farmer or reference to the debates of the Orkney Agricultural Discussion Society around the mid-1920s will show that the introduction of Wild White Clover in grass-seed mixtures was indeed a major milestone in Orkney's agricultural history. Its effect on the natural environment was extremely rapid. Within a few years, the use of heathland for summer pasture ended; herding and tethering were no longer necessary; and inby land (i.e., that near the farm buildings) could, with increased fertility, support all the stock carried on most farms.

The post-improvement mainstays of Orkney's farming economy have varied between poultry, pigs, dairying and beef cattle. Grain requires a drier and sunnier climate than exists in the north in most years, but the conditions for grass growth are almost ideal. Barley is also now widely grown, and harvested for silage while still green. An essential factor has been access to markets; efficient communications were vital before cash agriculture could flourish.

Improved communications

The steam service from Stromness to Scrabster commenced on 3 April 1856, and the first steamship to the North Isles nine years later. This stimulated the export of livestock and surplus cereals. Farm income changed very rapidly from that coming from primitive goods such as hides, to more advanced and perishable products such as eggs. The Orkney Road Act of 1857 was another landmark in the development of the islands.

Writing in 1936, W. S. Tait of Birsay tells of problems in previous days:

My father, who was a Caithness man, used to tell stories about crossing to Orkney with his father to buy cattle. The cattle were collected on places like the Point of Carness (near Kirkwall) and herded there for a week. On one occasion they had 18 sail-boats hired to take about 200 cattle across the Pentland Firth. When halfway across the Pentland Firth the wind changed, and it became so stormy they all returned to Longhope (on Hoy). The cattle were landed, and they all remained there for a week waiting for better weather. When the weather improved they set out again on a fine morning, but had not gone far till it became bad again. The first nine boats managed to get across all right, but the other nine had to put back and they lay at Longhope for another week before they could venture to cross to Caithness.

By the late 1860s about 10,000 head of cattle a year were being shipped out of Orkney, and by 1900 there were 28,000 cattle on the islands. This number remained fairly constant until the 1950s, when it doubled, and continued to increase until the mid-1990s; in the late 1980s there were about 90,000 beef cattle and 5,000 dairy cows. The former were mainly Aberdeen Angus, increasingly crossed with Herefords, Charolais, Simmentals, and Friesians. The old Orkney cattle are rarely seen: they produced tough meat and little milk; their chief virtue was their ability to survive on poor pasture.

Figure 10.6
Peat cutting – with modern wind generators in the background.
Photo: Richard Welsby

Proposals to enforce the extinction of 'wild sheep' were made at about the same time as those for the abolition of run-rig in the 1850s. Modern breeds of sheep are now kept almost entirely on improved pasture. Their numbers declined between 1939 and 1949 from 88,000 to 61,000. There are now about 30,000 breeding ewes on the islands, plus another 4,000 North Ronaldsay sheep. The comparatively few areas of peat-covered hill which are still grazed are very lightly stocked, and in some cases only used for a few months every year; in others, mixed sheep and cattle grazing is practised. There are even areas of heathland on peat or mineral soils which are virtually unstocked.

Orkney had 789,330 hens in 1950, and exported 80 million eggs annually. With the ever-increasing price of imported feed, the abolition of the Egg Marketing Board and its subsidies, and large-scale egg production in the south, the number of hens has now declined to 19,000. The cost of food has also brought about a decrease in pig numbers from a peak of 13,500 in the mid-1950s to under 1,000 in 1979. Associated with these falls, the acreage of land devoted to grain has been more than halved from 3,200 in 1970 to 1,500 in 1980. In 1977 the area of barley overtook that of oats, and the swing towards barley and silage production continues. Grain yields are around 11 tons per acre. Bere is still grown by a few farmers for grinding into meal for making bere bannocks. In 1923, 3,500 acres were grown, but less than 100 acres is currently under bere, and only one meal mill is still in operation.

Considerable reclamation of hill land has taken place since the Second World War. The rate of this is now decreasing, but the concern of conservationists remains. Nevertheless, substantial areas of semi-natural vegetation still remain: within the agricultural landscape there are numerous patches of wetland which owe their survival to problems of drainage; and along the coast there are many areas which are unsuitable for agricultural use, and the total area of semi-natural vegetation in coastal habitats must be considerable in view of the length of the coastline. However, wetlands are still being drained; their area has been more than halved in the recent years.

Man, kelp and the sea

Agriculture has always been the main occupation in Orkney, but the sea has been a permanent standby. All the Neolithic sites in the county are by the sea; fish and molluscs formed a substantial part of the diet. Flagstones for building were easily collected from the shore. This dependence continued through the centuries. In 1774, Low recorded vast quantities of cockles being gathered with rakes at Longhope, and noted that the shells were much in demand for lime for whitewashing houses, once the contents were eaten.

Figure 10.7
Drying herring, Papa
Westray.
Photo: Richard Welsby

In time of crop failure, the value of this natural food resource was greatly enhanced. At the time the Orkney ministers were sending descriptions of their parishes to Sir John Sinclair for the *Old Statistical Account*, there were a series of harvest failures due to cool and rainy summers; the Sanday minister noted 'the grey fish called cuths afforded some supply in 1782 and 1783; as also a cocklesand, where it was usual to see from 50 to 80 people gathering cockles in the months of April, May and June'.

Seaweed has long been important in Orkney. Winter gales cast huge quantities ashore, and it has been traditionally used widely as fertilizer. In past days, some of the North Isles kept work horses well in excess of those needed for ploughing in order to haul the weed from the shore. Seaweed also provides food for sheep, particularly in winter when normal pasture is short. This has been capitalized on particularly by the farmers of North Ronaldsay, whose seaweed-eating sheep are widely known. But for 50 years seaweed was the mainstay of the Orkney economy.

Kelp-making (as opposed to seaweed-gathering) was first introduced to Orkney in 1722 by James Fea of Stronsay. It involved the burning of dried seaweed, and collecting the ash ('kelp') formed. The initial reaction of the islanders was antagonistic, and led to the so-called 'Kelp Riot' of 1762. At the ensuing court case the instigators pleaded that:

It is the common opinion . . . that the burning of tang in this county has not only been the cause of bad crops these three years, but also that the same has been prejudicial to their persons and their cattle when in a sickly condition, and some of the cattle dyed of the smoke thereof, and the lampods growing upon the rocks . . . the poor people were derived of part of their food.

However, the potential was recognized by Fea's more enterprising neighbours, and the practice spread rapidly. In truth, it suited the way of life of both landlord and tenant. Small tenant farmers were in need of ancillary employment; they were traditionally accustomed to gathering large quantities of seaweed for manure, and they were bound by obligations of service to the principal tenant.

Remoteness meant that a good deal of compulsion could be exercised by eighteenth-century lairds. Later, when the Reform Bill had introduced dangerous ideas of equality, Captain William Balfour could look back with regret to the days when the laird's word was law: 'Lazy kelp burners have no longer any fear of my pouncing on them at 3 or 4 o'clock in the morning and if I could they would be far indeed from dreading my anger as in days of yore.'

But in the 1790s revolutionary ideas had made little progress on the islands, and the labour force was docile and easily subjected to that degree of compulsion which kelp-making required.

Kelp-making was labour intensive. It involved cutting the *Laminaria* stipes from the rocks (drift-weed was less valuable). The weed was spread out to dry, and then burned in simple beach kilns, circular depressions lined with stones. It was said that 'to the eye of the passing mariner the smoke from the kilns distinguished Stronsay from the other islands, and gave it the appearance of an active volcano'. The resulting slabs of ash, much adulterated with sand, stones and partly-incinerated seaweed, were much valued for their alkali content. It was shipped south in Orkney vessels and commanded good prices from glass manufacturers and soap-makers, particularly in the Newcastle area, but also those on the Forth and in Dumbarton, Liverpool, Hull, London and Bristol. During the period from 1780 to 1830, the Orkney economy was totally dominated by kelp-making. Wars and protective tariffs excluded foreign sources of alkali, particularly the much-prized Spanish

Figure 10.8
Spoot (razor-shell) gathering.
Photo: Richard Welsby

Figure 10.9 (opposite)
Collecting 'tangles' at Warbeth Beach, Outertown, Stromness and (lower picture) drying tangles on Sanday.
Photos: Richard Welsby

barilla. The price of kelp was high, and production soared in response. The *Old Statistical Account* records the early years of the great kelp boom when Orkney production reached 2,000 to 3,000 tons a year at a price approaching £10 a ton and occasionally much more. Profits from kelp were twice as great as income from rents, and about six times greater than the total value of agricultural exports.

The great rise in the value of kelp induced many to purchase land, and estates came to be valued more in terms of their shoreline than for the potential of their farmland. Orkney farming in the second half of the eighteenth century was barely profitable, so that an emphasis on the harvest of the shore rather than of farmland is understandable. Furthermore, the tenants involved in kelp-burning had an assured contribution towards paying off their rents, instead of having to rely absolutely on a grain crop which might suffer badly in a poor season.

In the North Isles, where vast quantities of kelp were produced, families such as the Traills, who owned whole islands, had most to gain. Every bit of shore that could produce kelp became involved in an activity which, at the time, offered a sure reward. Small offshore holms were inhabited, and the remains of the kelpers' hut can often still be seen. On Damsay and the Holm of Grimbister in Firth, the kelpers were supplied with food and peats, and their kelp shipped over to Eday and Kirkwall respectively. In the 1780s, many lairds would undoubtedly have gone bankrupt were it not for their kelp shores.

The poor state of much of Orkney agriculture at the time of the kelp boom both explained the dependence on kelp revenue, and came to be explained by it. Similarly, the preoccupation with kelp went far towards accounting for the poorly-developed state of commercial fishing in the islands. The kelp industry did not completely disappear after its boom years of the early nineteenth century, but never again attained the status that it had then.

Fishing

Commercial fishing in Orkney has a shorter history than in Shetland, with the exception of the South Isles lobster fishing which in *Old Statistical Account* times had been organized 'for many years past' by London companies. About 60 small open boats with two-man crews were employed in Scapa Flow and among the South Isles, and a fleet of fifteen smacks carried their catch to the London market. In the early nineteenth century, an estimated 120,000 lobsters were exported annually.

Shetland fishing was long dominated by line fishing for Ling and Cod from open boats. Indeed, the Shetland economy was distorted by this fishery in the same way that kelp later came to dominate the Orkney economy (p. 212).

The line (or haaf) fishing was very labour-intensive, and the landowners who controlled the marketing of the fish exercised sanctions against their tenants (notably payment in kind rather than money) to discourage them leaving. As a result Shetland became over-populated in the early part of the nineteenth century. The power of the lairds was finally broken by the Truck Acts of the 1870s and the Crofters' Act of 1886 which guaranteed tenure and fair rents. The Orkney equivalent of this thrall to landowners was the kelp boom of 1780 to 1830, but it was never so extreme as in Shetland.

What long-line fishing there was in Orkney was originally centred on Walls at the south end of Hoy; the Pentland Firth was fished mainly for Cod. In a good year, between 50,000 and 70,000 Cod were cured. The few families living on Swona and Switha at the southern entrance to Scapa Flow (both islands now uninhabited) were virtually entirely dependent on Saithe and Dogfish. They built small houses with open drystone through which the wind could blow freely, and thus preserve the fish, in like manner to the *cleitean* of St Kilda. The fish oil used in lamps was traded from these South Isles among surrounding communities, while places in the north received fish oil from the skiffs which were rowed across from Fair Isle. In the case of North Ronaldsay, fish oil from Fair Isle was traded for seed oats which were often in short supply after poor harvests in the latter's difficult environment and small cultivated area.

Some of the Dutch boats which regularly visited Shetland for herring fishing, used also to fish in Orkney waters. In addition Fife boats began to visit Orkney in the early 1800s. Then in 1815 an Orkney-based industry was begun when a fishing station was established on Stronsay. The original station was at Huip in the north of the island, but it soon moved to White-hall on Papa Sound, where the proprietor (Lang of Papdale, now the site of Kirkwall Grammar School) built a pier and houses for the fisherfolk, and established cooperages and airing yards. The settlement itself had a popula-tion derived from several places, including Caithness and the overpopulated Fair Isle. Despite the setting up of other stations on the Mainland and South Isles, the Stronsay station retained its pre-eminence not only among the North Isles, but in the whole of Orkney. In 1848, about 600 boats were fishing for herring each year, 240 of them out of Stronsay.

At the same time, efforts were made to exploit Cod and Ling. Eday and Westray were the main centres for this, using both line and drift-net. However fishing began to lose its importance by the 1860s, allegedly due to increased remuneration due to improvements in agriculture. Nevertheless, in 1872, 1,317 vessels were fishing out of Kirkwall (although many of them were travelling to the Faroe and Iceland grounds). In 1913, Kirkwall was the eighth-busiest fishing port in Scotland, with 340, 194 cwt (17.3 million kg) landed, but much of this was caught by boats owned outside Orkney.

Fishing (both white and shell fish) still plays an important part in the

FISHING BOATS RETURNING. STROMNESS. TK.

economy of Orkney, particularly in that of the North Isles, but in general it is much less important than agriculture. The Stronsay herring station closed in 1936. The last herring drifter (the *Beezaleel* from Burray) stopped fishing in the same year. There now seem to be far fewer fish in Orkney waters than there were 50 years ago. A crab-processing factory on Rousay has recently turned to canning rabbits.

Figure 10.10
Herring drifters returning to Stromness, about 1900.
Photo: Tom Kent Collection, Orkney Library. By courtesy of the Orkney Library – Photographic Archive

Orkney future

Can true Orkney survive? For the past 40 years, migrants have been moving into Orkney who have had no previous links or interests in the islands. Egilsay had only one native-born Orcadian in 1983 in a population numbering 24, and a number of the other islands (especially the North Isles) now have as many incomers as native Orcadians. A sociological study of the effect of this has been carried out in one of the islands, disguised under the name Stormay (*Urban-Rural Migration, Change and Conflict in an Orkney Island Community*, Diana Forsythe (1982)).

'Stormay' had a population in 1981 of 186, of which 77 (41 per cent) were incomers, all except nine of these from outside Orkney. This produced a degree of distancing between members of the community which did not exist previously:

Despite the incomers' expressed desire to preserve the Stormay way of life, their very presence is helping to destroy it. Although individually the incomers are generally pleasant and well-meaning additions to the island's community, they are also contributing to a cultural evolution in which ethnic, regional and national differences are being eroded away, to be replaced by a more standardized and homogeneous way of life. In 1981, incomers were still a minority on Stormay, albeit a vocal and powerful minority. But the receiving population on Stormay is relatively old, whilst continuing in-migration from Scotland and England brings in a steady stream of young adults in their prime child-bearing years. In the face of this in-migration, its influence augmented by national radio, television and standardized education, the number of people who actually use and identify with Stormay speech and customs will inevitably diminish. There is tragedy in this situation for both islanders and incomers. The Stormay folk have welcomed the migrants as bringing new life and new ideas to their depopulated and ageing community, but they already have reason to regret their generosity. The energy the incomers bring to the island is committed to a vision of the future in which local people have no active part. They have sought to attain this vision by moving to a remote island to partake of the mystique of country life. But these migrants are not countrymen, nor do they really wish to become so; instead they seek a stage on which to act out an urban conception of what rural life should be like. The coming of urban refugees may revitalize the community in a demographic sense, but it will also transform it beyond recognition, for most incomers have little understanding of the distinctiveness and value of

Figure 10.11
A deserted croft house on Faray, a common sight, particularly in the North Isles. Although depopulation has now almost stopped in the islands as a whole, there is still a drift from the outer islands to the Mainland.
Photo: Andrew Berry

Orkney's cultural heritage as different from their own. In the long run, the conflicts that have accompanied the incomers' move to the island probably will be resolved through the submergence of the way of life of the receiving community – a high price to pay for the personal fulfilment of a few.

It is difficult not to be depressed by this analysis, or to disagree with Forsythe's conclusion:

Through history the Orcadian way of life has continually changed and developed. Successive waves of in-migrants have helped to shape the course of island life, contributing to the mixture of Pictish, Norse, Scottish and English elements that make up the heritage of Orcadians today. Over time, Orkney has managed to retain an identity related to but consciously separate from those of Norway and mainland Britain. Now, once again, outsiders are coming into the archipelago, not as conquerors this time but as refugees from the cities of the south. Like those of earlier eras, this latest wave of migration will lead to a new cultural synthesis. However because of the nature of this particular in-migration, it is doubtful that the new synthesis will retain very much that is distinctively Orcadian.

Nonetheless 'Orkney-ness' still survives strongly. Westray has few incomers. Douglas Sutherland has written an enchanting account of returning to his roots in Stronsay (*Against the Wind,* 1996). The land shapes those who live in Orkney with a distinctive genius. It contributes to the 'mixter-maxter' of George Mackay Brown's poem at the head of Chapter 9. Robert Rendall called it 'necromancy':

> I sing the virtue of country living
> Of long days spent without misgiving
> In calm fulfilment of rustic labours
> Among good friends and kindly neighbours.
> I sing of Nature's necromancy,
> The beauty and wonder that wake the fancy,
> When after winter's cheerless rigour
> Gay summer flowers the earth transfigure.
> I sing of sea-swept burial places,
> Shore-graves where native legend traces Time's finger
> and glimpses as in vision
> Our ancient Orkney sea tradition.

Further reading

Calder, 1952; Charter, 1995; Davidson *et al.*, 1976; Dry, 1985; Dry and Robertson, 1982; Fenton, 1978; Firth, 1995; Forsythe, 1982; Goodier, 1975; Macdonald, 1967; Marwick, 1930; Mooney, 1931; O'Dell, 1939; Senior and Swan, 1972; Spence, 1981; Sutherland, 1996; Tait, 1936; Thomson, 1981, 1983; Willis, 1983; Young, 1985.

Chapter 11

Orkney Naturalists

It is impossible to live in a place like Orkney and be unaware of its animals and plants, its moods and seasons. Rain is foretold by the especially loud calling of the Loon (or Red-throated Diver); children are warned away from burns because of lurking Otters, which 'never let go once they bite you'; sea urchins are 'scaadman's heids' (the heads of drowned men); and so on. Children populate imaginary farms with shells chosen for their similarities to farm animals: a scallop shell becomes a sheep, and is called a 'gimmer'; 'cattie buckies' are farm cats; and gaper shells are like the snout of a pig, or a 'grice'. The names are old, probably dating back to Viking times; parallels are recorded in games played by children in Norway. One of the earliest accounts of Orkney (*Descriptio Insularum Orchadiarum*) was compiled by Jo Ben around 1529. He wrote of Sanday that

> a great monster, called Troiccis, often associates with women living there. When I resided there, a beautiful woman that was married to an able-bodied farmer was much tormented by a great spirit, and both were soon against the farmer's will lying on one bed. The woman became emaciated with worry. I advised that she might get freedom by prayer, almsgiving and fasting. The description of the monster is this: he was covered with seaweed over his whole body and resembled a dark horse with wrinkled skin, with limbs like a horse.

In his *Herbal* of 1597, John Gerard gave Orkney as one of the localities for the fabulous Barnacle Tree:

They are found in the north parts of Scotland and the Islands adjacent called Orchades, certain trees whereon do grow certain shells of a white colour tending to russet, wherein are contained little living creatures, which falling into the water do become fowles, which we call Barnacles (Geese).

The first serious work of natural history was compiled by the Revd James Wallace, minister of Sanday, and then from 1672 to 1688 of St Magnus Cathedral, who gathered material on Orkney at the request of Robert Sibbald, Scottish Geographer Royal to Charles II. Wallace's observations were published by his son, also called James, in 1693 after his father's death. Sibbald's own account of Orkney (1711) is not very informative, and was

Figure 11.1
Illustrations from James Wallace's *Account of the Islands of Orkney* (1700) with archaeological carvings and an 'Ember Goose'.

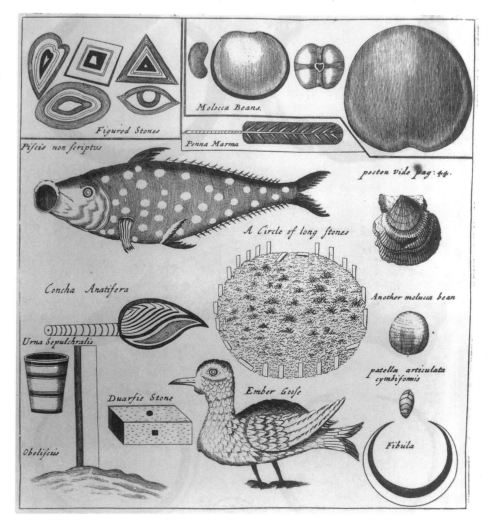

obviously based on second-hand knowledge. In contrast, Wallace's book seems to have been a reasonable success, because James Wallace junior brought out a revised edition in 1700 in which the anecdotal descriptions of the original version were supplemented by systematically arranged lists of marine molluscs and land plants. These were the first records of Orkney plants and animals. There is also a nice record of a Hoopoe: 'Sometimes they find exotick fowls driven in by the wind in time of a storm: myself saw one that had a long Beak, a large tuft on the head in the fasion of a crown, with speckled feathers, pleasant to behold: which I believe is the Upupa.'

In 1700, the General Assembly of the Church of Scotland sent seven ministers and one ruling elder 'to settle the ecclesiastical affairs of the islands on a presbyterian basis'. One of the ministers was John Brand, who published *A Brief Description of Orkney, Zetland, Pightland Firth and Caithness* in 1701. He was a wondermonger who is well worth reading. His description of the Arctic Skua (Scuti-allan in the North Isles) is far more entertaining than modern ornithological literary asceticism:

> There is a fowl called the Scutiallan, of a black colour and as big as a Wild Duck, which doth live upon the Vomit and Excrements of other Fowls whom they pursue and having apprehended them, they cause them to Vomit up what they have lately taken and not yet digested: the Lord's Work both of Nature and Grace are wonderful, all speaking forth His Glorious Goodness, Wisdom and Power.

Wallace and Brand were isolated figures; the real beginning of Orkney natural history took place at the end of the eighteenth century, and its father was undoubtedly the Revd George Low. Low arrived in Orkney in August 1768, a 21-year-old student of divinity and philosophy from Edzell in Forfarshire, appointed as tutor to the family of a Mr Robert Graham. By the time of his death in 1795 he had achieved an enduring contribution to Orkney scholarship (Cuthbert, 1995).

Orkney suited him. Ingenious enough to construct his own microscope, he quickly developed a talent for patient and meticulous observation which he expressed in accurate and beautiful drawings. He met Sir Joseph Banks, President of the Royal Society, when the latter visited Orkney on his way home from Iceland, and Banks introduced him to Thomas Pennant, a wealthy Welsh landowner and the influential author of *British Zoology*. Pennant, an indefatigible instigator and prestigious patron of naturalists, encouraged Low to embark on a tour of Orkney and Shetland. With some financial help from Pennant, Low set out on 4 May 1774. He visited most of the South isles of Orkney and the parishes of the East Mainland before returning to Kirkwall for a passage to Lerwick, arriving there on 19 June 1774. His description of Copinsay is a good example of his prosaic, but never dull, literary style:

Mony., May 30th. – Visited Copinsha, about a mile long, towards the mainland low, and a small part of it cultivated, the habitation of two families; on the sea side of the island there are altogether tremendous rocks about 50 fathoms high, the resort of millions of wildfowl, with which every shelf is so covered that it is impossible to figure a greater quantity. Observed Auks in 1000s., Skouts in like numbers, Cormorants, Shags, Taistes, Gulls of various kinds, and a single pair of a large specis of Hawk which people told me built in one spot of rock and have done so in past memory of man. This kind is much valued and saught after by the falconer, who gives the people 5sh. for the nest, which they procure by letting one another over the precipice. The old hawks kept at such a distance that it was impossible to know them with any certainty, the people told me that they have a white band round their neck, by their appearance, I imagined them to be *Falco peregrinus niger* . . .

In September, Low arrived back in Orkney from his journey around Shetland. Marriage and appointment as minister of the Mainland joint parishes of Birsay and Harray quickly followed. Birsay is one of the most beautiful of all the Orkney parishes: a rich mosaic of brown moorland, interspersed with silver lochs and fertile green farmland, with the clear blue of the North Atlantic stretching to the western horizon. Low's manse was situated at its heart.

For a short period after his marriage Low was happy; but tragically, Helen Low died on 2 September 1776 – a blow from which her husband never really recovered. Pennant, meanwhile, was procrastinating over the publication of the manuscripts Low had so assiduously prepared, while at the same time brutally plagiarizing them in his own works, particularly in his monumental *Arctic Zoology*. Low was in despair. He wrote to a mutual friend, '. . . But stay, what is to be published? Is it not all published already. One has taken a leg, another an arm, some a toe, some a finger and, MR PENNANT THE VERY HEART'S BLOOD OUT OF IT.'

By 1790, Low's eyesight had deteriorated to such an extent that he was compelled to give up fieldwork. He died a disappointed man on 13 March 1795, aged 49. Low's best-known works are his *Tour of Orkney and Shetland* (which remained unpublished until 1879), and a *Fauna Orcadensis*, or the *History of the Quadrupeds, Birds, Reptiles and Fishes of Orkney and Shetland*. He also produced the first flora of Orkney, most of which was lost in its original form until 1991 and remains unpublished (Cuthbert, 1995). Low was unsuccessful with publishers. His *Fauna* only appeared eight years after his death in 1803. The book was arranged according to the classification scheme devised by John Ray. In the foreword, Low wrote: 'I hope what follows will encourage everyman of curiosity in these isles to throw in his mite to bring the natural history of the Orkneys as near perfection as possible.'

Low's death created a vacuum, although his flora, the manuscript of which disappeared shortly after his death, resurfaced without acknowledgement in the Revd George Barry's formidable *History of Orkney*, published in 1805. Barry was minister of Shapinsay. He and Low provided two of the fuller accounts of Orkney parishes in response to Sir John Sinclair's 166 questions, sent to every parish minister, and published as *The Statistical Account of Scotland* between 1791 and 1799. (This is known as the 'Old Account' to distinguish it from the 'New Account' which appeared in 1845.) Barry's natural history is suspect but always colourful, and he seems to have been the first person to apply the word 'vole' to a small mammal. Here is his description of the Sea Eagle:

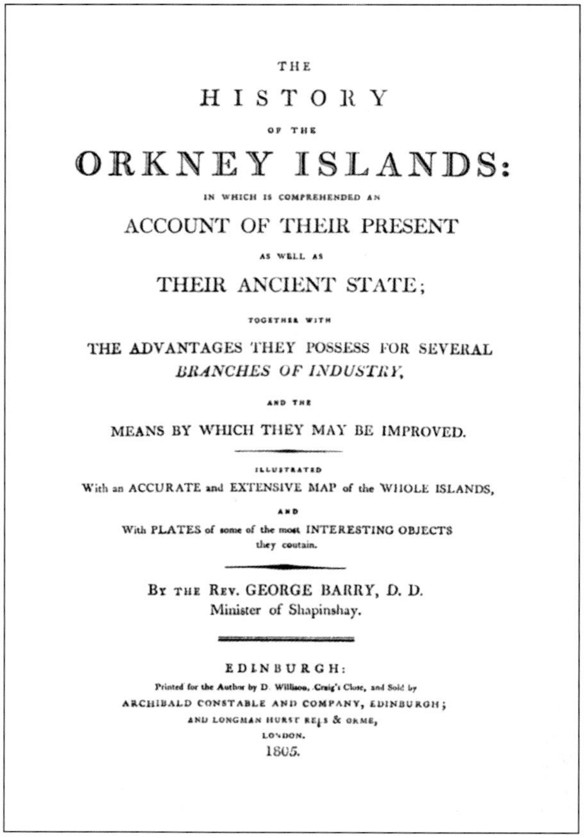

THE
HISTORY
OF THE
ORKNEY ISLANDS:
IN WHICH IS COMPREHENDED AN
ACCOUNT OF THEIR PRESENT
AS WELL AS
THEIR ANCIENT STATE;
TOGETHER WITH
THE ADVANTAGES THEY POSSESS FOR SEVERAL
BRANCHES OF INDUSTRY,
AND THE
MEANS BY WHICH THEY MAY BE IMPROVED.

ILLUSTRATED
With an ACCURATE and EXTENSIVE MAP of the WHOLE ISLANDS,
AND
With PLATES of some of the most INTERESTING OBJECTS
they contain.

BY THE REV. GEORGE BARRY, D. D.
Minister of Shapinshay.

EDINBURGH:
Printed for the Author by D. Willison, Craig's Close, and Sold by
ARCHIBALD CONSTABLE AND COMPANY, EDINBURGH;
AND LONGMAN HURST REES & ORME,
LONDON.
1805.

> . . . frequently seen in the hills, is of a large size, distinguished from the rest by a band of white encompassing the root of the tail, and the legs being covered with feathers down to the very feet; and it is such prodigious strength that it is said to have carried from a considerable distance to its eyry not only foulis, but lambs, pigs and in some instances young children . . .

Figure 11.2
Title page from George Barry's *History of Orkney* (1805).

At the time Barry was writing his book, the scholarly Dr Patrick Neill (1776–1851), Secretary of Edinburgh Natural History Society, was touring the northern isles. The results of his tour were published in 1806. Neill interspersed his natural history with perceptive comments on the social conditions of the Orkney people, especially the poor. He added 100 flowering plants and ferns, and 50 mosses to the Orkney list, raising it to a new total of 462 species. Conchology was another of his specialities and he recorded a number of previously unrecognized species.

By 1830, Orkney was well established on the itinerary of serious travellers. Charles Clouston, minister of Sandwick, contributed a comprehensive summary of what might be seen by the intrepid explorer, in Anderson's *Guide* (1834). Clouston was a man very much in the mould of Low. His west Mainland parish of Sandwick was a large one; Clouston served his parishioners as both minister and doctor, but also found time to pursue an

Figure 11.3
The Stones of
Stenness, as seen by
Barry in his *History of
Orkney* (1805).

astonishing wide range of interests – archaeology, geology, meteorology, ornithology and botany. Although he wrote and lectured on all these subjects, his chief interest lay in the study of marine algae and he is commemorated by having a kelp species, *Laminaria cloustonii*, named after him; he is also credited with adding *Chara aspersa* to the British list. Clouston was a dominant figure in Orkney natural history circles until well after the mid-decades of the nineteenth century. With professional biologists and collectors coming to the islands in ever-increasing numbers (a reflection of the national interest in natural history) and the steady increase in the numbers of local enthusiasts, it was an exciting period. It was perhaps inevitable that this should be institutionalized in some way; in December 1837, the Orkney Natural History Society was inaugurated. Clouston, the doyen of local naturalists, became its first President; membership in the first year reached 150. The first Annual Report of the Society declared that the Society: '. . . was instituted for the two-fold object of investigating the natural history and antiquities of the County, and stimulating the inhabitants of these Islands to the study of the Almighty's works.'

The Report noted proudly that the Herbarium could boast a collection of over 600 specimens, and that a 'truly excellent collection' of algae had been presented by the President and others. There was also great optimism for the future: '. . . what holds out the highest prospect of success, there are not wanting among the members some eminently, zealous cultivators of the natural sciences.' The Society, and its Museum in Stromness, still flourish today.

Some six years later another organization, the Antiquarian and Natural History Society of Orkney, was established in Kirkwall. Its first Annual Report is a minor masterpiece of Victorian verbosity:

> . . . the study of natural history is both interesting and instructive . . . is eminently calculated to improve the taste, enlighten the mind, and lead the contemplative student to recognise, in the delicacy of structure and adaptation of parts to the purpose intended, the finger of a being possessed of unerring wisdom, and infinite power.

Natural history was thought to be particularly suited to the young: '. . . as it is based directly on facts not abstract theorising'. A small museum was created in the home of the first secretary, and the Society was keen to obtain: 'natural and antiquarian specimens of all kinds', particularly 'whale remains, rare fish and marine animals'. Prominent on the list of desiderata were plans to 'open tumuli' and compile a comprehensive flora and fauna of the islands. However, continual problems over housing the ever-growing museum collection, and the departure from Orkney of two of the Society's most enthusiastic founding members, William Baikie and Robert Heddle, led to its demise after little more than ten years. The contents of the Museum were dispersed at public auction.

The insatiable appetite at this time for specimens representative of the British fauna had its darker side. It was the age of the professional collector: men whose stock-in-trade ranged from Wrens to Peregrines and Golden Eagles. Eggs and skins were equally in demand. One such man was Robert Dunn, a Hull taxidermist, who established himself in Stromness in the 1830s. Styling himself 'naturalist', he offered convivial lodgings: 'at reasonable rates for tourists and gentlemen collectors' and as part of an inclusive 'package deal', lessons in skinning, while shot and cartridges might be included. His comprehensive catalogue of specimens makes interesting, but somewhat alarming, reading. Dunn was able to offer Golden Eagle eggs at 23 shillings (115 pence, but allow for a century and a half's inflation) each. The skin of the same species was offered at £2, but for the skin of the majestic Great Northern Diver (in winter plumage) the price dropped sharply to 8 shillings (40 pence), and the same price was asked for the skins of Red-throated Divers (in summer plumage). The eggs of this last species were listed at one shilling and sixpence (7½ pence), a comparatively low price

Figure 11.4
The Great Auk from an old print. The last known breeding pair in Britain was on Papa Westray in 1812.

suggesting that they were relatively common in Orkney then as a breeding species; or more probably that the eggs could be collected without too much effort. In 1837, Dunn in his small book *The Ornithologist's Guide to the Orkneys and Shetland* (mostly reminiscences of his shooting exploits), lists 87 species of birds.

At the end of the first decade of the nineteenth century, the proprietor of the London Museum, W. Bullock, was directly responsible for the destruction of the last pair of Great Auks to nest in Orkney. The birds, approximately the size of a Gentoo Penguin, were completely flightless and very clumsy on land. However, away from their dependence on land breeding, they were supremely adapted to water. Once common over the whole of their North Atlantic range, they were, through the ease with which they could be caught at their nesting sites, becoming increasingly rare by the end of the eighteenth century. The appearance of the species at its Orkney breeding site on Papa Westray was very sporadic. The female was stoned to death in 1812. Bullock tried to obtain the male as well, but the bird managed to escape, only to be shot the following year by a local man named William Foulis, the skin being sold to Bullock. A local tradition survived on Papa Westray that the birds were: 'the King and Queen of 'a' the acks". Both birds are now in the Natural History Museum in London.

The relative remoteness of the Orkney archipelago was not without attraction for naturalist/collectors. A typical book of the period, Crichton's *Ramble to the Orcades*, (1866), enthuses: 'It is very pleasant to wander forth in the exhilarating morning air with no slaughtering Cockneys with their rusty artillery harrassing every inoffending bird . . . On rounding a point of rock I saw and shot a female wheatear.'

Despite the depredations of such people as Dunn, Bullock and Crichton, the serious study of Orkney natural history took hold. Apart from the patriachal influence of Clouston, much of the credit for this resurgence of interest must be given to two young Orcadians, William Balfour Baikie (1825–64) and Robert Heddle (1827–60). Robert Heddle was the son of an influential Orkney Laird, Heddle of Melsetter and Hoy, and the son-in-law of the highly respected doctor and botanist A. R. Duguid. He was educated at Edinburgh University, and his main interests lay in botany and ornithology. William

Baikie was a ship's surgeon and keen philologist. After leaving Orkney he earned international recognition for his exploration of the River Niger. Baikie seems to have been particularly adept at encouraging other naturalists to tackle difficult or under-recorded faunal groups (although he did undertake some dredging on his own account) and helping them prepare their results for publication. Together with Heddle, he sensed that the time was appropriate for descriptive work on the natural history of Orkney, and in 1848 the first part of their *Historia Naturalis Orcadensis* was published. This book rapidly established itself as *the* book on the birds and mammals of Orkney and it was not superceded until T. E. Buckley and J. A. Harvie-Brown published their *Vertebrate Fauna* towards the end of the century.

Subsequent volumes on the flora and on the invertebrates were planned. However, five years after the publication of the first part of their history, nothing else had appeared, although Baikie, when presenting a catalogue of the 'Echinodermata of Orkney' in the *Zoologist*, could still write optimistically:

> My friend, Mr R. Heddle and myself, being prevented by numerous pressing avocations from continuing at present, in a separate form, an account of the Natural History of Orkney, are nevertheless anxious to have one or two of our lists of species published in order to show what has hitherto been done in that locality, and also to preserve our claim to priority of publication.

The *Historia*, although sadly never completed, was a very 'modern' work with great attention paid to accurate description and nomenclature. The width of Baikie's scholarship can be seen in the time it took for his extensive library to be sold after his death. A great many of the books were on natural history, and the sale lasted for five days. Robert Heddle emigrated to America in 1856, but returned home to Orkney after only a year. He died in 1860.

Meanwhile, geologists were studying the rocks of Orkney. The beginning of this research can be attributed to Robert Jameson, a Shetlander by descent. His natural history interests led his father to apprentice him to an Edinburgh surgeon. While at university, he attended lectures given by the Professor of Natural History, John Walker, a noted geologist. He became fascinated with geology and in 1794 at the age of 20 gave up his medical career, and spent three summer months studying geology and natural history in Shetland. In 1799 he made a six-week survey in Orkney, declaring it the most interesting journey he ever made; an account of it appears in his *Outline of the Mineralogy of Scottish Isles* (1800).

In 1804, Jameson became Professor of Natural History at Edinburgh, and remained in this post until his death 50 years later. He was a poor lecturer, but students were attracted by his subject matter, his field excursions, his genial nature, and his ability to befriend them. His most famous student was Charles Darwin, who declared that Jameson's lectures were so dull that they made him determined never to read a book on geology – yet Charles Lyell's *Principles of Geology* was later to influence Darwin seriously; he was for a time Secretary of the Geological Society in London after his *Beagle* voyage.

One of Jameson's earliest students was an Orcadian, T. S. Traill, who went on to have an eminent career in medicine, becoming Professor of Medical Jurisprudence in Edinburgh. He had a lifelong interest in mineralogy, and made an important collection of fossil fish from Orkney (which were identified by Louis Aggasiz, who used them to establish the correlation of the Caithness and Orkney flagstones). Traill's account of Orkney geology was published in Neill's *Tour through some of the Islands of Orkney and Shetland* (1806). Another of Jameson's Orcadian students was W. F. Heddle. He was a medical student, qualifying in 1851. As a child he was already a fanatical collector but, when a prize-winning herbarium of his was dropped into a stream by a fellow student, he resolved to collect only indestructible objects, and became a mineral collector. He spent some of his undergraduate years in Germany studying mineralology and chemistry, and his graduation thesis was entirely mineralogical. He taught at St Andrew's University for twenty years. He was one of the most dedicated, ruthless and successful mineral collectors who ever lived. He attacked rocks with 28-lb hammers, wedges and explosives, and when possible, travelled by boat to save time. His description of *The County Geognosy and Mineralogy of Scotland, Orkney and Shetland* (1878) remained unchallenged for around 80 years. His collection of Scottish minerals grew to be the greatest collection of any single country made by one man. But he was much more than a collector, analysing his minerals both chemically and crystallographically, describing them in detail and publishing the results.

The first comprehensive account of Orkney geology was prepared by two career geologists, B. N. Peach and J. Horne; it appeared in 1880. Peach's father was a customs officer and keen amateur geologist, who recognized the effect of glaciation in Shetland during a cruise on a ship belonging to the Commissioners of Northern Lights. Horne and the junior Peach used to spend their holidays surveying together, and they established the major effects of the ice sheets in the Highlands and Islands, as well as confirming Heddle's conclusions.

Other important Orcadian naturalists of the mid-nineteenth century included the Revd J. H. Polexfen (1813–99), marine algae specialist; Alexander Russel Duguid (1798–1869), joint author with Robert Heddle of an important although unpublished flora of Orkney; William Layman Cowan (1824–1916), who contributed valuable records of Orkney marine fishes to the Natural History Museum in London; John Guthrie Iverach (1836–97), who studied marine invertebrates; George William Traill (1836–75) who produced the definitive nineteenth-century list of Orkney's marine algae; and his brother William Traill of Woodwick, noted local botanist and conchologist. The flora of Heddle and Duguid provided the basis for the studies of an Orphir farmer, A. R. Fortesque of Swanbister, who published a comprehensive list of Orkney vascular plants in the *Scottish Naturalist* during the early 1880s.

The *Scottish Naturalist* provides a direct link with the indefatigable J. A. Harvie-Brown who founded and co-edited the *Scottish Naturalist*'s precursor the *Annals of Scottish Natural History*. His book, *A Vertebrate History of the Orkney Islands*, written jointly with T. E. Buckley, an Englishman, was for long the standard work on Orkney birds and mammals. Harvie-Brown was, by any standards, a remarkable man. The son of a wealthy Stirlingshire landowner, with obsessive singlemindedness he pursued a quest to know everything there was to know about Scottish natural history. He was a great innovator and one of the first naturalists to use questionnaires as a standard means of soliciting facts from landowners, gamekeepers and lighthouse-keepers. Information and records poured into his home at Dunipace from all over Scotland. In 1887, he bought the Fraserburgh-built yacht *Shiantelle* to explore the Scottish Islands. Eminent fellow-scientists such as Professor Heddle, by then at St Andrew's University, and the ornithologist W. Eagle Clark, accompanied the Harvie-Brown entourage on their cruises around the islands. The need for a new fauna of Orkney was urgent: 'Considering the number of local faunas already issued, it seems not a little curious that Orkney should have been left so long to take care of itself, there having been no attempt made to write a fauna of the whole group, since Baikie and Heddle's work appeared in 1848.'

This was not mere chauvinism; Orkney was changing. As the *Vertebrate Fauna* points out:

A great impetus was given to Orcadian agriculture about 1832, when kelp burning became unremunerative and steam communication with the South commenced. Since then the reclamation of the wasteland has gone on to the present time, and now the advance guard of fields may be seen well up some of the lower hills, the surrounding walls showing by their whiteness their new appearing. And the Grouse, Golden Plover, Short Eared Owls, and other birds, interesting alike to sportsman and naturalist, are gradually getting crowded out. The draining of the moors drives out the snipe, once so extremely numerous, while the unnumbered, so called Shepherds' dogs – most happy misnomer, together with cats, are sadly reducing the breeding stocks of such birds as Lapwings, Ring Dotterels, etc., which once swarmed.

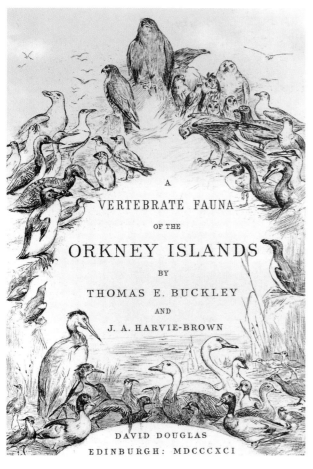

A

VERTEBRATE FAUNA

OF THE

ORKNEY ISLANDS

BY

THOMAS E. BUCKLEY

AND

J. A. HARVIE-BROWN

DAVID DOUGLAS

EDINBURGH: MDCCCXCI

Figure 11.5
Title page from the Orkney volume of the *Vertebrate Fauna of Scotland*, a series inspired by J. A. Harvie-Brown.

All Harvie-Brown's regional faunas followed a similar pattern: a general chapter on topography and geology, followed by descriptions of all but the smallest islands. The species accounts, which comprised the greater part, were considerably fleshed out by local information and anecdotes supplied by local 'gentlemen'. In the Orkney volume, Mr Moodie-Heddle of Hoy is one of the best. Writing of the disappearance of the Sea Eagles from Hoy he says: 'There has only occasionally been a nest here for the last 25 years. I remember when there used to be seven or eight breeding places. My father and grandfather used to keep a pair tame. I believe they have really been exterminated by people offering rewards for eggs, since I never knew of anyone shooting or trapping an eagle in Orkney in living memory.' Harvie-Brown devoted a considerable amount of space to the local extinction of the Sea Eagle. He made no apology for this, stressing that: 'the Sea Eagle is rapidly disappearing all through Scotland, so it behoves naturalists to try and make their memorials accurate and full, seeing that, in the Orkneys at least, this is all that is left to us.'

The increasing interest then being shown in the new study of bird migration is reflected by the inclusion of a long chapter analysing migration records submitted by the lighthouse-keepers on the isolated Pentland Skerries.

The *Vertebrate Fauna of the Orkney Islands* is one of the better-known volumes of a slightly uneven regional series. It raised the county bird list to 223 species. In Orkney it has rightly attained the status of a minor classic, and commands a high price whenever it is offered for sale. The book was illustrated in part by J. G. Millais (son of the pre-Raphaelite painter, Sir John Millais) who visited Orkney on several occasions. It was Millais who was to make an exciting discovery. One evening in 1886 on returning from an evening's fishing on the Loch of Stenness he 'noticed what looked like a water vole running swiftly along the sheeptrack in front of me'. Millais's water vole turned out to be a previously undescribed species of British vole, which he named *Microtus orcadensis*. Oldfield Thomas hailed the discovery as one of the most 'interesting and unexpected finds ever made in British

Figure 11.6
J. G. Millais' own illustration of the Orkney Voles, from the second volume of his *The Mammals of Great Britain and Ireland*.

mammalogy', while Eagle Clark asserted 'that from a scientific standpoint this little mammal is one of the most interesting and important of existing British vertebrates'.

Previous writers – Low, Barry, Baikie and Heddle, and Buckley and Harvie-Brown – had all assumed the Orkney Vole to be a variety of *Microtus agrestis*, the common British Vole. Despite this, Low gives a good description of the animal's runways:

> It is found very common in the mossy and fogay heaths, where it makes itself tracks of several miles along over the whole heath. These tracks are about 3" broad, much worn by continual treading and warped

through a thousand directions. Where the fog (grass) is short they are open, but where this is long, by it arched above.

Local scholarship and expertise continued to flourish in Orkney after the turn of the century, despite an increasing number of visiting professionals. In 1905, a slim volume was published entitled *Orcadian Papers* which included a diverse range of subjects such as the trap dykes of Orkney, the glacial history of the islands, the flora and fauna of an Orkney lagoon (oyce), and two papers on the birds of Sule Skerry.

Some of the more isolated islands of the archipelago were beginning to attract ornithologists. In 1913, one of Harvie-Brown's collaborators, W. E. Clark, best known for his pioneering researches into bird migration, endured the miseries of a tempestuous Orkney autumn for five weeks on the island of Auskerry. Notable among the list of rarities he recorded were Scarlet Grosbeak, Barred Warbler, Red-throated Pipit and Black Tern. He received valuable records from the lightkeepers and became firmly convinced that his fellow-ornithologists were failing to appreciate the potential of the islands as places to study migration.

At the turn of the nineteenth century Orkney botany was in the hands of a Deerness schoolmaster, Magnus Spence. Basically kind, he could also be cantankerous and obstinate. 'He was in the real sense symbolic of a type now passing "the village dominie"', said Robert Rendall, who vividly recalled his first encounter with him:

> First of all he took me through his entire herbarium (now preserved in Stromness museum) and I gained my first insight into scientific methods of handling and arranging specimens. I observed his extreme caution when offering opinions and his deliberate care in his examination of particular plants, all this being in marked contrast to my own precipitate boyish enthusiasm; it was my first lesson in scientific discipline.

Spence's years of patient fieldwork culminated in 1914 with the publication of his *Flora Orcadensis*. It was much more than a simple flora, for it contained chapters on geology, climate, natural selection (Spence quotes Darwin with approval, and he was obviously aware of the importance of islands as natural laboratories for testing the theories of evolution; he tentatively compared the floras of Orkney, Caithness and Shetland within a Darwinian framework), and the 'new' science of ecology.

Ecology was then in its infancy as a science (the British Ecological Society, the oldest in the world, was established in 1913) but a young Orcadian research student, George Scarth (1881–1951) wrote a seminal paper 'Ecology of Orkney vegetation in relation to different classes of soil' in 1911. Scarth was to become Professor of Botany at McGill University in Canada, but he always maintained a close interest in the natural history of his native islands.

A distinguished contemporary of Spence's was another botanist, Colonel H. Halcro-Johnstone. An army doctor, Halcro-Johnstone was, during his period of active service, able to visit Orkney only for short spells. His army career meant long tours of duty abroad, and this interrupted his real passion – the study of native Orkney plants. It was not until he retired that he could concentrate on his interest from his home in Orphir. His main period of collecting in Orkney covered the years 1923–39, during which he created a herbarium of over 4,000 specimens and an irreplaceable archive of field notes and observations.

Robert Rendall was fascinated, if not a little intimidated, by the sheer magnitude of Halcro-Johnstone's achievement; after asking to be shown *Primula scotica* in the herbarium, he recalled:

> the herbarium contained numerous specimens of this one species, gathered from different localities and during different seasonal periods of development. Behind the collected specimens was a wealth of recorded fact, stored in a series of exercise books somewhat illegible to anyone unaccustomed to the Colonel's handwriting. These notebooks left me dazed, for they not only recorded the normal data of scientific collecting, but a series of systematic arrangements, each illustrating some particular aspect of plant study; data over a period of years showing the seasonal variation in the annual dates of flowering and seed formation, the difference in flowering times in different stations in one year; the flora of each separate island and holm, to give but three examples . . . when it is considered that the rest of these trays in these six cupboards were left unexamined, something can be realised of the thoroughness with which the great Orkney botanist pursued his formidable task.

When Col. Halcro-Johnstone died, his herbarium was transferred to the Royal Botanic Gardens, Edinburgh. His field notebooks and diaries are still in Orkney. It is, perhaps, invidious to compare Spence and Halcro-Johnstone: Spence is remembered for his marvellous book; Halcro-Johnstone was undoubtedly the better botanist. Most of his results and records were published in specialist botanical journals.

A protegé of Colonel Halcro-Johnstone's, James Sinclair (1913–68), a farmer's son from Hoy, was to become, after the death of Johnstone, a kind of leading Orkney botanist in exile. That he successfully made the transition from gifted amateur to respected professional must be due, in part, to Halcro-Johnstone's influence. Incredibly, although we have Halcro-Johnstone's testimony for this, Sinclair had, by the age of 23, amassed a

Figure 11.7
Rackwick Bay, Hoy.
Photo: Richard Welsby

collection of 522 species and 89 varieties of flowering plants and ferns; almost 80 per cent of the then accepted total of 653 species.

After completing his university education at Edinburgh he spent two years teaching on the island of Stronsay until he was called up for military service. During his spell on Stronsay he took an intense interest in the marine algae of the island, supplementing the earlier work of G. W. Traill with many additional records. The Second World War took Sinclair to India and Pakistan, beginning a romance with the East that was to last for the remainder of his life. In 1946 he was appointed to the staff of the Royal Botanic Gardens, Edinburgh. During his time in Edinburgh he arranged the transfer of Colonel Halcro-Johnstone's herbarium from Stromness to Edinburgh in order that it might be properly curated. After the Colonel's death, Sinclair was generally regarded as the authority on Orkney botany, a reputation he sustained despite being appointed as Curator of the Herbarium of the Singapore Botanic Gardens in 1948. Although his personal knowledge of the Orkney flora was great, most of his published writing was devoted to his work on the flora of Malaysia. He did, however, contribute a chapter on the Orkney flora to the *New Orkney Book*.

Perhaps the best known, loved and respected of all Orcadian naturalists was Robert Rendall. He devoted his life to the study of Orkney shore life, especially the mollusca, but he was also a poet (*Country Sonnets, Orkney Variants, Shore Poems, The Hidden Land*), theologian, archaeologist and folk-lorist (Dickson, 1990). Rendall was born in Glasgow on 24 January 1898, the elder son of Orcadian parents. The family returned to Orkney in 1905. At the tender age of 13 the young Rendall left Kirkwall Grammar School to become an apprentice draper, embarking on what was to be a long and successful career in commerce. He read widely and voraciously and was almost entirely self-taught. As a boy he delighted in the freedom offered by the Orkney countryside:

> Gradually, I became accustomed to this new freedom, and my acquaintance with flowers grew. I came to know the scalies and the curly doddies, the sea pinks, the cocks and hens, the wild white clover (sucking this for its sweetness), the seggies in the Crantit meadows, golden dandylions run to seed, meadowsweet in the gullies of the cliffs at Scapa and Berstane, wiry 'sodgers' to slash in mimic battles. Insects, too, of all sorts laid a spell upon me: burnished beetles scuttling in the sun, cabbage butterflies in the garden, small blue ones by the roadside ditches, bumble bees in their ceremonial splendour of colour and many a thing besides.

Marine life in general and shells in particular fascinated him; he knew his Orkney beaches intimately and maintained an articulate and enquiring correspondence with all the leading conchologists of his day. Mrs N. McMillan (1968) wrote of his work: 'The non-marine species Rendall did not much care for, but he dredged and shore collected marine species with the utmost assiduity . . . His work was careful and thorough and his *Mollusca Orcadensia* will long be the standard list for these northern Isles.' *Mollusca Orcadensia* was published in 1958 by the Royal Society of Edinburgh, listing approximately 300 species with data on habitat and abundance.

Rendall also wrote a beautiful book, the *Orkney Shore* (1960), an evocative interweaving of autobiography with natural history. Light and colour spill from its pages, and in its own way it is a simple testament to the beauty of the Orkney landscape and the people who inhabit it:

> It was the end of the season, and the day's fishing was over. We landed on one of the small islands before making homeward. It was the last lingering hour of the day. Sitting on big lichened stones at the edge of the water we silently ate our 'Pieces' and drank our thermos tea. There the three of us were, old James, Dave and myself. Casting out the dregs of the tea from our flasks we rose and prospected the little islet, one of the chain-like group at the lower end of the loch. James picked up a few wing feathers (he had a use for these), and with a boylike simplicity

strange to see in an old man gathered a posy of water mint. I did likewise and added to them single specimens of a few wild flowers found in late bloom. They stood all winter in an Italian majollca vase; when next spring came they had become dull and colourless, with leaves shrivelled and dry, their fragrance gone. James, too, had gone, and lay buried beneath the turf. The last day of the season remains like a faded flower, preserving in thought moments and motions that never will return.

Robert Rendall died on 8 June 1967, not long after being awarded a Civil List pension for his services to literature and science. His collection of shells is now in Stromness Museum.

Orkney has attracted a good many competent birdwatchers into its midst, while Alfred Wood, James Omond, George Arthur, Duncan J. Robertson and William Groundwater, all Orcadians, have each added significantly to our knowledge of birds. Omond's *How to Know the Orkney Birds* (1925) raised the total Orkney list to 264 species.

In 1923, a solicitor and keen naturalist from Kirkwall, Duncan J. Robertson, purchased the lovely island of Eynhallow. Set in the violent tide rips of Rousay Sound, Eynhallow, or Holy Island, with its ruined Cistercian

Figure 11.8
The Peerie Sea at Kirkwall, an engraving from George Barry's *History of the Orkney Islands* (1805). The main road to Stromness now runs along the ayre which links the town to the shore in the left foreground.

monastery, is one of the most attractive and haunting of all the Orkney islands. Under Robertson's ownership it became, unofficially, Orkney's first bird reserve. Robertson knew his Eynhallow birds well, especially the Eider Ducks and the Fulmars, and his patient studies of them resulted in a fine behavioural and ecological study, *Notes from a Bird Sanctuary* (1934). He wrote of the Fulmar, with genuine affection: 'it is amazing how the whiteness of the snow is dimmed by contrast. In one way the Fulmar excels in beauty above any of the gulls. Its large and liquid eye gives it an appearance of gentleness which is unequalled in any bird I know.'

Edward (Eddie) Balfour of Rendall was, unquestionably, the finest ornithologist Orkney has produced. His early interest in birds was encouraged by Alfred Wood of Finstown, and strengthened by collaboration with Kirkwall baker and expert ornithologist, George Arthur, who introduced him to the varied bird community of Orkney's moorlands, which became Balfour's main love. Balfour's long association with the Royal Society for the Protection of Birds began in 1937 when the Society appointed him honorary watcher in Orkney. In 1954 he became a paid employee and a year later the RSPB's first full-time Orkney officer, a position he held until his death in 1974. He published valuable studies on Orkney Cormorants and Kestrels and contributed a plethora of shorter papers to the leading ornithological journals, as well as writing many popular bird articles. One bird came to dominate his life, the majestic raptor of the Orkney moors, the Hen Harrier, on which Eddie Balfour was rightly acknowledged the world authority. His study of the Orkney population of Hen Harriers lasted 43 years, the longest study of any raptor anywhere in the world. His last major paper on the species was published posthumously in collaboration with Dr J. Cadbury in 1979.

Eddie Balfour was a passionate advocate of conservation, but his arguments were always carefully tempered by realism. The rate at which good natural history sites in Orkney were disappearing under plough and bulldozer in the late 1960s and early 1970s saddened him greatly. In 1959, Eddie Balfour and others were the moving spirits behind the formation of an Orkney Field Club. The aims of the Club were straightforward: 'to promote the study and the conservation of the natural and cultural heritage of the County of Orkney'. The Club was well served by its early chairmen – John Scott and Eddie Balfour (Balfour's commitment was astonishing: in fifteen years' involvement he only missed three full committee meetings and one Annual General Meeting), and by acting as a forum for naturalists, it was able to play a significant and influential role in a variety of natural history and conservation issues (seals, mink, uranium, etc.) which have been such a feature of Orkney life in recent years.

Further reading

Agassiz, 1834; Anderson, 1834; Baikie and Heddle, 1848; Barry, 1805; Ben, 1529; Brand, 1701; Buckley and Harvie-Brown, 1891; Burkill, 1968; Charleson, 1905; Crichton, 1866; Cuthbert, 1995; Dickson, 1990; Donaldson, 1966; Dunn, 1837; Groundwater, 1974; Lea, 1976; Love, 1982; Low, 1813, 1879; McMillan, 1968; Millais, 1904; Neill, 1806; Ormond, 1925; Peach and Horne, 1880, 1883; Pennie, 1964; Rendall, 1948, 1956, 1960; Robertson, 1934; Sibbald, 1711; Sinclair, 1950; Spence, 1914; Traill, 1830; Wallace, 1693; Wallace, 1700; Withrington and Grant, 1978.

Chapter 12

Conservation, Development and the Future

Orkney's rich pre-history, significant on both a local and European scale, is widely recognized. The islands are much less well known for the international importance of their natural history and natural heritage. One reason for this may be that the landscape does not hold the high drama and remoteness of the Highlands or even Shetland to the north. There are few places in Orkney that one can truly experience complete wilderness, although weather and scenery regularly join to offer nature at its most majestic. Another reason is that, as we have seen, much of Orkney's wildlife is strongly influenced by human activities. Most of the species found today within the archipelago owe at least something to the long and often uneasy alliance between mankind and nature. That combination has brought about considerable change to the landscape over the last six millennia, with the last few decades of agricultural change and economic development representing some of the most rapid transformations in the islands' history. These changes reveal how delicate the balance is between conservation and other land uses. Notwithstanding, modern Orkney is unique – in Europe, at least – in its mix of biological richness within a relatively intensive agricultural practice.

This chapter examines the very considerable conservation value of the various habitats and species found in Orkney. It outlines some of the steps taken to safeguard them, together with the problems of maintaining the islands' natural heritage for future generations.

The most recent Structure Plan for Orkney, approved in 1994, states that

> The Council is keenly aware of its role as custodian of Orkney's cultural and natural heritage, . . . and [it] recognises also that this heritage is one that, properly managed, can bring substantial economic benefits to the community. There is in the Council's view, therefore, no necessary conflict between objectives for boosting the economy of the island and for protecting its natural and cultural assets. Indeed these assets provide a vital foundation for the Island's future prosperity and can contribute positively to achieving the Council's goal of redistributing economic activity more evenly throughout the archipelago.

One key factor in Orkney's nature conservation importance is the many wildlife refuges within the predominant farming landscape – areas of wet grassland and undrained meadow, flooded peat banks, disused farm tracks, and the proximity of extensive moorland edge and coastal fringe. These provide oases, especially for birds which feed on the productivity of adjacent farmland. Even species that seem to use exclusively semi-natural habitats such as moorland, for example the Hen Harrier and Short-eared Owl, depend heavily on intermediate areas of rough grassland to provide them with voles and other prey. Moreover, whilst much of Orkney's farming is modern and intensive, comparatively few pesticides and herbicides are used. Until recently, much of the moorlands were not heavily sheep-grazed. There are no deer with the associated problems of over-grazing which afflicts so much of the Scottish Highlands. Grouse are not common, and there is no tradition of predator persecution which formed part of the over-enthusiastic and over-prolonged Victorian approach to gamekeeping. Remoteness and limitations of infrastructure have meant that development has been relatively slow, and although this has had social consequences, it has also had wildlife benefit. In addition, the extensive shoreline and unpolluted coastal waters represent some of the finest marine habitats in Scotland, and an abundant food source for the birds and mammals reliant upon them.

Natura 2000

There is a raft of legislative and voluntary designations helping to safeguard Orkney's flora, fauna and landforms, much of it stemming from European directives. The most important have given rise to the 'Natura 2000' sites, which include Special Protection Areas for Birds and Special Areas of Conservation for other species and habitats. These are designated by the

Table 12.1   Sites classified as Special Protection Areas (SPAs) under the Wild Birds Directive

Site	Species of International Importance	Population	Designated
Mainland			
Marwick Head	Kittiwake	2% of GB, 1% of EU	1994
	Guillemot	4% of GB, 3% of EU	
South Isles			
Auskerry	Storm Petrel	4% of GB, 1% of World	1998
	Arctic Tern	2% of GB	
Copinsay	Great Black-backed Gull	3% of GB, 2% of EU	
	Kittiwake	2% of GB, 2% of EU	
	Guillemot	3% of GB, 2% of EU	
Pentland Firth Islands	Arctic Tern	2% of GB	1997
North Islands			
Calf of Eday	>20,000 seabirds, incl.		1998
	Cormorant	3% of GB	
	Great Black-backed Gull	5% of GB	
	Guillemot	1% of GB	
Papa Westray (incl.	Arctic Tern	4% of GB	1996
Holm of Papa Westray)	Arctic Skua (not qualifying criterion)	5% of GB	
	Black Guillemot (not qualifying criterion)	1% of GB	
East Sanday Coast	Purple Sandpiper	4% of GB, 2% of EU Atlantic Flyway	1997 (also RAMSAR site)
	Turnstone also:	2% of GB, 2% of EU	
	Ringed Plover	1% of GB wintering population	
	Sanderling	2% of GB	
	Bar-tailed Godwit	1% of GB	
West Westray	Kittiwake	5% of GB, 4% of West Europe	1996
	Guillemot	4% of GB, 1% of West Europe	
	Arctic Tern	1% of GB	
		113,000 individual seabirds of 12 species	
Sule Skerry and Sule Stack	Storm Petrel	1–6% GB, 1–2% of world	1994
	Leach's Petrel	1–5 pairs	
	Gannet	4% of GB, 3% of West Europe and EU	
	Puffin *grabae* race	5% of World, 10% of GB & EU	

European Union as sites of significance in a European context. In Scotland, designation has been the responsibility of the Secretary of State for Scotland, acting on the advice of Scottish Natural Heritage. Fifteen Special Protection Areas (SPAs) have or are likely to be selected in Orkney, providing convincing testimony of the archipelago's international ornithological standing and reflecting the range of rare, vulnerable and migratory species found regularly within the islands (Table 12.1). The majority of these sites are already existing Sites of Special Scientific Interest under British legislation. Orkney's spectacular seabird colonies form the bulk of the sites so far designated. For example, Sule Skerry and Sule Stack, those remote islands to the west of the Orkney Mainland, qualify for selection because of their vast numbers of puffins and gannets, and both Marwick Head on the west Mainland coast, and the cliffs of West Westray and Copinsay harbour sufficient breeding pairs of species such as kittiwake and guillemot to make them of European importance.

There are in addition six potential SPAs likely to be selected in Orkney which would involve the protection of such species as Red-throated Diver, Great Skua, Hen Harrier, Pintail and Pochard.

All Natura 2000 sites must also be Sites of Special Scientific Interest (SSSI), and most of the proposed SPAs in Orkney are already existing SSSIs. However, the re-assessment of Scottish bird populations has revealed that the wintering coastal wader populations around Orkney are some of the most significant in the UK (see p. 175). Unlike more northerly breeding grounds for these species, the Orkney coastline, although subject to severe winter weather, is rarely frozen. Moreover, the complex tidal situation means that high tide differs from place to place, so that for example sanderling on the Sanday coast need fly only a few miles to North Ronaldsay to extend the length of their feeding time between high tides, and at the same time evade the rats on Sanday. In addition, the severe winter storms around Orkney deposit vast quantities of kelp (*Laminaria)* and other detritus on the shore. This material supports huge quantities of invertebrates such as Sandhoppers (*Talitrus* spp.) and kelp fly larvae (*Coelopa* spp.) which are valuable food for many species. The East Sanday Coast SPA, which extends for about 30 miles (55 kilometres) around the Sanday coast is the most important of these coastline areas, although beaches on the islands of the Mainland, Stronsay, Westray and North Ronaldsay, are also of significance.

Special Areas for Conservation

The equivalent of SPAs for habitats and species other than birds are the Special Areas for Conservation (SACs). They are defined in the European Habitats and Species Directive (1992). Habitats Directive sites can be either marine or terrestrial. Four candidate sites are in Orkney.

On Hoy, the north of the island is a candidate SAC on several grounds. The first of these is the presence of hard-water springs with tufa formations. These are springs or flushes of calcareous water (in the case of Hoy, derived from calcium carbonate bands within the Old Red Sandstone) that precipitate to form hard deposits of lime known as tufa, a relatively rare habitat in both continental Europe and the UK outside limestone areas. The vegetation of these springs consists of a dense yellow mat of the Feather Moss *Cratoneuron commutatum* along with various lime-loving species, hence their technical name: cratoneurion. Hoy also supports large areas of wet heathland containing Cross-leaved Heath *(Erica tetralix)*, a community typical of cool oceanic areas, occuring on wet, acid, peaty soils. On Hoy the lichen component is unusually luxuriant, probably due to the low level of disturbance, including little grazing by sheep or other herbivores. Finally, the alpine and sub-alpine heaths on Hoy are some of the best in Europe, and are dominated by dwarf-shrubs of the Heather family, Bearberry *(Arctostaphylos uva-ursi)* Arctic Bearberry *(Arctostaphylos alpinus)*, and Dwarf Willow *(Salix herbacea)*. A noticeable feature is the wind-clipped nature of these plant communities due to their exposure. Such plant communities are typically found at high altitude, but exposure to Orkney's windy climate has resulted in their development on the much lower westerly and southern slopes of Hoy. The vegetation on the summit of Ward Hill on Hoy at 1,500 feet (479 metres) is comparable with vegetation on the Cairngorms at 3,000 feet (1,000 metres).

Figure 12.1
The lack of air pollution in Orkney is well illustrated by the extraordinary luxuriance of lichen growth on these trees in Trumland, Rousay.
Photo: Richard Welsby

Stromness Heaths and Coast is another candidate SAC, on the basis of its vegetated sea cliffs and the dry heath community. The cliffs themselves are so storm battered that no plants survive, but the cliff top has extensive areas dominated by Thrift *(Armeria maritima)* and Sea plantain *(Plantago maritima)* along with Red Fescue *(Festuca rubra)* and Spring Squill *(Scilla verna)*. Further back from the cliff edge, but still strongly sea influenced, are the maritime heath communities, characterized by Crowberry *(Empetrum nigrum)*, Bell Heather *(Erica cinerea)* and Heather *(Calluna vulgaris)*. There are also species of sedge *(Carex* spp.*)* and lichens (the so-called reindeer mosses) *(Cladonia* spp.*)*; colonies of the rare Scottish Primrose *(Primula scotica)* also occur.

The Loch of Stenness is also a candidate SAC. The European Community's Habitat Directive defines lagoons as 'areas of shallow coastal saltwater of varying salinity separated from the sea by sand banks, shingle, or less frequently rocks'. These saline enclosed waters have declined considerably in number and quality across Europe, and are considered a priority habitat under the Directive. Scotland has many of the pristine lagoons remaining in Britain. The Loch of Stenness has a narrow entry to Scapa Flow at the Brig of Waithe, and as a shallow predominantly saline body of water, represents a particularly good example of a lagoon; it is also the largest lagoon in the UK (see p. 124).

Just outside this proposed site is the Loch of Harray. This is a freshwater loch but with a saline input from the Brig of Brodgar, where tidal water enters from the Loch of Stenness. This inflow is limited by one-way flaps on the causeway, installed as a response to a marine algal bloom (caused by a species called *Prymnesium*) which in 1968 resulted in large-scale mortality of Brown Trout. Fortunately for the scientific interest of the site the flaps are not completely effective and the causeway itself is also somewhat permeable. Most biologists agree that the best action would be to remove the flaps, which do little for the fish population and hamper water exchange, thus contributing to the nutrient enrichment of Harray Loch.

Sites of Special Scientific Interest

There are 34 Sites of Special Scientific Interest (SSSI) in Orkney, notified by Scottish Natural Heritage and its predecessor the Nature Conservancy Council under the Wildlife and Countryside Act (1981). They cover approximately 20 per cent of the land area of the islands and are notable for their flora, fauna, geology or geomorphology (landforms). Some sites are nationally important while others have a more regional significance, but in total they contribute to a UK-wide series, and every site must be seen from this national perspective. A full list of Orkney's SSSI together with the reasons for notification are given in Table 12.2.

The re-notification of Orkney SSSIs under the Wildlife and Countryside Act 1981 was met with considerable local opposition when it began in the mid-1980s. Emotions ran strongly in the islands, with their tradition of owner-occupancy and a fiercely independent outlook; an outside government body intervening in the management of farms was unlikely to be popular. Much has changed since then, and the value of conservation has become generally recognized, including the financial benefits it may bring. In order to secure sound conservation management on sites, SNH now pays over £200,000 per annum into the Orkney farming community through more than 40 management agreements with farmers, part of a general operating principle that no one should suffer loss simply as a result of owning an SSSI. Increasingly, such agreements are devised to secure positive management in order to enhance the special interest of the site concerned.

Table 12.2   Sites of Special Scientific Interest in Orkney (SSSIs)

Site	Area (ha)	Grid reference	Scientific interest
Auskerry	103	HY2319	Breeding Arctic tern and colonies; Storm Petrel.
Bay of Skaill	7.85	HY2319	Middle Devonian fossil flora.
Calf of Eday	242	HY5839	Large Cormorant colony.
Central Sanday	655	HY7040	Sand dune landforms, salt marsh and machair vegetation, wetland areas, waders.
Copinsay	151	HY6001	Breeding seabird communities, notably Guillemot and Kittiwake; maritime vegetation including Oyster plant (Mertensia maritima).
Cruaday Quarry	7	HY2421	An exposure of the Middle Devonian Lower Stromness Flags, particularly important for the numbers of fossil fish it contains.
Den Wick	0.5	HY5708	Earth science site, with 'multiple till' sections, illustrating changes in ice dynamics during last ice age.
Doomy and Whitemaw Hill	209	HY5634/ HY5432	Site for breeding Whimbrel and Arctic Skuas.
East Sanday Coast	1,505	HY7040	Internationally important for winter numbers of: Purple Sandpiper Turnstone. Nationally important for winter numbers of: Ringed Plover Sanderling Bar-tailed Godwit.
Eynhallow	102	HY3629	Breeding seabirds, notably Fulmar on which a long-term study has been carried out. Common Seal breeding site and haul-out.
Faray and Holm of Faray	80	HY5238	Internationally important Grey Seal breeding site.
Glims Moss and Durkadale	225	HY3123	Mire vegetation: raised mire; and most northerly calcareous valley mire in Britain.
Holm of Papa Westray	47	HY5052	Large colony of Black Guillemots, other birds include Eiders and Storm Petrels.
Hoy	8,186	HY2201	Very diverse upland and coastal habitat, with excellent examples of dwarf shrub heaths, and arctic alpines especially on the more calcareous soils; only Orcadian ancient woodland remnant; lepidoptera; moorland birds including Great Skuas and Red-throated Divers; only place in Orkney where Mountain Hare occurs. St John's Head at 338 metres is one of the highest headlands in Britain, excellent geological exposures of Hoy Volcanics and Hoy Sandstones, glacial and periglacial features.
Keelylang Hill and Swartabeck Burn	925	HY3909	Important breeding site for Merlin, Hen Harrier and Short-eared Owls. Moorland of interest for the regeneration of unmanaged heather stands and extensive areas of Greater Woodrush.
Loch of Banks	43	HY2723	Basin mire formed from an area of formerly largely open water. Wetland habitats, winter roost for Hen Harriers, diverse breeding bird community, regularly used by Otters.
Loch of Isbister and the Loons	104	HY2524	Basin mire with excellent examples of open-water transition communities; diverse breeding bird community.

Site	Area (ha)	Grid reference	Scientific interest
Lochs of Harray and Stenness	1,930	HY2916 HY2813	Open water with transition from fresh water (Harray) to brackish (Stenness). Large number of *Potamogeton* pondweeds, including three nationally scarce species. Unusual invertebrate interest. Nationally significant numbers of breeding wildfowl.
Marwick Head	9	HY2225	One of biggest seabird breeding colonies in Orkney, particularly Guillemots, Kittiwakes, Fulmars and Razorbills (small numbers of Puffins can also be seen at this RSPB reserve).
Mill Bay, Stronsay	1.9	HY6625	Best available exposures of the classic shelly till and includes a wide range of erratic materials. The site is thus important in demonstrating glacial ice movement and as a potential dating site using shell fragments.
Mill Loch, Eday	23	HY5636	In recent years this loch small loch has held one of the largest densities of breeding Red-throated Divers in Britain.
Muckle and Little Greenholm	53	HY5227	Nationally important colonies of breeding Grey Seals.
Muckle Head and Selwick	1.7	HY2105 HY2205	Two areas of raised beach deposits, representing a relatively rare record in Scotland of a period or periods when sea level was slightly above that of the present day prior at least to the last glaciation
North Hill, Papa Westray	206	HY5055	Extensive area of maritime heath, botanically very diverse. Large Arctic Tern and Arctic Skua breeding colonies. The cliffs surrounding the site hold breeding seabirds.
Northwall, Sanday	251	HY7444	Extensive dune machair, encloses along with the Central Sanday SSSI the most extensive area of this habitat outwith the Western Isles. There are also five machair lochs in the site and a range of wetland habitat.
Orphir and Stenness Hills	890	HY3308	Moorland birds, especially birds of prey: Hen Harrier, Merlin, Kestrel, Short-eared Owl. Botanically diverse with typical moorland vegetation and tall herb and flush communities typical of Orkney dales.
Pentland Firth Islands	168	ND3844/ 4678	Internationally important Arctic tern colonies.
Rousay	2,313	HY4031	Ornithological interest includes breeding Red-throated Divers, Merlin, Kestrel, Short-eared Owl, a large Arctic Tern and Arctic Skua colony and seabirds. Botanically the site includes Brings and Faraclett Head, where maritime and coastal wet heath remain, and Scottish Primrose (*Primula scotica*) is to be found. The inland vegetation is typically moorland within which the nationally scarce species the Serrated Wintergreen (*Orthilia secunda*) can be found. On the hilltops exposure and latitude allow vegetation more typical of higher altitudes elsewhere, including the Dwarf Willow (*Salix herbacea*), Arctic Bearberry (*Arctostaphylos alpinus*) and Alpine Saw-wort (*Saussurea alpina*).

Site	Area (ha)	Grid reference	Scientific interest
Stromness Heaths and Coast	755	HY2213	Coastal and moorland habitats. Cliff-top vegetation is co-dominated by Sea Plantain (*Plantago maritima*) and Thrift (*Armeria maritima*). Coastal heath communities including Scottish Primrose (*Primula scotica*) give way to acidic heaths and flushes further away from the maritime interest. The coast is subject to some of the highest energy storm waves in Britain, and the examples of geomorphological features, such as arches, stacks, caves and geos are outstanding. The geology is also important, featuring the Sandwick Fish Beds Cycles, and possessing the best stromatolite beds in the Orcadian basin.
Sule Skerry	15	HX6224	A very large Puffin colony, and large numbers of Shag breed here, together with a number of other species of seabirds.
Sule Stack	3	HX5617	An internationally significant, and Orkney's only, Gannet colony
Ward Hill Cliffs	35	ND4688	A further site with sea cliff-top vegetation, which grades into lichen rich heath. There are localized calcareous flushes typically dominated by the Black Bog-rush (*Schoenus nigricans*). Small colonies of seabirds also occur and the small beaches and cliffs are some of the few Mainland Orkney breeding sites for Grey Seal.
Waulkmill	71	HY3706	A sheltered bay facing Scapa Flow, at the head of which behind a shingle spit is one of the most extensive salt marshes in Orkney. There is also heathland vegetation and on the sheltered sides of the bay a richer community of herbs, shrubs and ferns. Aspen (*Populus tremula*) and willows (*Salix* spp.) are also to be found. The cliffs are generally considered to be one of the best lepidopteran (moths and butterflies) sites in Orkney.
West Mainland Moorlands	2,523	HY3521	An extensive upland site, almost entirely sub-montane in character, with few alpine plants, but with large extents of blanket bog, wet and dry heaths. In the sheltered 'dales' patchy willow (*Salix* spp.) scrub occurs along with tall-herb communities including Valerian (*Valerian officinalis*), Water Avens (*Geum rivale*) and Rosebay Willowherb (*Chamerion angustifolium*). The moorlands are the premier area for Hen Harrier in Orkney, and Merlin, Short-eared Owl and Kestrel also breed in significant numbers. Arctic Skuas and Great Skuas also breed on the site and approximately eleven pairs of Red-throated Divers breed on the moorland's lochans.
West Westray	371	HY4246	Eight kilometres of coastline supporting an immense colony of nesting seabirds: including one of the largest colonies of Guillemots and Kittiwakes in the British Isles. Other species include Razorbills, Puffins, Fulmars and Shags. Inland both Arctic and Great Skuas breed. The vegetation includes a range of maritime heath and grass-land, and some of the outcrops have well-developed fern communities; wetter ledges are characterized by Moss Campion (*Silene acaulis*).

Figure 12.2
Tourism is now a major factor in the economy of Orkney. The islands are a wonderful record of human–nature inter-actions, even in the Block Ships sunk to guard the entrances to Scapa Flow during the Second World War.

Furthermore, tourism is second only to agriculture in the Orkney economy, and landscape and wildlife are significant commercial assets. A sense of trust and some experience of working together has greatly improved relationships between farmers and conservationists. A notable step forward was the establishment in 1985 of the Orkney Wildlife and Farming Group (FWAG). This has provided a constructive forum to deal with problems between farming and conservation, and to promote the message of environ-mentally friendly agriculture in a way that offers Orkney's farmers an opportunity to be involved in the conservation of their lands. Membership has steadily grown; there are now two full-time advisory officers. In 1995, FWAG's tenth year, a specially written handbook, *Farming with Wildlife in Mind* was presented to every farmer in Orkney (Charter, 1995).

Outside the statutorily protected sites there are a number of second-tier sites – RSPB and local nature reserves. And beyond these, over 5,000 hectares in 153 marginal moorland and wetland sites have been identified as biologically important in a Royal Society for the Protection of Birds survey during 1986 and 1987. The RSPB study took place in early summer and focused primarily on breeding birds, but basic habitat details were also col-lected. Although these scattered sites have no particular protection, they are regarded as *de facto* third-tier sites, in planning applications involving proposed development. This status has been formalized in the Orkney Islands Council Structure Plan in terms of a general presumption against development in those areas. In 1993 and 1994 the survey was extended by the RSPB to include information on a total of 202 sites. Of the 153 originally surveyed, 24 had been substantially damaged, including six that had been completely lost – over 15 per cent in seven years, a rate equivalent to nearly a quarter every ten years. Most of the damage was due to agricultural improvement, particularly drainage and re-seeding of semi-natural areas, which is exempt from planning controls. It highlights one of the biggest dilemmas for those concerned for Orkney's wildlife.

Agricultural change

Agriculture has been a major agent of change in Orkney ever since the first human settlers arrived. Abandonment of the run-rig practice of strip farming and the Clearances, together with the introduction of large numbers of sheep, dramatically affected many parts of Orkney in the nineteenth century. Subsequently the huge loss of moorland from the First World War to the 1980s has had a profound effect on wildlife. The results of these changes are poorly documented, and good information is only available for the last few decades. We know that between the late 1940s and 1970s Orkney lost around 30 per cent of its moorland through ploughing, liming and re-seeding with grass. A more detailed study on Mainland and South Ronaldsay, using maps, survey data and aerial photographs found that there had been an astonishing 72 per cent loss of moorland on South Ronaldsay, from 1,556 hectares to 435 hectares between 1932 and 1985. On the Mainland, many of the corridors linking the main moorland blocks had been lost by 1958 and the original 20,202 hectares of moorland was reduced by 56 per cent to 11,355 hectares. The data can be extrapolated to the whole archipelago (Table 12.3).

Large-scale moorland 'reclamation' has now ceased, since the grants supporting it have been withdrawn. However, smaller wildlife oases remain highly vulnerable. The RSPB estimate that Orkney's lowland areas in early summer support around 9,800 pairs of Oystercatchers, 5,400 pairs of Lapwings, 4,100 pairs of Curlews, 3,150 Snipe and 1,700 pairs of

Table 12.3   Agricultural land in Orkney (including rough grazing) 1833–1995

Year	Area used for agriculture (in hectares)	% of total land area
1833	10,110	10.4
1870	28,300	29.1
1900	34,000	35.0
1923	37,600	38.7
1936	36,213	37.3
1952	71,600	73.3
1960	77,974	76.9
1981	77,974	80.9
1995	78,600	81.5

Redshank. The 153 unprotected sites mentioned above were estimated to hold 3,642 pairs of waders, approximately 70 pairs per square kilometre, an astonishing figure when compared with the average in suitable areas else-where of perhaps ten to fifteen pairs per square kilometre. This illustrates the importance of these sites, and the consequences of further damage or loss.

Some species have benefited from agricultural changes; the population of breeding Curlews in Orkney is probably in excess of 5,000 pairs, when birds using the margins of moorland are included – over a seventh of Britain's total of a Red Data Book bird. But other species have declined. For example, Lapwing are thought to have been three to four times more numerous in the 1930s than now. The main reason for such declines are almost certainly habitat loss. Less rough grazing, shorter pasture availability in early summer, and other changes in farming practice are factors, while the continuing loss of wet pasture has had a marked affect on birds that require not only cover, but also the invertebrate food that this sort of habitat provides. The disap-pearance of many arable weeds has affected the abundance of invertebrates. It is worth noting that agricultural improvement continues today, even without agricultural grants, fragmenting remaining semi-natural habitats.

Some other species have increased in numbers this century – Hen Harrier and Red-throated Diver, for example, are certainly more numerous than otherwise would be the case, because they have suffered little or no persecu-tion, although the Harrier has declined markedly from its peak population in the late 1970s, probably through land-use changes reducing its prey. Certain seabirds have increased, as have Seal numbers. Other species have declined. The Scottish Primrose (*Primula scotica)*, virtually an Orkney emblem, occurs in far fewer sites than it once did (p. 74). The maritime grassland and maritime heath communities in which it is found are highly sensitive to fer-tilizer or slurry applications, let alone ploughing and re-seeding. (*P. scotica* is damaged by grazing during flowering, but actually requires grazing in late summer and autumn). Fortunately most sites on which *P. scotica* occurs are now protected, and there is even talk of reintroductions. However, there is little point in reintroducing *P. scotica* to sites when the pressures that caused its loss still exist. Perhaps the best approach will be to reintroduce *P. scotica* to 'safe' sites (i.e. those in which land-use favours *P. scotica*) where plants usually associated with the Primrose are found, but *P. scotica* itself is absent. Considerable success has also been enjoyed by the Scottish Wildlife Trust management at Loft and the Hill of White Hamars, where adjustment to the pattern of sheep grazing has produced a dramatic recovery of *P. scotica* numbers in semi-natural habitats. The factors that determine whether *P. scotica* colonies will establish and thrive are complex, and include the degree of exposure, changing winds, and localized bombardment by salt spray.

Juniper (*Juniper communis)*, the Stag's Horn Clubmoss (*Lycopodium clavatum*) and Alpine Clubmoss (*Diphasiastrum alpinum*) appear to have declined due to a combination of reclamation and heather burning. The latter has been practised in Orkney for many years, often in an uncontrolled fashion with no direct management purpose intended. A firewatch warden on the Mainland hills in the 1990s has reduced the severity of the fires. Increased sheep grazing of the hills also affects these species. Yellowhammers, once a common breeding bird, have been lost, perhaps due to the removal of gorse. Many weeds of cultivation have become rarer; Corn Cockle (*Agrostemma githago*), Greater Yellow-rattle (*Rhinanthus seroyinus*) and Cornflower (*Centaurea cyanthus*) have disappeared, and the Long-headed Poppy (*Papaver dubium*) is now much less common. As well as the loss of agricultural weeds, more efficient harvesting of barley, which is now cut greener and with less spilt grain, has contributed to the decline of birds such as the Corn Bunting, Twite and Skylark. A further factor must also be the reduction in land under arable cultivation as production has switched to greater grass production.

Positive initiatives

The Corncrake Initiative described above (p. 160) is a good example of a project aiming to favour conservation, as is the Barnacle Goose programme (p. 175). The Agricultural Development Programme (ADP) was run in the late 1980s by the Scottish Office Agriculture and Fisheries Department (SOAFD) with European Community support which made payments to safeguard environmentally valuable areas on farms. This programme helped to secure many of the second-tier marginal moorland and wetland sites which might otherwise have been lost. More recently, SOAFD have introduced other schemes with environmental benefits. The first was a successor to the ADP, the Highlands and Islands Agricultural Programme. Under this, money has been available for specific environmental projects. There appears to have been little use made of this, perhaps because its focus is on capital expenditure. The second scheme was the Agri-environment Programme, now the Countryside Premium Scheme, under which assistance is available to support habitat restoration or creation in the form of annual area payments. The scheme has been popular in Orkney, although it is underfunded and uptake has involved only a few tens of farmers. The provisions to restore maritime heath, moorland, upland scrub and semi-natural grassland have resulted in some excellent projects. A weakness of the Scheme is that it concentrates on habitat creation and restoration, and makes no provision for the maintenance of existing habitats. Another venture which proved very successful has been SNH Farm Conservation Plan Grants, in which farmers have been encouraged to have a farm plan drawn up, detailing the conservation interest of the farm and how they could modify their

Figure 12.3
Colours seem particularly vivid in Orkney. Untreated road verges are a particular delight.
Photo: Richard Welsby

husbandry to encourage wildlife. Offering a very favourable rate of grant, over 50 plans were completed between 1995 and 1998.

Farming and conservation

Orkney farmers take great pride in their farms, and this includes a genuine enthusiasm for the wildlife present on the land. This is well illustrated by the support given by both individual farmers and by the local branch of National Farmers Union of Scotland to FWAG. There is no doubt of the value of this bridge-building, nor of the need to promote a wider understanding of the requirements of wildlife. The loss of moorland might be regrettable to naturalists, but few knowing the hardship of farming in Orkney between the wars would wish to turn the clock back. Unfortunately, comments on the decline of wildlife on farmland are often taken personally by farmers as a criticism of their agricultural practice. This is understandable, but the problem lies firmly with a governmental support structure that fails to grasp the nettle of sustainable farming. Until this issue is dealt with, conservation will largely remain an unaffordable luxury in a community where the average farm size is only around 65 hectares, and agricultural incomes very modest.

Landscape

Loss of habitat is not the only threat to the Orkney countryside. A recent survey identified 23 different landscape types in Orkney and pinpointed new rural housing as a major threat to the traditional mosaic of scattered farms. New houses, often constructed in unsympathetic styles and materials, are too often sited without reference to landscape character. Policies favouring new-for-old housing and allowing the building of two or three houses in a group, have resulted in ribbon development. The best approach is not obvious. People need to live close to where they work, and in agricultural Orkney, rural settlement must be encouraged. Modern kit houses are cheaper and warmer than more traditionally styled new buildings or the renovation of existing properties; moreover, current VAT legislation encourages new building rather than upgrading old properties. Too restrictive planning policies will fossilize the countryside, but too *laissez-faire* an approach will result in long-term ugliness. Another problem is the demise of stone walls. Although these provide good wind-breaks, they are expensive to build and maintain, while barbed wire fences are relatively easy to erect. Yet in areas such as Stromness, lying within a National Scenic Area, the existence of this traditional form of field division is an important and attractive component of the landscape.

Uranium deposits

Uranium is present in the basal beds of the Stromness Flags in Yesnaby and Stromness area, and in their extension in Caithness (p. 47). The amount of uranium is unknown. As a part of its investigation of the geochemical resources of Britain, the South of Scotland Electricity Board some years ago proposed to explore the uranium resources in Orkney. This was interpreted by the anti-nuclear lobby as a preliminary to mining. Feelings ran high over the issue. More recently there were rumours that the sea-bed around Orkney was being considered as a repository for radioactive waste. Today uranium mining seems unlikely, with nuclear energy less fashionable than it was a couple of decades ago and cheaper sources of uranium available from elsewhere. A more urgent radioactivity story is that relating to the experimental and reprocessing plant for the nuclear industry at Dounreay, located on the north coast of Caithness and now under sentence of closure. Over the last few years it has become clear that a number of breaches in safety procedures have occurred during the life of the plant, and local opinion has been unsettled at reports of radiation 'leaks'.

The oil industry

Of other industries, oil poses the most obvious environmental threat – but also contributes significantly to the economic prosperity of the islands. Since January 1977 oil has been pumped from a field 150 miles (200 kilometres) south-east of Orkney to a terminal on Flotta, whence it is transferred to tankers to be shipped world-wide. Apart from providing deep-water anchorage, Flotta was well suited as a location for an oil terminal. The decision to locate it there took the development away from the main areas of settlement to a small island suffering considerable depopulation. In designing the terminal, considerable efforts were made to integrate it visually into the island. A surprising discovery was the ignorance that existed about water movements in Scapa Flow, despite its history as a naval base during two World Wars. The oil companies commissioned a series of measurements of winds, tides and currents, to establish the likely effects of oil pollution. These led to the treated ballast water outfall being situated outside the Flow, and an effluent water treatment monitoring system being installed, which re-treats water before discharge if it falls below a predetermined standard.

An associated biological monitoring programme was set up as part of the Harbours Department. Sea water and faunal samples are collected in and around the Flow, to detect changes in shore life and both zoo- and phytoplankton. Control sample sites outside the Flow have shown changes, albeit none attributable to the presence of the terminal. In addition, the Nature Conservancy Council established a seabird monitoring programme in 1976, based on sample counts at five mainland cliff sites each June. Counts

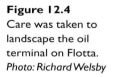
Figure 12.4
Care was taken to landscape the oil terminal on Flotta.
Photo: Richard Welsby

included individual Guillemots, Razorbills, Kittiwakes and Fulmars, and apparently occupied nests of Kittiwakes and Fulmars. A difficulty has been the variability of the counts. Statistically, changes of as little as three per cent per annum can be detected within the Kittiwake population, but for Guillemots the change in numbers needed must be over 13 per cent, and for Razorbills the population alteration must be even larger, over 22 per cent.

In fact the terminal has a good safety record, and the main cause of oil pollution has been the disposal of ballast and tank water from ships outside Scapa Flow. Leakage in the Flow from the torpedoed battleship *Royal Oak* led to a patch being fitted over the wreck in 1999. The RSPB runs a Beach Bird Survey, in which corpses of all birds found on a sample of some 30 Orkney beaches are recorded. The dead birds are identified, noted as to whether oil is present (the vast number of deaths are due to natural causes) and the corpses removed from the beach. In the early years of the operation of the terminal, 26 per cent of beached birds were oiled, but then the terminal introduced a policy of refusing to load vessels unless all tanks were emptied via the terminal's ballast water treatment facilities. This, and the provision of similar facilities at the Sullom Voe Terminal in Shetland, has reduced the proportion of oiled birds to less than 5 per cent in recent years.

When the *Braer* tanker ran aground near Sumburgh Head, Shetland in January 1993, and spilt all her oil cargo, concerns re-surfaced that a similar incident could happen in Orkney, possibly with much worse consequences (extremely stormy weather combined with the particular characteristics of the oil meant that most of the latter was quickly dissipated in the *Braer* incident, with relatively light environmental consequences for a spill of such magnitude). The Harbour Authority would like to see improved radar coverage of the Pentland Firth and the introduction of radar coverage of the Fair Isle channel. In addition, direction of tankers in transit away from Orkney in-shore waters has been suggested, coupled with clear separation of traffic moving east–west and west–east between Orkney and Shetland. The stationing of a helicopter and an ocean-going tug in Orkney would also speed up any oil-spill response.

The discovery of oil to the west of Orkney has intensified concerns. These relate mainly to the technique of bringing the oil to Orkney by transferring oil to tankers at sea and shipping it to Flotta, rather than by a pipeline. The method increases the chance of a spillage as two loading/unloading procedures are required instead of one. However, the oil companies maintain that modern technology and safety standards make this no more risky than pumping the crude to Orkney. If there was a major spill, equipment is locally available to assist in containing and collecting the spilt oil. National resources can also be called upon if the incident warrants. Both the Harbour Authority and the terminal operators have contingency plans, and in the case of the Harbours Authority, details of the coastline around Orkney are held

Figure 12.5
The Churchill Barriers have influenced water exchange between Scapa Flow and the open sea, and affected inshore fishing as well as linked the human communities of Burray and South Ronaldsay with the Mainland.

(left) Barrier blocks.

(right) Third Churchill Barrier.

Photos: Richard Welsby

on a computer database. However, in most cases any measures would represent little more than a cosmetic cleaning-up operation and would only marginally lessen the environmental impact of a really big spill, especially as much of the clean-up technology, such as booms and skimmers, relies on near-ideal weather conditions.

The marine and coastal habitats are some of the most pristine around Orkney. They are also probably some of the most significant areas from a conservation viewpoint. However, there has been comparatively little work on their ecology. In 1995 and 1996, SNH specialists and the members of the Joint Nature Conservation Committee's Marine Nature Conservation Review team surveyed some of Orkney's marine and coastal habitats. A small amount of data has also been collected by sports divers, under the Sea Search programme. Slowly we are building up a fuller knowledge of the marine ecosystem, but it will be a long time before the ecology of the seas around the archipelago is known.

Fishing

Fish-based industries are of considerable importance to Orkney's economy. A number of trawlers operate out of Orkney, but the decline of the drifters that used to follow the herring around Scottish coasts is a reminder of an unsustainable fishery. In past times fishing provided far more jobs than at present, with Whitehall on Stronsay, St Margaret's Hope, South Ronaldsay, and Burray, being particularly important locations during the late eighteenth and first part of the nineteenth centuries.

One factor influencing the in-shore fishery has been the construction of the Churchill Barriers. These have reduced water exchange within Scapa Flow, and fish stocks are now much reduced. Today inshore fishing for shell fish is particularly important, and although lobster catches have declined, edible crab are still taken in good numbers. One proposal being seriously considered is the re-stocking of Scapa Flow with captive bred lobsters. Other species fished include the whelk (or buckie) for the Japanese market and the velvet swimming crab, which is a delicacy in parts of the Mediterranean. A voluntary ban operates in the summer to assist the conservation of the latter. Scallops too are taken in Orkney, but most are dived for, rather than dredged. The latter can be a particularly damaging operation to sea-bed habitats. Collecting kelp has long been of importance to Orkney (p. 210). Recently proposals have been put forward to establish an industry within Orkney to harvest live seaweed and extract a growth promoter for horticultural use. Provided the amount of seaweed removed is not excessive, this will not be damaging, but the situation will obviously need to be monitored to ensure that the operation remains sustainable.

Fish farming

Fish farming grew explosively in Scotland in the 1970s; virtually every sheltered loch seemed to spawn a set of floating tanks. However, the industry requires considerable capital outlay, and the crop of fish (mainly Salmon in Orkney) takes several years to mature. Disease can quickly spread with so many fish so closely contained. Fish farming can therefore be a risky enterprise. In recent years an increase in the production of farmed Salmon has depressed prices, which may be good news for the consumer, but within the industry has forced a degree of rationalization. There are now fewer small operators and several farms in Orkney have gone out of business, but new fish farms are still being established. At the same time the industry has become more environmentally aware, although problems remain. Especially important is good water exchange, as detritus falling below the cages can cause anoxic conditions, and a carpet 'sewage fungus'. There are also concerns that the farms can become a source of infection to wild fish. In particular, large numbers of sea-lice (fish ecto-parasites) can build up in captive Salmon. The response of fish-farmers is to treat cages containing infected fish, and this leads to toxic pesticides becoming an environmental threat.

Seal culling

Seal biology is dealt with elsewhere in this book, but seal populations in Orkney waters are of significant conservation importance. There are around 38,000 Grey Seals breeding on Orkney's shores each autumn, and this represents one of Europe's most important areas for Grey Seals. Over 50 per cent of the world population of Grey Seals breed in British waters. Orkney's Common Seals are less numerous than the Grey Seals, but the resident population of around 8,000 is a significant proportion of British Common Seal numbers which in turn represent 5 per cent of the world population and about 40 per cent of the European sub-species.

Seals were traditionally hunted by fishermen around Orkney, and even after strict controls were introduced in 1962, small numbers of seals were annually taken as a fisheries protection measure. Generally seals have recovered well from previously very low numbers in the post-war period, due to the fact that animals were hunted less and left undisturbed to breed on uninhabited islands such as Faray. Numbers of Grey Seals began to rise steeply from around 700 in 1962, to 1,000 in 1976 and 12,000 in 1982. In recent years the population seems to have stabilized at over 30,000 breeding individuals. Some protection was given to all species of seals in 1970 with the passing of the Conservation of Seals Act. This provided for a closed season when it was illegal to shoot or otherwise kill seals, and controlled how seals might be taken outside the closed season. Protection was given to both species during the pupping period: June to August for Common Seals, September to December for Grey Seals. The Act makes an exception for shooting seals that threaten fishing gear (which is interpreted to include fish farms), but generally the Act has proved a successful conservation measure.

In 1977 the Department of Agriculture and Fisheries for Scotland decided to carry out a major cull of Grey Seals on fishery protection grounds. This was in response to pressures from fisheries interests, and intended to return seal numbers to 1960s levels. It was a policy based on unsound principles and bad science. There was no research to substantiate the need for such a major cull and the policy failed to balance conservation of a wild species with human exploitation of the seas. After a huge campaign mounted by opponents of the proposals, attracting national press attention, the cull was abandoned.

Unfortunately protests against seal culls have been called conservation which is, by definition, the management of resources. The number of pups killed in Orkney is less than the harvesting of a surplus at a level which the population can easily sustain. The objections to seal culling in Orkney are about animal welfare rather than conservation, and in fact has confused local people about the work of nature conservation, since the distinction between conservation and animal welfare is not generally recognized by the public.

In the last few years fishermen have also complained of seals robbing their creels of bait, as well as threatening fish farms. Scottish National Heritage funded a survey of fishermen to assess the extent of reported losses from creel robbing. The problem seemed very patchy, and the seriousness with which it was perceived depended a lot on the attitude of individual fishermen.

Predation of fish by seals evokes strong feelings. If fish cages are unprotected, seals can bite fish through holes in the net and damage a large number of Salmon, making them unsaleable and vulnerable to disease. This is in addition to any fish they may take, and the risk that a net may be damaged and allow the fish to escape. Fish farmers now use anti-predator nets: a second wall of net outside the fish cage to keep seals away. Most farms now do this or use a net-tensioning system which appears to overcome most of the problems if maintenance is good. Attitudes vary within the industry as to the seriousness of seal predation, but examples of best practice suggest that problems from seals can largely be overcome. Scarers are employed at some sites. In recent years powerful ultra-sonic scarers have raised fears as to whether the high-intensity ultra-sonic pulses may disrupt seal and cetacean behaviour in general. In fact ultra-sonic scarers seem to be rather ineffective in deterring seals.

Seals undoubtedly take fish which might otherwise be caught commercially, but not all fish eaten by seals are commercial species nor indeed are available to fishermen. Any cull proposed in the future needs to be based on good science and carried out humanely. Even more importantly, it needs to be part of a truly sustainable approach to fisheries management. This is in the interests of both marine wildlife and fishermen. Despite various fish-stock conservation measures, we are still a long way away from an integrated and long-term policy. In fact both political and practical attitudes make a cull currently unlikely. Orkney sells itself on its natural image, and this would inevitably become tarnished in the event of a seal cull. The economic consequences would probably far outweigh any short-term benefits a reduction in seal numbers would bring to the islands' fishing industry.

Whales

Whales are fairly regularly seen off Orkney's shores and are occasionally washed ashore. In past times these would have been a bountiful and unexpected supply of welcome food. In recent years, for reasons not fully understood, cetaceans have more regularly become stranded on Orkney's – and indeed, Scotland's – shores. In 1994, eleven Sperm Whales stranded on Sanday. The whales were alive when they beached but were too large to allow any rescue to be mounted, and died within a few hours as a result of the enormous body weight pressing down on their internal organs.

However, an event which attracted greater interest was the appearance of six male Sperm Whales in Scapa Flow in the previous year. These whales, the same species as the Moby Dick of Herman Melville's book, were about 15 metres long and about 30 tonnes in weight. The most likely cause was that the relatively shallow waters and complex coastline of the Flow interfered with the acoustic communication of the whales and, coupled with strong tides at its entrance, resulted in their entrapment. At first local naturalists were simply excited about the sight of such whales within the confined waters of the Flow, but after some weeks concern mounted. The food available to the whales was very limited. It was agreed that efforts should be made to mount a rescue. Attempts were made to entice the whales from Scapa using recordings of female whale sound, but this was unsuccessful. 'Operation Gentle Shepherd' was then launched. On 25 March 1993, over six weeks after the whales were first sighted, a flotilla of seventeen local boats was assembled. After several attempts the boats managed to corral the whales and successfully usher them out into the Pentland Firth. It was the first time in the world such an operation of this type had been successful.

In May 1998 seven Sperm Whales spent three weeks in Scapa Flow – and then found their own way back to the open sea just as another rescue operation was being planned.

The case for conservation

In recent years, more and more attention has been given to environmental issues, and particularly global concerns such as global warming and depletion of the ozone layer. In Orkney, predicted rises in sea level and increase in coastal erosion would have very serious consequences. For example Deerness (east Mainland) might become an island. However, in Orkney there is not the global or emotional imperative of the loss of tropical rain forest or the black rhino to press the case for conservation. Yet as we have seen, Orkney is home to a number of species which are internationally important, and at least one (the Corncrake) is globally threatened.

Figure 12.6
Rubbish disposal is a chronic problem for isolated communities. Fortunately scenes like this are now rare in Orkney as the Islands Council takes steps to remove waste, large and small. This particular eyesore is now no more.
Photo: Richard Welsby

The most commonly-argued justification for conservation is the importance of the natural world to us human beings. For example, it is asserted that the tropical forests may be a source of valuable new drugs. It seems unlikely that any of Orkney's native terrestrial species will yield this sort of human gain, nor do its semi-natural habitats offer the same apparent benefits in terms of preventing soil erosion and flooding as, say, the conservation of hillside vegetation in truly mountainous areas might. Yet Orkney gains tremendously from its semi-natural areas, and stands to lose much from even their partial loss. Tourism is Orkney's biggest earner, and although prehistoric and historic monuments are a major draw, the beauty and wildlife of Orkney's setting are vital to most visitors' experience of the islands. The farming and fishing industries depend on Orkney's natural environment to promote a positive image when selling their products. Nor are Orcadians different from other folk in sharing a concern for the natural environment. If we are to convince those in developing countries that they should look after their own environment, we need to take the conservation of our own country seriously. Special places like Orkney cannot rely wholly on their own resources; they need the support of Government through agencies such as Scottish Natural Heritage and SOAFD, and the assistance of voluntary agencies to fulfil their responsibilities. At the same time it is essential to respect the strong local sensitivities of such places.

Following the 1992 Rio Earth Summit, countries and local authorities were challenged to take forward their own local plans to develop more sustainable approaches to the natural environment. In Britain, the UK Government supported the development of local Biodiversity Action Plans. In the post-Earth Summit euphoria, Orkney seemed at first to be falling behind other areas in devising strategies for managing its biodiversity in a sustainable way. However, in 1996 Orkney was selected by the Scottish Office as one of four pilot areas in Scotland to develop a Local Biodiversity Action Plan. A Project Officer was appointed with SNH, RSPB and Scottish Office support and a Biodiversity Forum established by the Islands Council, with all the local-interest groups represented, from the Fisheries Association and Field Club to the Chamber of Commerce and the Tourist Board. In due course, the Islands Council took over the Scottish Office share of financing the Project Officer, who then launched into an educational programme and a consultation to agree Biodiversity Action Plans on the scale of individual islands or parishes.

In parallel with these encouragements and linked with both the statutory and natural history organizations, an Orkney Biodiversity Records Centre was established on Kirkwall, with a mandate to link with the emerging National Biological Recording Network. This will inform and monitor Action Plans within Orkney. It will complement FWAG and the Council's Structure Plan and hopefully ensure that local environmental issues are addressed.

All these enthusiasms and initiatives raise the underlying and moral question 'Why conserve?' In examining its own *raison d'être* (*Nature Conservation in Great Britain*, 1984), the Nature Conservancy Council (the predecessor of SNH) stated that 'the primary reason for conservation in Britain is the cultural, educational, recreational, aesthetic and inspirational value of the countryside'. In other words, the whole environment is greater than the sum of its parts. This makes good sense in Orkney. The natural systems there are not threatened in the same way as the tropical rainforests or the ozone layer. The Government working party that recognized the need for an official Natural Conservancy in Britain, and whose report (Cmd 7122, 1947) led to its establishment, urged an integrated concept of nature conservation, with the renewable resources of the country developed whilst being sustained for the manifold benefit of society, through the application of scientific insight to management and control. *Nature Conservation in Great Britain* identified that the most serious and disappointing shortcoming in nature conservancy practice was the failure to translate into reality the broad and integrated concept of conservation which was the great vision of Cmd 7122. This judgement was underpinned and re-emphasized in another official document *This Common Inheritance* (Cm 1200, 1990), which formed the formal UK submission to the Earth Summit of 1992:

> The starting point (for enviromental policy) is the ethical imperative of stewardship . . . We have a moral duty to look after our planet and to hand it on in good order to future generations. That is what experts mean when they talk of 'sustainable development': not sacrificing tomorrow's people for a largely illusory gain today. We must put a proper value on the natural world: it would be to cherish a Constable but not the landscape he depicted.

In the context of Orkney this should mean that the success or failure of conservation should not be judged as to where there are more or fewer Hen Harriers, Grey Seals or *Primula scotica*, but whether the Orkney known to Edwin Muir, Robert Rendall and George Mackay Brown still exists, whether we can continue to share the experience of Eric Linklater:

> As I walked downhill, over grass starred with tormentil to a shore where black rocks were parti-coloured with the yellow tangle of the sea, and the sea was still glass-grey, I became aware of an extraordinary physical pleasure. It suffused my body and possessed my mind. Eyes and ears contributed to it, but my lungs were filled with it – I breathed the euphory that blows down from an arctic spring.

The future of nature conservation in Orkney is inextricably linked with attitudes which are moulded by past history and current incentives (often

Figure 12.7
Evening at Marwick Head.
Photo: Richard Welsby

financial ones). We must work to convince people of the threat to the dwindling natural assets around them and of the need to conserve for future generations examples of Orkney habitats and Orkney species. We must gain the confidence of the farming community and the decision-makers of the Islands Council. And we must implant a sense of respect and responsibility in Orkney's schoolchildren, the decision-makers of tomorrow.

The natural heritage of Orkney is far from completely assured, but the long association between human activity and the rich wildlife of the islands, and the fact that this link is generally recognized, gives good hope for the future. There has to be concern over some aspects of modern farming, and certain new industries. However, balanced development, and a sustainable approach to existing and new industry, holds the key to ensuring that the

Orkney will remain, not unchanged, but still a beautiful and welcoming place for generations to come.

> What would the world be, once bereft
> Of wet and of wildness? Let them be left,
> Oh let them be left, wildness and wet
> Long live the weeds and the wilderness yet.
> (Gerard Manley Hopkins)

Further reading

Baker *et al.*, 1981; Berry, 1983b, 1999; Calder, 1952; Charter, 1995; Coughtrey, 1983; Flint, 1979; Gallagher *et al.*, 1971; Goodier, 1975; Hardin, 1964; Harwood, 1978; Kruuck and Hewson, 1978; Linklater, 1981; Mabey, 1980; Nature Conservancy Council, 1984; O'Dell, 1939; Orkney Islands Council, 1994; Rendall, 1960; Senior and Swan, 1972; Summers, 1978; Walker, 1950; Wanless *et al.*, 1982; Young, 1985.

Getting About Orkney

Orkney is a good county for a naturalist who wants to see a wide range of species and habitats. There is an abundance of good ground for walking; some of the cliff walks rank with the best in the United Kingdom. Most of the land is farmed, but Orcadians are in general very tolerant of people walking on their property, so long as their crops, stock and privacy are properly respected (and it is, of course, only courteous to seek permission if one wants to cross private land). The Islands Council in association with Scottish National Heritage has produced a leaflet of walks, and a further selection is described by Mary Welsh in *Walks in Orkney* (Westmoreland Gazette, Kendal, 1994).

For newcomers, the Tourist Office in Broad Street near the Cathedral in Kirkwall (phone 01856 872856, or its satellite at Stromness Harbour) provides all necessary information about local transport and accommodation. Several general guidebooks are available. Probably the most comprehensive is the locally produced *Orkney Guide Book* by Charles Tait (2nd edition, 1997). An annually updated guide to the outer isles is available from the Tourist Office. Cars and bicycles can be hired in Kirkwall and Stromness, and cars on most of the islands. *Orkney by Bike* by Les Cowan and Mike Sinclair (Information Plus, Finstown, 1998) describes 24 cycle routes on the Orkney Mainland and some of the other islands. There are frequent boat sailings to Hoy, Flotta, Graemsay, Shapinsay, Rousay, Wyre and Egilsay, and to the larger North Isles (which are also connected by air services with Kirkwall). The Mainland and South Isles are better served by buses than most rural areas in mainland Britain.

Orkney is covered by three sheets (nos. 5, 6, 7) of the Ordnance Survey 1:50,000 series, and by a single sheet of Bartholomew's 1:100,000 series. Many of the island Community Councils have provided information leaflets setting out places of interest. The Orkney Field Club has produced Car Trails to the west and east Mainland. Several operators provide guided tours of the Mainland, including places of natural history interest (details from the

Getting around
Orkney is possible by
plane, bus, car, bike,
boat and on foot.
Photo: Richard Welsby

Tourist Office or the *Orcadian* newspaper, published every Thursday). Scottish Natural Heritage (who have an office at 54-56 Junction Road in Kirkwall (phone 01856 875302) produce a number of useful leaflets, and the RSPB (who have an Orkney office: phone 01856 850176) have published *Islands of Birds. A guide to Orkney birds* by Eric Meek.

Many of the archaeological and historical monuments are in the care of the Department of the Environment; a useful general introduction to them is Anna Ritchie's *Orkney* in the Exploring Scotland's Heritage series (HMSO, 1996). Valuable complements to this are Willie Thomson's *History of Orkney* (Mercat, 1987) and Caroline Wickham-Jones's *Orkney: a Historical Guide* (Birlinn, 1998).

The Orkney Museum Service maintains Tankerness House in Kirkwall, dating from the sixteenth century and for 300 years the town house of one of the leading merchant-laird families of Orkney; and also a restored farm-house at Corrigall, Harray, featuring some of the characteristic artefacts of Orkney agriculture. The Orkney Natural History Society supports the Stromness Museum (founded 1836), near the south end of Stromness. Besides exhibitions of the maritime traditions of Orkney, the Stromness

The edge of Orkney:
the north end of
Westray.
Photo: Andrew Berry

Museum houses one of Scotland's best collections of stuffed birds, local birds' eggs, the Robert Rendall collection of Orkney shells and seaweed, the Magnus Spence herbarium of Orkney plants, the Ian Lorimer collection of Orkney butterflies and moths, local fossils and geological samples, and a small archaeological display, chiefly from Skara Brae.

Appendix

Orkney's plants and animals

The aim of this book is to provide an introduction, summary and source of information about the natural history of Orkney in its wide sense – rocks and climate as well as plants and animals. It could be argued that this necessarily involves listing all the species which have been recorded in Orkney. There are two difficulties about this. The first is that such lists are in constant need of revision as new forms are found, old names change, and distributions fluctuate. The second is perhaps more contentious: most so-called lower organisms (invertebrate animals and cryptogamic plants) are familiar only to a small number of specialists in each group. In such groups the number of species known in a place like Orkney depends more on the interests and collecting opportunities of the specialists concerned, and a list of species is largely meaningless except to a very small handful of experts.

The forerunner of this book, the New Naturalist *Natural History of Orkney* attempted to list all species recorded in Orkney from all groups. This certainly performed a useful function and provided a baseline for the systematic ordering of biological records in Orkney. In 1992, the Orkney Field Club began producing a *Biological Records Supplement* to its annual *Bulletin,* marking the establishment of the Orkney Biological Records Centre as a repository for 'all biological records so that they can be periodically and separately published (to) form an up-date or addition to the records published in Berry, R. J. *The Natural History of Orkney*'.

The Orkney Biodiversity Records Centre is now established with Council, Orkney Enterprise, SNH, Field Club, RSPB and EC funding at 10 Bridge Street, Kirkwall KW15 1HR (phone/fax 01856 875127). For a small handling charge, the Centre will provide an up-to-date list of the Orkney records for any group. In the light of this and also the availability of comprehensive lists of the more easily recognized groups (Ian Lorimer, *Lepidoptera of the Orkney Islands*, 1983 with a supplement *Unfinished Business*, 1998; Elaine Bullard, *Wildflowers in Orkney; a new checklist*, 1995; and Chris and Jean Booth, *Status and Checklist of the Vertebrate Fauna of Orkney*, 1998) it did not seem worth including the complete listings provided in *The Natural History of Orkney*. Most people interested in the natural history of the islands are likely to want to know the occurrence or not of birds and flowering plants. A list of the birds of Orkney and their status are given included here (pp. 287–292); a checklist of flowering plants has been kindly prepared by Miss E. R. Bullard on the basis of and updating her 1995 publication, and is also included in this appendix (pp. 271–283). It has been difficult to know whether to include full lists of such 'popular' groups such as Lepidoptera or Mollusca, but a line has to be drawn somewhere. For some groups it is easy. For example, the national Biological Records

Centre at the Institute of Terrestrial Ecology at Monks Wood holds records of the occurrence in Orkney of only five species of millipedes, one centipede, one dermapteran (the common Earwig, *Forficula auricularia*), three cladocerans, one copepod and five isopods. It may be that there really are only seven species of Dragonflies found in Orkney. Notwithstanding, it has to be recognized that most of the available lists vary greatly in their completeness and usefulness. Consequently, for all groups except birds and flowering plants, I have provided merely a note of any Orcadian interest and relevant references, and rely on the presumably small number of people who wish to know more to contact the Biodiversity Centre in Kirkwall.

FLOWERING PLANTS AND FERNS

The list that follows has been provided by Miss E. R. Bullard of Kirkwall who has acted as BSBI Recorder for Orkney over many years. It represents the latest version of the study of the Orkney flora which began at the end of the seventeenth century. Although there were often gaps in time between the compilation of one list and the next, most people tended to make use of those of their predecessors in a somewhat uncritical fashion. More rigorous studies can be regarded as starting with Col. Henry Halcro-Johnstone who, in the early part of the present century, backed up all his own records with herbarium specimens and made strenuous attempts to check all earlier unauthenticated records. He sent specimens to all the major Herbaria in Great Britain and his own very extensive collection is now housed at the Royal Botanical Garden, Edinburgh. While knowledge of the Orkney flora was increased immeasurably by his painstaking work, there were losses as the result of over-zealous collecting. It was not unknown for the Colonel to collect as many as 90 specimens from one colony of a single species, and as he often took and pressed a whole plant, roots and all, some very rare plants, e.g. *Hammarbya paludosa*, were probably exterminated.

A group of islands poses problems in obtaining thorough coverage, and inevitably some of the early suspect records have been proved to be correct since his time. The apparently unlikely *Atriplex littoralis* turns up occasionally as strand-line seedlings which fail to overwinter, and many other unconfirmed records – omitted from the following list – may yet appear. Although it is known that Halcro-Johnstone and other earlier botanists explored very close to the sites where the species now exist, they managed to miss such rarities as *Rubus chamaemorus*, *Poa alpina* and *Heirochloë odorata*. New understandings from time to time disclose a species hitherto unrecognized in the UK, e.g. *Puccinellia capillaris* was passed over by earlier specialists as a form of *P. distans*. The real possibility of other European species appearing in Orkney is to some extent offset by the failure of visiting botanists to recognize the replacement there of familiar southern species by ones of northern distribution, so that false records of *Poa pratensis* appear in lieu of the widespread *P. humilis*, and *Festuca ovina* in lieu of *F. tenuifolia*. Other common plants are slightly different in appearance, being larger or smaller, or differently coloured than their southern counterparts. Some others occupy unfamiliar habitats: visitors simply do not expect to find *Thalictrum alpinum* in low-lying fen or maritime heath, nor *Galium sterneri* in machair or on grassy banks.

Apart from two *Euphrasia* species and *Heirochloë odorata*, Orkney appears to have no 'nationally rare' plants, but does have a special abundance of northern species such as *Dryopteris expansa*, *Ligusticum scoticum*, *Mertensia maritima*, *Saussurea alpina* and *Carex maritima*; it shares with Caithness and north Sutherland one of the UK's few endemics, *Primula scotica*; and has such oddities of distribution as *Ophioglossum azoricum*, *Dryopteris aemula*, *Pyrola rotundifolia* and *Jasione montana*.

Many groups, genera and microspecies require further work, and there are good opportunities for searchers of *Equisetum* (hybrids), *Fumaria*, *Atriplex*, *Salix* (hybrids), *Epilobium* (hybrids), *Rhinanthus*, *Odontites*, *Pilosella* (microspecies), *Taraxacum* (microspecies – only one, *T. rubellum*, has been discovered in recent years, but there must be more), *Zostera*, *Dactylorhiza* and perhaps *Festuca*.

A large number of plants definitely known in Orkney in the early part of this century are probably now extinct. At first the losses were mostly of 'weeds of cultivation', probably originally introduced with improperly cleaned crop seeds. More serious is the loss now taking place of truly native plants of wetland, heath and machair as their habitats are lost due to agricultural development and sand extraction. The spread of such recently introduced aliens as *Montia sibirica*, *Mimulus* species and London Pride, however pretty, can in no way compensate future generations of Orcadians for these losses.

The nomenclature follows in most cases that used in the BSBI's list of *Vascular Plants of the British Isles*. This has meant that some familiar names have been changed from those given in popular handbooks and previously published lists of Orkney flora. Synonyms are given in most cases. It should be noted that a large number of plants found in Orkney, particularly those with a restricted or northern distribution, are not fully described in the BSBI *list*. The list here is based on Miss Bullard's *Wildflowers in Orkney. A new checklist* (Kirkwall, 1995). I am in Miss Bullard's debt for allowing this list to be reproduced and for updating it for this book.

STATUS. N = Native. A = Alien. E = Established (alien). S = Survives (alien). C = Casual (alien). P = Planted (alien). A few Orkney plants can be both Native and Alien owing to known introductions.

FREQUENCY. A = Abundant. F = Frequent. O = Occasional. F = Rare. All may be qualified by L = Local. Ex = Extinct. ? = unknown or doubtful. RDB = Red Data Book. BSS = British Scarce Species.

Huperzia selago	Fir Clubmoss	N	O L
Lycopodium clavatum	Stag's-horn Clubmoss	N	O L
Lycopodium annotinum	Interrupted Clubmoss	N	Ex?
Diphasiastrum alpinum	Alpine Clubmoss	N	R
Selaginella selaginoides	Lesser Clubmoss	N	F
Isoetes lacustris	Quillwort	N	R L
Equisetum hyemale	Dutch Rush	E	R
Equisetum fluviatile	Water Horsetail	N	F
Equisetum fluviatile x arvense = E. x litorale	Hybrid Horsetail	N	R
Equisetum arvense	Field Horsetail	N	A
Equisetum pratense	Shady Horsetail	N	R BSS
Equisetum sylvaticum	Wood Horsetail	N	O L
Equisetum palustre	Marsh Horsetail	N	F
Ophioglossum vulgatum	Adder's-tongue	N	O L
Ophioglossum azoricum	Small Adder's-tongue	N	O L BSS
Botrychium lunaria	Moonwort	N	O
Hymenophyllum wilsonii	Wilson's Filmy-fern	N	R L
Polypodium vulgare	Common Polypody	N	O
Polypodium vulgare x interjectum = P x mantoniae	Hybid Polypody	N	R
Pteridium aquilinum	Bracken	N	F
Phegopteris connectilis	Beech Fern	N	R
Oreopteris limbosperma	Lemon-scented Fern	N	O L
Phyllitis scolopendrium	Hart's-tongue Fern	N	R
Asplenium adiantum-nigrum	Black Spleenwort	N	O
Asplenium marinum	Sea Spleenwort	N	O
Asplenium trichomanes	Maidenhair Spleenwort	N	O
Asplenium ruta-muraria	Wall-rue	N	R
Athyrium filix-femina	Lady-fern	N	F
Cystopteris fragilis	Brittle Bladder-fern	N	R
Polystichum aculeatum	Hard Shield-fern	N	R
Polystichum lonchitis	Holly Fern	N	R
Dryopteris filix-mas	Male Fern	N	F L
Dryopteris affinis s.l.	Scaly Buckler-fern	N	O
Dryopteris affinis ssp affinis	Scaly Buckler-fern	N	O
Dryopteris affinis ssp borreri	Scaly Male-fern	N	O
Dryopteris aemula	Hay-scented Buckler-fern	N	O L
Dryopteris dilatata	Broad Buckler-fern	N	F

Dryopteris dilatata x expansa = D x ambrosiae	Hybrid Broad Buckler-fern	N	R
Dryopteris expansa	Northern Buckler-fern	N	R, L
Blechnum spicant	Hard Fern	N	F
Pinus mugo	Mountain Pine	E	R, L
Pinus contorta	Lodgepole Pine	E	R, L
Juniperus communis ssp alpina	Juniper	N	O L
Caltha palustris	Marsh Marigold, King-cup	N	F
Aconitum napellus x variegatum =			
A. x cammarum	Monkshood	S	R BSS
Anemone nemorosa	Wood Anemone	E	R
Ranunculus acris	Meadow Buttercup	N	F
Ranunculus repens	Creeping Buttercup	N	A
Ranunculus bulbosus	Bulbous Buttercup	N	O L
Ranunculus arvensis	Corn Buttercup	C	E
Ranunculus sceleratus	Celery-leaved Crowfoot	A	R or E
Ranunculus flammula	Lesser Spearwort	N	F
Ranunculus ficaria ssp. ficaria	Lesser Celandine	N	F
Ranunculus ficaria ssp. bulbifer	Lesser Celandine	E	R
Ranunculus hederaceus	Ivy-leaved Water-crowfoot	N	O L
Ranunculus baudotii	Brackish Water-crowfoot	N	OL BSS
Ranunculus trichophyllus	Thread-leaved Water-crowfoot	N	O
Ranunculus aquatilis	Water-crowfoot	N	O
Aquilegia vulgaris	Columbine	S	R
Thalictrum minus	Lesser Meadow-rue	N	O L
Thalictrum alpinum	Alpine Meadow-rue	N	F L
Papaver somniferum	Opium Poppy	C	R
Papaver rhoeas	Poppy	C	R
Papaver dubium	Long-headed Poppy	N	O L
Meconopsis cambrica	Welsh Poppy	E	O BSS
Fumaria capreolata	White Ramping Fumitory	N	O BSS
Fumaria bastardii	Tall Ramping Fumitory	N	R BSS
Fumaria muralis ssp boraei	Common Ramping Fumitory	N	O
Fumaria purpurea	Purple Ramping Fumitory	N	O BSS
Fumaria officinalis	Common Fumitory	N	F
Fumaria densiflora	Dense-flowered Fumitory	C	R BSS
Ulmus glabra	Wych Elm	P	R
Cannabis sativa	Hemp	C	R or Ex
Humulus lupulus	Hop	C	R
Urtica dioica	Stinging Nettle	N	F
Urtica urens	Small Nettle	N	O L
Soleirolia soleirolii	Mind-your-own-business	E	O
Myrica gale	Bog Myrtle	N	R
Fagus sylvatica	Beech	P	R
Castanea sativa	Sweet Chestnut	P	R
Quercus sp.	Oaks	P	R
Betula pubescens	Downy Birch	N	R
Alnus glutinosa	Alder	P	O
Corylus avellana	Hazel	N and P	R
Chenopodium album	Fat Hen	C	R
Chenopodium hybridum	Goosefoot	C	R or Ex
Atriplex prostrata agg.	Orache	N	F
Atriplex glabriuscula	Babington's Orache	N	F
Atriplex littoralis	Shore Orache	C	R
Atriplex patula	Common Orache	N or C	O
Atriplex laciniata	Frosted Orache	N	R
Salicornia europaea agg.	Common Glasswort	N	R
Salicornia nitens	Shiny Glasswort	N	R
Salicornia dolichostachya	Long-spiked Glasswort	N	?
Suaeda maritima	Sea-blite	N	O L
Salsola kali	Salt-wort	?	Ex
Claytonia perfoliata	Spring Beauty	C	R or Ex
Claytonia sibirica	Pink Purslane Smiling Jessie	E	F
Montia fontana agg.	Blinks	N	F
Montia fontana ssp. fontana	Blinks	N	F
Montia fontana ssp. variabilis	Blinks	N	R
Montia fontana ssp. minor	Blinks	N	R
Arenaria serpyllifolia	Thyme-leaved Sandwort	C	R

Honckenya peploides	Sea Sandwort	N	F L
Stellaria media	Chickweed	N	A
Stellaria holostea	Greater Stitchwort	S	R
Stellaria graminea	Lesser Stitchwort	N	O
Stellaria uliginosa	Bog Stitchwort	N	F
Cerastium arvense	Field Mouse-ear Chickweed	C	R or Ex
Cerastium fontanum ssp vulgare	Common Mouse-ear Chickweed	N	F
Cerastium fontanum ssp holosteoides	Common Mouse-ear Chickweed	N	R
Cerastium glomeratum	Sticky Mouse-ear Chickweed	N	F L
Cerastium diffusum	Sea Mouse-ear Chickweed	N	F
Sagina nodosa	Knotted Pearlwort	N	F
Sagina subulata	Awl-leaved Pearlwort	N	R
Sagina procumbens	Procumbent Pearlwort	N	A
Sagina apetela	Annual Pearlwort	N	R
Sagina maritima	Sea Pearlwort	N	O L
Spergula arvensis	Corn Spurrey "ruithe"	N	F
Spergularia media	Greater Sea-spurrey	N	F L
Spergularia marina	Lesser Sea-spurrey	N	O L
Lychnis coronaria	Rose Campion	C	Ex?
Lychnis flos-cuculi	Ragged Robin	N	F
Lychnis viscaria	Sticky Catchfly	C	Ex?
Agrostemma githago	Corncockle	C	R or Ex
Silene dichotoma	Forked Catchfly	C	R or Ex
Silene vulgaris	Bladder Campion	C	R or Ex
Silene uniflora	Sea Campion	N	F
Silene acaulis	Moss Campion	N	R
Silene latifolia	White Campion	N & C	R
Silene latifolia x dioica = S. hampeana	Hybrid Campion	N	R L
Silene dioica	Red Campion	N	F
Persicaria bistorta	Common Bistort	E	R
Persicaria vivipara	Alpine Bistort	N	O
Persicaria amphibia	Amphibious Bistort	N	O
Persicaria maculosa	Redshank	N	O
Persicaria lapathifolia	Pale Persicaria	N	R
Persicaria hydropiper	Water-pepper	?N	Ex?
Polygonum oxyspermum	Ray's Knotgrass	C	R or Ex
Polygonum arenastrum	Equal-leaved Knotgrass	N	O
Polygonum aviculare	Knotgrass	N	F
Polygonum boreale	Northern Knotgrass	N	O BSS
Fallopia japonica	Japanese Knotweed	E	R
Fallopia convolvulus	Black Bindweed	C	O
Rheum x hybridum	Rhubarb	E	O
Rumex acetosella	Sheep's Sorrel	N	F
Rumex acetosa	Sorrel	N	A
Rumex longifolius	Long-leaved Dock	N	O L
Rumex longifolius x obtusifolius = *R. x hybridus*	Hybrid Dock	N	R
Rumex crispus	Curled Dock	N	A
Rumex crispus spp. crispus	Curled Dock	N	F
Rumex crispus ssp. littoreus	Curled Dock	N	O
Rumex crispus x obtusifolius = R. x pratensis	Hybrid Dock	N	R
Rumex obtusifolius	Broad-leaved Dock	N	A
Oxyria digyna	Mountain Sorrel	N	R
Armeria maritima	Thrift, Sea-pink	N	F
Hypericum tetrapterum	Square-std St John's-wort	S	R
Hypericum pulchrum	Slender St John's-wort	N	F
Hypericum hirsutum	Hairy St John's-wort	C	R
Hypericum elodes	Marsh St Johns-wort	N	E
Tilia x vulgaris	Lime	P	R
Malva moschata	Musk Mallow	C	R or Ex
Malva pusilla	Small Mallow	C	R or Ex
Drosera rotundifolia	Common Sundew	N	O
Drosera longifolia	Great Sundew	N	R L
Viola riviniana	Common Dog-violet	N	F
Viola canina	Heath Dog Violet	?N	?
Viola palustris	Marsh Violet	N	F
Viola cornuta	Horned Pansy	C	R or Ex

Viola tricolor ssp. tricolor	Heart's-ease Pansy	N	O L
Viola arvensis	Field Pansy	N	R
Populus tremula	Aspen	N	O L
Populus trichocarpa	Balsam Poplar	P	R
Populus candicans Aiton		P	R
Salix pentandra	Bay-leaved Willow	P	O
Salix fragilis	Crack Willow	P	R
Salix viminalis	Osier	P	O
Salix x calodendron = *S. viminalis x capreax ciner*	Hybrid Willow	P	R
Salix viminalis x cinerea = S. x smithiana	Hybrid Willow	P	O
Salix viminalis x aurita = S. x fruticosa	Hybrid Willow	P	R
Salix caprea	Goat Willow	P	R
Salix caprea hybrids		P	R
Salix cinerea ssp. oleifolia	Rusty Sallow, Rice	N	O
Salix cinerea x aurita = S. x multinervis	Hybrid Willow	N	R
Salix cinerea x phylicifolia = S. laurina	Hybrid Willow	N	O
Salix aurita	Eared Willow, Rice	N	F
Salix aurita x repens = S. x ambigua	Hybrid Willow	N	R
Salix myrsinifolia	Dark-leaved Willow	P	R BSS
Salix phylicifolia	Tea-leaved Willow, Rice	N	O L
Salix phylicifolia x repens = x schraderiana	Hybrid Willow	N	R
Salix repens var. repens	Creeping Willow	N	F
Salix repens var. argentea	Silver Creeping Willow	N	O
Salix myrsinites	Myrtle-leaved Willow	N	R BSS
Salix herbacea	Dwarf Willow	N	R
Sisymbrium officinale	Hedge Mustard	C	R
Descurainia sophia	Flixweed	C	R
Arabidopsis thaliana	Thale Cress	N	O
Hesperus matronalis	Sweet Rocket, Dame's-violet	E	O
Barbarea vulgaris	Winter-cress	C	O
Barbarea intermedia	Intermediate Wintercress	C	R
Rorippa nasturtium-aquaticum	Watercress	N	O
Rorippa x sterilis	Cultivated Watercress	S	R
Rorippa islandica	Northern Yellow-cress	N	R BBS
Armoracia rusticana	Horse-radish	S	R
Cardamine pratensis	Lady's Smock	N	F
Cardamine flexuosa	Wavy Bitter-cress	N	O
Cardamine hirsuta	Hairy Bitter-cress, Poppers	N	F L
Arabis causcasica	Garden Arabis	C	R or Ex
Arabis hirsuta	Hairy Rock-cress	N	R or Ex
Draba incana	Hoary Whitlowgrass	N	R
Erophila verna (sens. lat.)	Common Whitlowgrass	N	O
Cochlearia officinalis	Scurvey-grass	N	F
Capsella bursa-pastoris	Shepherd's-purse	N	F
Thlaspi arvense	Field Pennycress	C	O
Lepidium virginicum	Least Pepperwort	C	R or Ex
Lepidium draba	Hoary Cress	E	R
Lepidium perfoliatum	Perfoliate Pepperwort	C	R or Ex
Diplotaxis muralis	Wall Rocket	C	R
Brassica napus	Rape	C	O
Brassica rapa	Wild Turnip	C	R
Brassica nigra	Black Mustard	C	R or Ex
Sinapis arvensis	Charlock	N	F
Sinapis alba	White Mustard	C	R
Cakile maritima	Sea Rocket	N	F L
Raphanus raphanistrum	Runch, Wild Mustard	N	F
Raphanus sativus	Radish	C	R
Reseda luteola	Dyer's Rocket	C	R or Ex
Empetrum nigrum ssp nigrum	Crowberry	N	A
Loiseleuria procumbens	Trailing Azalea	N	R
Arctostaphylos uva-ursi	Bearberry	N	R
Arctostaphylos alpinus	B. Blaeberry, Alp. Bearberry	N	R BSS
Calluna vulgaris	Heather, Ling	N	A
Erica tetralix	Cross-leaved Heath	N	A
Erica cinerea	Bell Heather	N	F
Vaccinium vitis-idaea	Cowberry	N	R L

Vaccinium uliginosum	Bog Blaeberry	N	R L
Vaccinium myrtillus	Blaeberry	N	F
Pyrola rotundifolia ssp. rotundifolia	Round-leaved Wintergreen	N	R BSS
Orthilia secunda	Serrated Wintergreen	N	R BSS
Primula vulgaris	Primrose	N	F L
Primula vulgaris x veris = P. polyantha	False Oxlip	N	R
Primula veris	Cowslip	N	R L
Primula scotica	Scottish Primrose Primula scotia	N	O LBSS
Lysimachia nemorum	Yellow Pimpernel	N	R
Lysimachia punctata	Dotted Loosestrife	E	R
Trientalis europaea	Chickweed Wintergreen	N	R
Anagallis tenella	Bog Pimpernel	N	F
Anagallis arvensis	Red Pimpernel	C	R
Glaux maritima	Sea Milkwort	N	F
Samolus valerandi	Brookweed	N	R
Escallonia macrantha	Escallonia	P	O
Ribes nigrum	Black Currant	S	R
Ribes rubrum	Red Currant	S	R
Ribes uva-crispa	Gooseberry	S	R
Sedum rosea	Roseroot	N	R L
Sedum telephium	Orpine	S	R
Sedum acre	Wall Pepper	E	R
Sedum album	White Stonecrop	E	R
Saxifraga stellaris	Starry Saxifrage	N	R
Saxifraga umbrosas x spathularis = S. x urbium	London Pride	E	R
Saxifraga oppositifolia	Purple Saxifrage	N	R L
Saxifraga aizoides	Yellow Saxifrage	N	R L
Chrysosplenium oppositifolium	Opposite-lvd Golden-saxifrage	N	R
Parnassia palustris	Grass-of-Parnassus	N	F
Filipendula ulmaria	Meadow-sweet	N	A
Rubus chamaemorus	Cloudberry	N	R
Rubus saxatilis	Stone Bramble	N	O L
Rubus idaeus	Raspberry	E	R L
Rubus spectabilis	Salmonberry	E	O L
Rubus fruticosus	Bramble	N & E	R L.
Potentilla palustris	Marsh Cinquefoil	N	F L
Potentilla anserina	Silverweed	N	F
Potentilla argentea	Hairy Cinquefoil		?
Potentilla sterilis	Barren Strawberry	C	Ex?
Potentilla erecta	Tormentil, Hill-bark	N	A
Fragaria vesca	Wild Strawberry	N	R
Fragaria x ananassa	Strawberry	C	R
Geum rivale	Water Avens	N	O
Geum urbanum	Herb Bennet	E	R
Dryas octopetala	Mountain Avens	N	R BSS
Sanguisorba minor	Salad Burnet	P	R or E
Alchemilla filicaulis	Lady's-mantle	N	F
Alchemilla glabra	Lady's-mantle	N	O
Alchemilla vulgaris agg.		N	F
Aphanes arvensis agg.	Parsley-piert	N	O
Rosa agg.	Wild rose	N	O
Rosa arvensis	Field Rose	E	Ex?
Rosa x sabinii = mollis x pimpinellifolia	Hybrid Rose	?N	R
Rosa pimpinellifolia x sherardii = R. x involuta	Hybrid Rose	?N	R
Rosa rugosa	Ramanas Rose	E	O
Rosa x dumalis =			
* R.caesia ssp glauca x R.canina*	Dog Rose hybrid	N	O
Rosa canina x sherardii = R. rothschildii	Dog Rose x Downy Rose hybrid	N	O
Rosa caesia ssp glauca	Glaucous Northern Dog-Rose	N	O
Rosa caesia x sherardii	Dog Rose x Downy Rose hybrid	N	R
Rosa caesia x mollis = glaucoides	Dog Rose x Downy Rose hybrid.	N	R
Rosa sherardii	Sherard's Downy Rose	N	O
Rosa sherardii x mollis = R. shoolbredii	Downy Rose hybrid	N	R
Rosa mollis	Soft Downy Rose	N	O
Rosa molliformis =R.mollis x rubiginosa	Hybrid Rose	N	Ex?
Rosa micrantha	Sweet Briar	S	R
Malus domestica	Apple	S	R

Sorbus aucuparia	Rowan	N	R L
Sorbus hybrida	Swedish Service-tree	E	R
Sorbus intermedia	Swedish Whitebeam	E	R
Sorbus aria s.s.	Whitebeam	P	O
Cotoneaster integrifolius	Thyme-leaved Cotoneaster	E	O
Crataegus monogyna	Hawthorn, Quick	P	O
Anthyllis vulneraria s.l.	Lady's-fingers, Kidney Vetch	N	F
Anthyllis vulneraria ssp. vulneraria	Lady's-fingers, Kidney Vetch	N	O
Anthyllis vulneraria ssp lapponica	Lady's-fingers, Kidney Vetch	N	F
Lotus corniculatus	Bird's-foot Trefoil	N	A
Lotus pedunculatus	Greater Bird's-foot Trefoil	N	O
Vicia cracca	Tufted Vetch	N	F
Vicia hirsuta	Hairy Tare	P	R
Vicia sepium	Bush Vetch	N	F
Vicia sativa	Common Vetch	P	R
Vicia sativa ssp. nigra	Narrow-leaved Vetch	C	R
Lathyrus linifolius	Bitter Vetch	C	R or Ex
Lathyrus pratensis	Meadow Vetchling	N	F
Ononis repens	Rest-harrow	N	E?
Melilotus altissimus	Tall Melilot	C	R or Ex
Melilotus indicus	Small Melilot	C	R or Ex
Medicago lupulina	Black Medick	C	O
Medicago sativa ssp. falcata	Sickle Medick	C	R or Ex
Medicago sativa ssp. sativa	Lucerne	C	O
Trifolium repens	White Clover	N	A
Trifolium hybridum	Alsike	P	O
Trifolium aureum	Large Trefoil	C	R or Ex
Trifolium campestre	Hop Trefoil	C	R
Trifolium dubium	Lesser Yellow-trefoil	N	O
Trifolium pratense	Red Clover	N	F
Lupinus nootkatensis	Nootka Lupin	E	O
Cytisus scoparius	Broom	P	O
Ulex europaeus	Whin, Gorse	E	O L
Myriophyllum spicatum	Spiked Water-milfoil	N	O
Myriophyllum alterniflorum	Alternate Water-milfoil	N	O
Lythrum portula ssp. longidentata	Water Purslane	N	R
Epilobium hirsutum	Great Hairy Willowherb	S	R
Epilobium parviflorum	Small-flowered Willowherb	N	O
Epilobium palustre x parviflorum = E.x rivulare	Hybrid Willow-herb	N	R
Epilobium montanum	Broad Leaved Willowherb	N	F
Epilobium obscurum	Short-fruited Willowherb	N	O
Epilobium palustre	Marsh Willowherb	N	F
Epilobium brunnescens	New Zealand Creeping Willowherb	E	O
Chamerion angustifolium	Rosebay Willowherb, Fireweed	N or E	O
Fuchsia magellanica	Fuchsia	E	O L
Circaea x intermedia	Intermediate Enchanter's Nightshade	N	R
Cornus suecica	Dwarf Cornel	N	R
Ilex aquifolium	Holly	P	R
Euphorbia peplus	Petty Spurge	C	R
Euphorbia helioscopia	Sun Spurge	N	O
Linum usitatissimum	Flax	C	R
Linum catharticum	Purging Flax	N	F
Radiola linoides	Allseed	N	O
Polygala vulgaris	Common Milkwort	N	O
Polygala serpyllifolia	Heath Milkwort	N	F
Aesculus hippocastanum	Horse Chestnut	P	R
Acer pseudoplatanus	Sycamore, Scots Plane	P	R
Oxalis acetosella	Wood Sorrel	N	R
Geranium sylvaticum	Wood Crane's-bill	C	R
Geranium pratense	Meadow Crane's-bill	S	R
Geranium dissectum	Cut-leaved Crane's-bill	N	O
Geranium pusillum	Small-flowered Crane's-bill	C	R
Geranium molle	Dove's-foot Crane's-bill	N	O
Geranium lucidum	Shining Crane's-bill	A	R
Geranium robertianum	Herb-Robert	N & E	R
Erodium cicutarium	Common Stork's-bill	N	R
Impatiens glandulifera	Indian Balsam	E	O

Hedera helix ssp helix	Ivy	N	R
Hedera hibernica var'Hibernica'	Irish Ivy	E	F
Hydrocotyle vulgaris	Marsh Pennywort, White-rot	N	F
Astrantia major	Astrantia	S	R
Anthriscus sylvestris	Cow Parsley	N	F
Anthriscus caucalis	Bur Parsley	C	R
Scandix pecten-veneris	Shepherd's Needle	A	R or Ex
Myrrhis odorata	Myrrh, Sweet Cicily	E	O
Bunium bulbocastanum	Great Pignut	C	R
Conopodium majus	Pignut	N	O
Pimpinella saxifraga	Burnet-saxifrage	N	R
Aegopodium podagraria	Ground Elder, Bishop-weed	E	F
Berula erecta	Lesser Water-parsnip	N	R
Apium inundatum	Marsh-wort	N	F
Oenanthe crocata	Hemlock Water-dropwort	A	R
Conium maculatum	Hemlock	S	R or Ex
Carum carvi	Caraway	C	R
Ligusticum scoticum	Scottish Lovage	N	O L
Angelica sylvestris	Wild Angelica	N	F
Angelica archangelica	Angelica	E	R
Levisticum officinale	Lovage	E	R
Peucedanum ostruthium	Masterwort	E	R
Heracleum sphondylium	Hogweed	N	F
Torilis japonica	Upright Hedge-parsley	A	R
Daucus carota	Wild Carrot	C	R
Gentianella campestris	Field Gentian	N	F L
Gentianella amarella sl.	Felwort, Autumn Gentian	N	O
Lycium barbarum	Duke of Argyll's Teaplant	E	R
Hyoscyamus niger	Henbane	C	R BSS
Solanum nigrum	Black Nightshade	C	R
Solanum dulcamara	Woody Nightshade	S	O
Convolvulus arvensis	Field Bindweed	S	R
Calystegia soldanella	Sea Bindweed	N	R
Calystegia sepium	Hedge Bindweed	S	O
Menyanthes trifoliata	Bogbean, Crawshoe	N	F
Echium plantagineum	Purple Viper's Bugloss	C	R
Echium vulgare	Viper's Bugloss	C	R or Ex
Symphytum x uplandicum	Russian Comfrey	E	O
Symphytum tuberosum	Tuberous Comfrey	E	O
Anchusa arvensis	Bugloss	N	F L
Mertensia maritima	Oyster Plant	N	OL BSS
Myosotis scorpioides	Water Forget-me-not	E	F
Myosotis secunda	Creeping Forget-me-not	N	O
Myosotis laxa	Tufted Forget-me-not	N	F
Myosotis arvensis	Field Scorpion-grass	N	F
Myosotis ramosissima	Spring Scorpion-grass		R or Ex
Myosotis discolor	Variegated Scorpion-grass	N	F
Stachys sylvatica	Hedge Woundwort	N	R
Stachys sylvatica x palustris = S. x ambigua	Lamb's-lugs	N & E	F
Stachys palustris	Marsh Woundwort	N	O
Stachys arvensis	Field Woundwort	C	R
Lamium album	White Dead-nettle	A	Ex?
Lamium maculatum	Spotted Dead-nettle	A	R or Ex
Lamium purpureum	Red Dead-nettle	N	F
Lamium confertum	Northern Dead-nettle	N	F
Lamium amplexicaule	Henbit Dead-nettle	N	O L
Galeopsis speciosa	Large-flowered Hemp-nettle	C	Ex?
Galeopsis tetrahit	Common Hemp-nettle	N	A
Galeopsis bifida	Bifid Hemp-nettle	N	R
Scutellaria galericulata	Skull-cap	N	R
Teucrium scorodonia	Wood Sage	N	O
Ajuga reptans	Creeping Bugle	N	O
Ajuga reptans x pyramidalis = *x pseudopyramidalis*	Hybrid Bugle	N	R or Ex
Ajuga pyramidalis	Pyramidal Bugle	N	R BSS
Glechoma hederacea	Ground Ivy	E	R
Prunella vulgaris	Self-heal	N	F

Thymus polytrichus ssp britannicus	Wild Thyme	N	F L
Mentha x verticillata = M aquatica x arvensis	Mint	E	R
Mentha aquatica	Water Mint	N	F
Mentha x piperita = aquatica x spicata	Peppermint	E	O
Mentha spicata	Spearmint	E	R
Mentha x villosa	Apple Mint	C	O
Mentha suaveolens	Round-leaved Mint	A	R
Hippuris vulgaris	Mare's-tail	N	F
Callitriche agg.	Water-starwort	N	F
Callitriche hermaphroditica	Autumnal Water-starwort	N	O
Callitriche stagnalis	Common Water-starwort	N	F
Callitriche platycarpa	Various-l'ved Water-starwort	N	F
Callitriche hamulata	Intermediate Water-starwort	N	O
Plantago coronopus	Buck's-horn Plantain	N	F
Plantago maritima	Sea Plantain	N	A
Plantago major	Greater Plantain	N	F
Plantago media	Hoary Plantain	S	R
Plantago lanceolata	Ribwort	N	F
Littorella uniflora	Shoreweed	N	F
Fraxinus excelsior	Ash	P	R
Verbascum thapsus	Aaron's Rod, Great Mullein	C	R
Scrophularia nodosa	Figwort	N	R or Ex
Scrophularia auriculata	Water Figwort	A	R
Mimulus agg	Monkey Flower	E	O
Mimulus guttatus	Monkeyflower	E	O
Mimulus burnetti = guttatus x cupreus	Coppery Monkeyflower	E	R
Mimulus guttatus x luteus = x robertsii	Hybrid Monkeyflower	E	O
Mimulus x smithii	Monkeyflower	E	O
Mimulus caledonicus	Monkeyflower	E	O
Linaria vulgaris	Common Toadflax	C	R or Ex
Digitalis purpurea	Foxglove	N	O L
Veronica serpyllifolia	Thyme-leaved Speedwell	N	F
Veronica officinalis	Common Speedwell	N	F
Veronica chamaedrys	Germander Speedwell	E	O
Veronica scutellata	Marsh Speedwell	N	O
Veronica beccabunga	Brooklime	N	F L
Veronica anagallis-aquatica	Water-speedwell	N	O
Veronica catenata	Pink Water-speedwell	N	R
Veronica arvensis	Wall Speedwell	N	O
Veronica agrestis	Field Speedwell	N	O
Veronica polita	Grey Speedwell	C	R or Ex
Veronica persica	Buxbaum's Speedwell	N	O
Veronica filiformis	Slender Speedwell	E	O
Veronica hederifolia	Ivy-leaved Speedwell	N	O
Hebe elliptica x speciosa = H. x franciscana	Hedge Veronica	E	R
Melampyrum pratense	Common Cow-wheat	N	R
Euphrasia agg.	Eyebright	N	A
Euphrasia arctica ssp arctica	Eyebright	N	O
Euphrasia arctica ssp borealis	Eyebright	N	O
Euphrasia arctica x micrantha	Eyebright	N	R
Euphrasia arctica x nemorosa	Eyebright	N	R
Euphrasia arctica x confusa	Eyebright	N	R
Euphrasia nemorosa	Eyebright	N	F L
Euphrasia foulaensis x nemorosa	Eyebright	N	R
Euphrasia confusa	Eyebright	N	F
Euphrasia foulaensis	Eyebright	N	O BSS
Euphrasia foulaensis x ostenfeldii	Eyebright	N	R
Euphrasia foulaensis x micrantha	Eyebright	N	R
Euphrasia ostenfeldii	Eyebright	N	R BSS
Euphrasia marshallii	Eyebright	N	R BSS
Euphrasia rotundifolia	Eyebright	N	R RDB
Euphrasia micrantha	Eyebright	N	F
Euphrasia micrantha x scottica	Eyebright	N	R
Euphrasia scottica	Eyebright	N	F L
Euphrasia heslop-harrisonii	Eyebright	N	R RDB
Odontites vernus	Red Bartsia	N	F
Rhinanthus angustifolius	Greater Yellow-rattle	N	R or Ex

Rhinanthus minor agg.	Yellow-rattle	N	F
Rhinanthus minor ssp. minor	Yellow-rattle	N	F
Rhinanthus minor ssp. stenophyllus	Yellow-rattle	N	F
Rhinanthus minor ssp. monticola	Yellow-rattle	N	O
Pedicularis palustris	Red Rattle	N	F L
Pedicularis sylvatica	Lousewort	N	F L
Pinguicula vulgaris	Butterwort	N	F
Utricularia vulgaris	Bladder-wort	N	R
Utricularia australis	Bladder-wort	N	R
Utricularia minor	Lesser Bladder-wort	N	O
Campanula rapunculoides	Creeping Bellflower	C	R or Ex
Campanula rotundifolia	Harebell, Scottish Bluebell	N	R or Ex
Jasione montana	Sheeps'-bit	N	R L
Lobelia dortmanna	Water Lobelia	N & E	R
Sherardia arvensis	Field Madder	N	R L
Galium palustre ssp palustre	Marsh Bedstraw	N	F
Galium palustre ssp elongatum	Marsh Bedstraw	N	R
Galium verum	Lady's Bedstraw	N	F BSS
Galium mollugo x verum = G. pomeranicum	Hybrid Bedstraw	N	R
Galium mollugo ssp mollugo	Hedge Bedstraw	N	R
Galium mollugo ssp. erectum	Marsh Bedstraw	N	R
Galium sterneri	Limestone Bedstraw	N	O L BSS
Galium saxatile	Heath Bedstraw	N	A
Galium aparine	Goosegrass, Cleavers	N	F L
Sambucus nigra	Elder, Bo'er-tree	P	O
Sambucus ebulus	Danewort	P	R
Symphoricarpos albus	Snowberry	E	R
Lonicera periclymenum	Honeysuckle	N & E	F L
Valerianella locusta	Lamb's Lettuce	C	R or Ex
Valeriana officinalis	Valerian	N	O L
Valeriana pyrenaica	Pyrenean Valerian	E	R
Knautia arvensis	Field Scabious	C	R or Ex
Succisa pratensis	Devil's-bit Scabious	N	F
Arctium minus s.l.	Lesser Burdock	N	O
Saussurea alpina	Alpine Saw-wort	N	R
Cirsium vulgare	Spear Thistle	N	F
Cirsium heterophyllum	Melancholy Thistle	E	R
Cirsium palustre	Marsh Thistle	N	F
Cirsium arvense	Creeping Thistle	N	F
Centaurea scabiosa	Greater Knapweed	C	R
Centaurea cyanus	Cornflower	C	Ex
Centaurea nigra x C. jacea = *moncktonii C.Britton*	Hybrid Knapweed	C	R or Ex
Centaurea solstitialis	Yellow-star-thistle	C	R or Ex
Centaurea nigra	Hardheads, Knapweed	N	O L
Cichorium intybus	Chicory	P	R
Lapsana communis	Nipplewort	N	O
Hypochaeris radicata	Cat's-ear	N	F
Leontodon autumnalis	Autumnal Hawkbit	N	F
Leontodon saxatilis	Lesser Hawkbit	S	R
Picris echioides	Bristly Oxtongue	C	R
Sonchus arvensis	Corn Sowthistle	N	F
Sonchus oleraceus	Common Sowthistle	N	O
Sonchus asper	Prickly Sowthistle	N	F
Taraxacum agg	Dandelion	N	A
Taraxacum tanylepis	Dandelion	N	R
Taraxacum faeroense	Dandelion	N	F
Taraxacum europhyllum	Dandelion	N	R
Taraxacum maculosum	Dandelion	N	O
Taraxacum naevosiforme	Dandelion	N	O
Taraxacum rubellum	Dandelion	N	R
Taraxacum naevosum	Dandelion	N	O
Taraxacum stictophyllum	Dandelion	N	O
Taraxacum subnaevosum	Dandelion	N	R
Taraxacum duplidentifrons	Dandelion	N	O
Taraxacum fulvicarpum	Dandelion	N	O
Taraxacum gelertii	Dandelion	N	O?

Taraxacum landmarkii	Dandelion	N	O
Taraxacum orcadense	Dandelion	N	R or Ex
Taraxacum unguilobum	Dandelion	N	O
Taraxacum hamatum	Dandelion	N	O
Taraxacum cyanolepis	Dandelion	N	O
Taraxacum polyodon	Dandelion	N	R
Crepis biennis	Rough Hawk's-beard	C	R or Ex
Crepis capillaris	Smooth Hawk's-beard	N	O
Crepis nicaeensis	French Hawk's-beard	C	R or Ex
Pilosella officinarum	Mouse-ear Hawkweed	N	O
Pilosella aurantiaca	Fox-and-Cubs	E	R
Hieracium maritimum	Hawkweed	N	R
Hieracium latobrigorum	Hawkweed	N	R
Hieracium orcadense	Hawkweed	N	R
Hieracium orimeles	Hawkweed	N	R
Hieracium scoticum	Hawkweed	N	R
Hieracium caledonicum	Hawkweed	N	R
Hieracium argenteum	Hawkweed	N	R
Hieracium sarcophylloides	Hawkweed	N	R
Hieracium iricum	Hawkweed	N	R
Hieracium anglicum	Hawkweed	N	R
Antennaria dioica	Cat's-foot, Mountain Everlasting	N	F
Anaphalis margaritacea	Pearly Everlasting	S	R
Gnaphalium sylvaticum	Heath Cudweed	N	R BSS
Gnaphalium uliginosum	Marsh Cudweed	N	F
Inula helenium	Elecampane	E	O
Solidago virgaurea	Golden-rod	N	O L
Aster x salignus	Michaelmas Daisy	C	R.
Aster tripolium	Sea Aster	N	R
Bellis perennis	Daisy	N	A
Tanacetum parthenium	Feverfew	E	O
Tanacetum vulgare	Tansy	E	O
Artemisia vulgaris	Mugwort; Bulwands	N	O
Achillea ptarmica	Sneezewort	N	O
Achillea millefolium	Milfoil, Yarrow	N	F
Chamaemelum nobile	Chamomile	C	R
Anthemis arvensis	Corn Chamomile	C	R or Ex
Anthemis cotula	Stinking Chamomile	C	R
Chrysanthemum segetum	Corn Marigold	N	O L
Leucanthemum vulgare	Ox-eye Daisy	N	O
Matricaria recutita	Scented Mayweed	C	R
Matricaria discoidea	Pineapple Weed	E	F
Tripleurospermum maritimum	Sea Mayweed	N	F
Tripleurospermum inodorum	Scentless Mayweed	E	O
Cotula squalida	N Zealand Pincushion-plant	C	R or Ex
Senecio smithii	Magellan Ragwort	E	O
Senecio jacobaea	Ragwort	N	O L
Senecio jacobaea x aquaticus = S. x ostenfeldii	Hybrid Ragwort	N	F
Senecio aquaticus	Marsh Ragwort	N	F
Senecio vulgaris	Groundsel	N	F
Senecio sylvaticus	Wood Groundsel	N or C	R
Tussilago farfara	Tushilaga, Colt's-foot	N	F
Petasites hybridus	Butterbur	E	O
Petasites fragrans	Winter Heliotrope	S	R
Calendula officinalis	Pot Marigold	C	R or Ex
Eupatorium cannabinum	Hemp Agrimony	N	R
Elodea canadensis	Canadian Pondweed	E	O
Triglochin palustris	Marsh Arrow-grass	N	F
Triglochin maritima	Sea Arrow-grass	N	F
Potamogeton natans	Broad-leaved Pondweed	N	O
Potamogeton polygonifolius	Bog Pondweed	N	F
Potamogeton x suecicus =			
filiformis x pectinatus	Pondweed hybrid	N	R
Potamogeton lucens	Shining Pondweed	N	R
Potamogeton x zizii = lucens x gramineus	Hybrid Pondweed	N	R BSS
Potamogeton gramineus	Various-leaved Pondweed	N	O
Potamogeton x nitens	Hybrid Pondweed	N	O BSS

Potamogeton praelongus	Long-stalked Pondweed	N	R BSS
Potamogeton perfoliatus	Perfoliate Pondweed	N	F
Potamogeton friesii	Flat-stalked Pondweed	N	O BSS
Potamogeton pusillus	Lesser Pondweed	N	O
Potamogeton obtusifolius	Blunt-leaved Pondweed	N	Ex
Potamogeton berchtoldii	Small Pondweed	N	O
Potamogeton crispus	Curled Pondweed	N	O
Potamogeton filiformis	Slender Pondweed	N	F BSS
Potamogeton pectinatus	Fennel-leaved Pondweed	N	F
Ruppia maritima	Tasselweed	N	O
Ruppia cirrhosa	Spiral Tasselweed	N	R BSS
Zannichellia palustris	Horned Pondweed	N	O
Zostera marina	Eelgrass Common Grass-wrack	N	O
Arum maculatum	Lords-and-Ladies, Cuckoo Pint	E	R
Lemna minor	Common Duckweed	N	O
Juncus squarrosus	Heath Rush	N	F L
Juncus tenuis	Slender Rush	C	R or Ex
Juncus gerardii	Mud Rush	N	F L
Juncus bufonius	Toad Rush	N	F
Juncus articulatus	Jointed Rush	N	A
Juncus x acutiformis x articulatus =			
J x surrejanus	Hybrid Rush	N	R
Juncus acutiflorus	Sharp-flowered Rush	N	O L
Juncus bulbosus	Bulbous Rush	N	F
Juncus triglumis	Three-flowered Rush	N	Ex
Juncus balticus	Baltic Rush	N	R
Juncus effusus	Soft Rush	N	F
Juncus conglomeratus	Compact Rush	N	F
Luzula pilosa	Hairy Woodrush	N	O
Luzula sylvatica	Great Woodrush	N	A L
Luzula campestris	Field Woodrush	N	F
Luzula multiflora	Heath Woodrush	N	F
Eriophorum angustifolium	Common Cottongrass	N	A
Eriophorum latifolium	Broad-leaved Cottongrass	N	R
Eriophorum vaginatum	Hare's-tail	N	F
Trichophorum cespitosum	Deer-grass	N	F
Eleocharis palustris	Common Spike-rush	N	F
Eleocharis uniglumis	One-glumed Spike-rush	N	O
Eleocharis multicaulis	Many-stemmed Spike-rush	N	O
Eleocharis quinqueflora	Few-fled Spike-rush	N	F L
Bolboschoenus maritimus	Sea Club-rush	N or C	E
Schoenoplectus lacustris	Bulrush	N	R L
Schoenoplectus tabernaemontani	Glaucus Bullrush	N	O L
Isolepis setacea	Bristle Scirpus	N	O
Eleogiton fluitans	Floating Scirpus	N	R
Blysmus rufus	Narrow Blysmus	N	O
Schoenus nigricans	Black Bog-rush	N	F L
Carex paniculata	Greater Tussock Sedge	N	O
Carex diandra	Lesser Tussock Sedge	N	R
Carex spicata	Spiked Sedge	?	R or Ex
Carex arenaria	Sand Sedge	N	F L
Carex disticha	Brown Sedge	N	R
Carex maritima	Curved Sedge	N	O L BSS
Carex ovalis	Oval Sedge	N	O
Carex echinata	Star Sedge	N	F
Carex dioica	Dioecious Sedge	N	F
Carex curta	White Sedge	N	R
Carex hirta	Hairy Sedge	C	R
Carex lasiocarpa	Slender Sedge	N	R or Ex
Carex riparia	Greater Pond-sedge	N	R
Carex riparia x rostrata	Hybrid sedge	N	R
Carex rostrata	Bottle Sedge	N	F L
Carex sylvatica	Wood Sedge	E	R
Carex capillaris	Hair Sedge	N	R
Carex flacca	Glaucous Sedge	N	F
Carex panicea	Carnation Sedge	N	A
Carex binervis	Green-ribbed Sedge	N	F

Carex extensa	Long-bracteate Sedge	N	O
Carex hostiana	Tawny Sedge	N	F
Carex x fulva = hostiana x viridula	Hybrid Sedge	N	F
Carex viridula ssp. brachyrrhyncha	Long-stalked Yellow-sedge	N	F
Carex viridula ssp. oedocarpa	Yellow Sedge	N	F
Carex viridula ssp viridula	Small-fruited Yellow-sedge	N	O
Carex pilulifera	Pill Sedge	N	O
Carex limosa	Mud Sedge	N	O L
Carex nigra	Common Sedge	N	F
Carex bigelowii	Stiff Sedge	N	R
Carex pulicaris	Flea Sedge	N	F
Nardus stricta	Mat Grass	N	F
Festuca pratensis	Meadow Fescue	N & E	O
Festuca arundinacea	Tall Fescue	E	O
Festuca rubra agg.	Red Fescue	N	A
Festuca rubra ssp scotica	Red Fescue	N	R
Festuca rubra ssp megastachys	Red Fescue	N	O
Festuca rubra ssp rubra	Red Fescue	N	F
Festuca ovina	Sheep's Fescue	N	R
Festuca vivipara	Viviparous Fescue	N	F
Festuca filiformis	Fine-leaved Sheep's Fescue	N	O
Lolium perenne	Perennial Ryegrass	N	F
Lolium multiflorum	Italian Ryegrass	A	O
Vulpia bromoides	Squirrel-tail Fescue	C	R or Ex
Cynosurus cristatus	Crested Dog's-tail	N	F
Puccinellia maritima	Common Saltmarsh-grass	N	F L
Puccinellia capillaris	Northern Saltmarsh-grass	N	O L
Briza media	Quaking-grass	N	R
Poa annua	Annual Meadow-grass	N	A
Poa trivialis	Rough Meadow-grass	N	A
Poa humilis	Spreading Meadow-grass	N	F
Poa pratensis	Smooth Meadow-grass	N & E	O
Poa alpina	Alpine Meadow-grass	N	R BSS
Dactylis glomerata	Cocksfoot	N or P	F
Catabrosa aquatica	Whorl-grass	N	R
Catapodium marinum	Stiff Sand Grass	N	R
Glyceria fluitans	Floating Sweet-g, Flote-g	N	F
Glyceria fluitans x notata = G x pedicellata	Hybrid Sweet-grass	N	R
Glyceria declinata	Small Sweet-grass	N	R
Glyceria notata	Plicate Sweet-grass	N	R
Helictotrichon pubescens	Hairy Oat-grass	N	O
Arrhenatherum elatius	False Oat-grass; Swinebeads	N	F
Avena strigosa	Bristle Oat, Black Oat	C	R
Avena fatua	Wild-oat	C	R
Avena fatua x sativa	Hybrid wild oat		
	(Spring Oat with cultivated Oat	C	R
Koeleria macrantha	Crested Hair-grass	N	R
Deschampsia cespitosa	Tufted Hair-grass	N	F
Deschampsia flexuosa	Wavy Hair-grass	N	O L
Holcus lanatus	Yorkshire Fog Punds	N	A
Holcus mollis	Creeping Soft-grass	E	O
Aira caryophyllea	Silver Hair-grass	N	O
Aira praecox	Early Hair-grass	N	F
Hierochloe odorata	Holy-grass	N	R RDB
Anthoxanthum odoratum	Sweet Vernal-grass	N	F
Anthoxanthum aristatum	Annual Vernal-grass	A	Ex?
Phalaris arundinacea	Reed Canary-grass	N	F
Agrostis capillaris	Common Bent	N	F
Agrostis capillaris x stolonifera = *A x murbeckii*	Hybrid Bent	N	R or Ex
Agrostis capillaris x vinealis	Hybrid Bent	N	R
Agrostis gigantea	Black Bent	E	O
Agrostis gigantea x stolonifera	Hybrid Bent	N	R
Agrostis stolonifera	Creeping Bent	N	F
Agrostis canina	Velvet Bent	N	F
Agrostis vinealis	Brown Bent	N	F
Calamagrostis epigejos	Wood Small-reed	N or E	R

Ammophila arenaria	Marram	N	O L
Alopecurus pratensis	Meadow Foxtail	N	O
Alopecurus geniculatus	Marsh Foxtail	N	F
Phleum pratense	Timothy	N & C	F
Bromus hordeaceus ssp hordeaceus x B lepidus	Hybrid Brome	C	R
Bromus hordeaceus ssp hordeaceus	Soft Brome	C	R
Bromus hordeaceus ssp thominei	Soft Brome	C	R
Bromus lepidus	Slender Brome	C	R
Anisantha sterilis	Barren Brome	C	R
Brachypodium sylvaticum	Slender False-brome	N	O
Elytrigia repens	Couch	N	F
Elytrigia x laxa	Hybrid Couch	N	O
Elytrigia juncea	Sand Couch	N	O L
Leymus arenarius	Lyme Grass	N	F
Hordeum vulgare	6-Row Barley, Bere.	N	R
Hordeum jubatum	Foxtail Barley	C	R
Danthonia decumbens	Heath Grass	N	F
Molinia caerulea	Purple Moor-grass	N	F
Phragmites australis	Reed	N	O L
Panicum miliaceum	Millet		R or Ex
Sparganium erectum	Branched Bur-reed	N	O L
Sparganium emersum	Unbranched Bur-reed	N	R
Sparganium angustifolium	Floating Bur-reed	N	R L
Typha latifolia	Great Reedmace	E	R
Narthecium ossifragum	Bog Asphodel	N	F
Fritillaria meleagris	Snakes-head Fritillary	E	R
Lilium pyrenaicum	Pyrenean Lily	E	R
Scilla verna	Spring Squill	N	F
Hyacinthoides hispanica x non-scripta	Hybrid Bluebell Wild Hyacinth	E	O
Allium schoenoprasum	Chives	A	R
Allium paradoxum	Three-cornered Garlic	E	O
Allium ursinum	Ramsons	A	R
Iris pseudacorus	Yellow Flag, Segs	N	A
Crocosmia x crocosmiflora	Montbretia	E	O
Phormium tenax	New Zealand Flax	P	O
Listera ovata	Twayblade	N	O
Listera cordata	Lesser Twayblade	N	O
Goodyera repens	Creeping Lady's-tresses	?	Ex BSS
Hammarbya paludosa	Bog Orchid	N	Ex BSS
Platanthera bifolia	Lesser Butterfly Orchid	N	R or Ex
Pseudorchis albida	Small White Orchid	N	R
Pseudorchis albidaa x Dactylorhiza maculata	Hybrid Orchid	N	R
Gymnadenia conopsea ssp. densiflora	Fragrant Orchid	N	R
Gymnadenia conopsea ssp borealis	Fragrant Orchid	N	R
Coeloglossum viride	Frog Orchid	N	O
Dactylorhiza fuchsii	Spotted Orchid	N	R or Ex
Dactylorhiza maculata ssp ericetorum	Moorland Spotted Orchid	N	F
Dactylorhiza x formosa	Hybrid Spotted Orchid	N	O
Dactylorhiza incarnata	Early Marsh Orchid	N	O
Dactylorhiza purpurella	Northern Fen Orchid	N	F
Orchis mascula	Early Purple Orchid	N	R

Other groups

Myxomycetes

Ing (1982) used the *Provisional Atlas of the Myxomycetes of the British Isles* to illustrate a number of points about the distribution of the group. The data therein should not therefore be taken to be a complete list of species, although 46 taxa are included for Orkney.

Fungi

Tom Eggeling (1994) recognizes 1,132 species in Orkney (excluding doubtful records) compared to 998 in Shetland and 547 in Faroe. The Orkney list builds on collections made by Dennis (1972; Dennis and Spooner, 1992, 1993), building on records by J. W. H Traill (1889, 1890) and M. Wilson (1934).

Marine Algae

A comprehensive list of marine algae recorded from Shetland has been compiled by David Irvine (in Berry and Johnstone, 1980). In it he noted that 'several southern species appear to come no further north than the Orkneys, for instance *Bostrychia scorpioides* and *Nemalion helminthoides*'. The Orkney list (Wilkinson,1975) is based on a visit of the British Phycological Society to Orkney in 1973, when 45 species were found. Earlier accounts of Orkney marine algae are given by Traill (1891, 1893, 1895), Lyle (1929), Dunn (1937) and Sinclair (1950).

Characeae

The status of this unusual group of macroscopic green algae is probably less well known nowadays than when Henry Halcro-Johnstone collected in 1920–26. The data are summarized in the *Provisional Atlas of the Characeae of the British Isles* (Moore and Greene, 1983) with more recent records in Charter (1993) and Stewart (1995).

Lichens

Dalby (1996) noted that 258 species have been recorded in Orkney, compared to 436 in Shetland. Most data are contained in the *Atlas of Lichens of the British Isles* (Seaward and Hitch, 1982); additional records come from the record scheme of the British Lichen Society (Purvis *et al.*, 1992). The clean air of Orkney is indicated by the rarity of *Lecanora coniziaeoides*, which apparently benefits from pollution and is abundant on trees and wood throughout England and Wales. Other species (e.g. *Diploicia canescens* and *Candelariella medians*) are at the northern edge of the range in Orkney, and are rare on that account, although abundant in south-east Britain. Conversely *Xanthoria candelaria* is often abundantly fertile in Orkney, whereas it is virtually sterile in the south. *Lichina confinis*, normally a lichen found at or just above high-tide level, occurs up to 100 metres on exposed hillsides in Orkney, where it is exposed to strong winds and salt spray for much of the year.

Bryophyta

Berry (1985) contains an extensive list of both mosses and liverworts compiled by Mrs Ann Thomson of Kirkwall. New County Records continue to be added (McCance, 1997, 1998), but no comparative analysis of the Orkney bryophyte flora has been made.

ANIMALS

Hirudinea

Maitland and Kellock (1971) list eighteen species recorded in Orkney.

Coleoptera

Extensive collections have been made in recent years by Vincent Lorimer of Orphir and Stuart Ball of the Joint Nature Conservation Committee (see also Sadler and Buckland, 1998). Their records are contained in Berry (1985). Since then Fairclough (1995, 1998) has listed another 26 species including five recorded only as sub-fossils from a Norse archaeological site in Westray and one further last recorded in Orkney in 1897. Colin Welch (formerly of the Institute of Terrestrial Ecology, Monk's Wood) has compared the beetle fauna of Orkney and Shetland. Probably most of the differences are due to the relative amount of collecting in the two groups. For example the carabid and curculionid lists are similar in the two groups, but there are three times as many chrysomelids known from Orkney than Shetland, and many more water beetles recorded in Orkney than in Shetland, the latter largely as a result of the work of Balfour-Browne (1949); in contrast only about 90 staphylinid species have been found in Orkney, compared with 128 for Shetland.

Hemiptera
Only three species recorded (Fairclough, 1998)

Odonata
Berry (1985) noted that only five of the 37 British dragon and damsel flies breed in Orkney. At least two more species should be added to this list: *Cordulegaster boltonii* and *Libellula quadrimaculata*.

Orthoptera
Three species were listed by Berry (1985). Since then the Common Green Grasshopper (*Omocestus viridulus*) known only from the Rackwick area may have become extinct. The House Cricket (*Acheta domesticus*) was reported from two houses in Kirkwall in 1995.

Trichoptera
Berry (1985) listed 48 species collected by J. D. Walker of Kirkwall. Andrew (1992) added a further eighteen species from trapping and netting on Hoy and the Mainland. He notes that none of the newly recorded species are rare in terms of their UK occurrence.

Ephemoptera, Plecoptera
Two additional stone-fly species have been added to the list of thirteen species of may-flies and ten species of stone-flies listed by Kellock and Maitland (1969) and repeated in Berry (1985).

Lepidoptera
The first list of Orkney lepidoptera was published by J. Traill in 1869 when he was only 18 (he produced a more complete list in 1888). Weir (1882) listed the results of a season's work on Hoy by a professional collector, probably H. McArthur. The next visitor was E. R. Curzon, who also spent a summer on Hoy, in 1885. His captures were listed independently by Gregson (1885) and South (1888).

A few other lepidopterists worked in Orkney before the turn of the century (details are given by Lorimer, 1983), but it was the publication of E. B. Ford's New Naturalist on *Butterflies* in 1945 that really stimulated interest in Orkney's butterflies and moths. Current knowledge is summarized in Lorimer's *Lepidoptera of the Orkney Islands* (1983, 1998), where detailed lists are given, regularly supplemented by new records in the Field Club *Bulletin*.

Hymenoptera
Berry (1985) had no list of Orkney hymenoptera. They are certainly understudied in Orkney. The common Wasp (*Paravespula vulgaris*) occurs on the Mainland, and the Norwegian Wasp (*Dolichovespula norvegicus*) has been found on Hoy and Rousay as well as on the Mainland. A nest of a tree wasp *Doliochovespula sylvestris* was found on Hoy in 1996.

Ants occur on Orkney, but the only species definitely identified is the common red ant *Myrmica ruginodis*; it is apparently the only species to occur in Shetland (Johnstone, 1998).

Diptera
The only dipteran group known in any detail is the *Syrphidae* or Hover-flies. Fifty species are known to occur in Orkney (Andrew and Watt, 1993; Laurence, 1997), about one quarter of the Scottish fauna. Two of the Orkney records are of rare species, in that they are included in the *Invertebrate Red Data Book*. Most of the Orkney species are ones characteristic of grassland, cow-dung, sewage or silage pits, or damp habitats.

Other Diptera are listed by Laurence (1997), who has compared the records from Orkney, Shetland and the Hebrides. He notes 'There is a general impression that the Western Isles contain a greater range of these species expected in collections made further south', that 'comparisons between the faunas of Orkney and Shetland is difficult because some species which were found only in one locality, even on more than one occasion, may well be found by similar collecting methods elsewhere in the islands', and while 'one characteristic of the island fauna is the presence at sea level of species which are found at higher altitudes further south'. However he believes that some conspicuous species found in Orkney are unlikely to be found in Shetland, instancing *Rhamphomyia subcinerescens* and *Leucozona lucorum* which feed on roadside flowers in Orkney but have not been seen in Shetland.

Arachnida

Spiders are very efficient dispersers and the spiders of the eastern North Atlantic form a 'common faunal area' (Braendegaard, 1958). However there are species which are certainly limited by climate. For example *Segestria senoculata* (Dysderidae) and *Dictyna arundinacea* (a cribellate) occur in Orkney, but have not been recorded in Shetland, Faroe or Iceland; the former does not occur much north of 60 degrees in Fennoscandia. Similarly, *Amaurobius fenestralis* is highly successful in Orkney and Shetland, but is absent from both the Faroes and Iceland (which have been well studied for spiders); it has been recorded only a little north of 60 degrees in Norway. Quite a number of species reach their northernmost limit in Orkney, particularly woodland species like *Pholcomma gibbum*, *Diplocephalus latifrons*, *Centromerus sylvaticus* and *Maso sundevalli*.

Several species are absent in particular groups for reasons difficult to understand. For example, *Pardosa amentata* occurs in Orkney and up to the Arctic Circle in Scandinavia, but it has not been found in Shetland, Faroe or Iceland despite the presence of apparently suitable habitats. Presumably its absence is due to a failure in colonization.

The first major spider collecting in Orkney was done by W. S. Bristowe in 1927 and 1931 (Bristowe, 1931). Apart from a single-species records made by Duffy in 1955, the next study of spiders was by M. J. Surtees in 1975, who added 22 new County Records out of 35 species found, mainly from Rackwick in Hoy. He was followed by P. D. Hillyard, who collected on the Mainland, Hoy and Burray in 1976, and added another 30 species to the Orkney list (with the help of Miss A. M. Coyle). There are now 130 species which have been found in Orkney, similar to the 121 for Shetland (Johnstone, 1998; J. E. Milner, personal communication), where the list has been boosted by recent collecting.

Mollusca

Seventy-seven species of terrestrial and fresh-water snails and slugs have been recorded in Orkney, most of the snails being small in size. The most complete list has been compiled by Mrs Nora MacMillan (Berry, 1985), building on the work of many earlier collectors. Up to 1990, 359 species of marine molluscs were recorded by collectors, beginning with the Revd James Wallace in 1700 and culminating with Robert Rendall's magisterial *Mollusca Orcadensis* in 1956. The problem is to know which are truly Orcadian: some of the records are of shells only or of specimens collected out at sea many miles from Orkney. Skene (1994) noted that between 1991 and 1994 only 96 species were recorded, and less than half of these (42 species) were based on live specimens. However, some of them were unexpected. Brightly coloured *Gari fervensis* and *Tricolia pullus* are found on east-facing coasts, although they are generally Atlantic species in Scotland. Some species like *Donax vittatus*, *Palliolum tigerinum* and the nudibranch *Crimora papillata* reach their northern limit in Orkney; *Scrobicularia plana* is found of the south shore of the Pentland Firth but not in Orkney.

Despite the attraction and accessibility of molluscs, there is much still unknown about the local species. A new taxon (*Coryphella browni*) was described from an Orkney animal in 1989; and in 1967 three small individuals of *Cima minima* found crawling on a large shell brought in from Hoy waters were the first British live record for years.

Vertebrata

The Vertebrata of Orkney are recorded by Chris and Jean Booth in their *Status and Checklist of the Vertebrate Fauna of Orkney* (1998). The different groups are very unevenly represented. The fish list is extensive and only recently compiled; there are hardly any amphibia and reptiles (p. 129) and only a few more mammals, of which only the Otter, the Pygmy Shrew and Pipistrelle Bat of the terrestrial species can be regarded as breeding natives (see Booth and Booth, 1994).

The birds are described in detail in Chapter 8; the breeding and non-breeding birds and their status are:

Breeding birds

Red-throated Diver	*Gavia stellata*	Rain Goose/Loon	3
Little Grebe	*Tachybaptus ruficollis*	Dabchick	1
Fulmar	*Fulmarus glacialis*	Mallimack	5
Manx Shearwater	*Puffinus puffinus*	Lyre	2
Storm Petrel	*Hydrobates pelagicus*	Alamottie	4
Gannet	*Morus bassanus*	Solan Goose	4
Cormorant	*Phalacrocorax carbo*	Skarf/Hiblin	3
Shag	*P.aristotelis*	Skarf	4
Grey Heron	*Ardea cinerea*		1
Mute Swan	*Cygnus olor*		2
Greylag Goose	*Anser anser*		2
Shelduck	*Tadorna tadorna*	Sly Goose	2
Wigeon	*Anas penelope*		2
Gadwall	*A.strepera*		1
Teal	*A.crecca*		3
Mallard	*A.platyrhynchos*	Stock duck	3
Pintail	*A.acuta*		2
Shoveler	*A.clypeata*		2
Pochard	*Aythya ferina*		OB
Tufted Duck	*A.fuligula*		2
Scaup	*A.marina*		OB
Eider	*Somateria mollissima*	Dunter	3
Red-breasted Merganser	*Mergus serrator*	Harle	3
Ruddy Duck	*Oxyura jamaicensis*		OB
Hen Harrier	*Circus cyaneus*	Catabelly	2
Sparrowhawk	*Accipiter nisus*		1
Buzzard	*Buteo buteo*		1
Kestrel	*Falco tinnunculus*	Moosie-haak	2
Merlin	*F.columbarius*		2
Peregrine	*F.peregrinus*		2
Red Grouse	*Lagopus lagopus*	Muir-hen	3
Grey Partridge	*Perdix perdix*		I.OB
Quail	*Coturnix coturnix*		OB
Pheasant	*Phasianus colchicus*		I.3
Water Rail	*Rallus aquaticus*		1
Corncrake	*Crex crex*		2
Moorhen	*Gallinula chloropus*	Water-hen	3
Coot	*Fulica atra*	Snaith	2
Oystercatcher	*Haematopus ostralegus*	Shalder/Skeldro	4
Ringed Plover	*Charadrius hiaticula*	Sanloo	3
Golden Plover	*Pluvialis apricaria*	Pliver	3
Lapwing	*Vanellus vanellus*	Teeick	4
Dunlin	*Calidris alpina*	Boondie	3
Snipe	*Gallinago gallinago*	Horse Gowk	4
Woodcock	*Scolopax rusticola*		OB
Black-tailed Godwit	*Limosa limosa*		1
Whimbrel	*Numenius phaeopus*	Titterel	2
Curlew	*N.arquatus*	Whaup	4
Redshank	*Tringa totanus*	Watery Pleeps	4
Common Sandpiper	*Actitis hypoleucos*		2
Arctic Skua	*Stercorarius parasiticus*	Scootie Allan	4
Great Skua	*Stercorarius skua*	Bonxie	4
Black-headed Gull	*Larus ridibundus*	Rittick	4
Common Gull	*L.canus*	White-maa	4

Lesser B-b Gull	*L.fuscus*		4
Herring Gull	*L.argentatus*	White-maa	4
Great B-b Gull	*L.marinus*	Swart-back/Swarbie	4
Kittiwake	*Rissa tridactyla*	Kittick/Wekko	5
Sandwich Tern	*Sterna sanvicensis*		3
Common Tern	*S.hirundo*		3
Arctic Tern	*S.paradisaea*	Pickie/Ritto	5
Little Tern	*S.albifrons*		OB
Guillemot	*Uria aalge*	Aak	5
Razorbill	*Alca torda*	Coulter-neb	4
Black Guillemot	*Cepphus grylle*	Tystie	4
Puffin	*Fratercula arctica*	Tammy Norie	5
Rock Dove	*Columba livia*	Doo	4
Woodpigeon	*C.palumbus*	Doo	3
Collared Dove	*Streptopelia decaocto*		2
Cuckoo	*Cuculus canorus*	Gokk	OB
Short-eared Owl	*Asio flammeus*	Cattie-face	2
Long-eared Owl	*A.otus*		OB
Skylark	*Alauda arvensis*	Laverock	4
Swallow	*Hirundo rustica*		3
House Martin	*Delichon urbica*		1
Meadow Pipit	*Anthus pratensis*	Teeting	4
Rock Pipit	*A.petrosus*	Tang Sparrow	3
Yellow Wagtail	*Motacilla flava*		OB
Grey Wagtail	*M.cinerea*		1
Pied Wagtail	*M.alba*	Willie Wagtail	3
Dipper	*Cinclus cinclus*		OB
Wren	*Troglodytes troglodytes*	Jenny Wren	3
Dunnock	*Prunella modularis*		2
Robin	*Erithacus rubecula*	Robin Redbreast	2
Whinchat	*Saxicola rubetra*		OB
Stonechat	*S.torquata*		2
Wheatear	*Oenanthe oenanthe*	Chackie/Stonechat	3
Ring Ouzel	*Turdus torquatus*	Flitterchack	OB
Blackbird	*T.merula*	Blackie	3
Song Thrush	*T.philomelos*	Mavis	2
Redwing	*T.iliacus*	Wind-thrush	OB
Sedge Warbler	*Acrocephalus schoenobaenus*		2
Marsh Warbler	*A.palustris*		OB
Lesser Whitethroat	*Sylvia curruca*		OB
Whitethroat	*S.communis*		OB
Garden Warbler	*S.borin*		OB
Blackcap	*S.atricapilla*		OB
Willow Warbler	*Phylloscopus trochilus*		2
Chiffchaff	*P.collybita*		OB
Goldcrest	*Regulus regulus*		2
Spotted Flycatcher	*Muscicapa striata*		OB
Jackdaw	*Corvus monedula*	Jackie	3
Rook	*C.frugilegus*	Corbie/Craa	4
Hooded Crow	*C.corone*	Hoodie	3
Raven	*C.corax*	Corbie/Ramna	2
Starling	*Sturnus vulgaris*	Strill/Stirling	4
House Sparrow	*Passer domesticus*	Sprog	4
Chaffinch	*Fringilla coelebs*		2
Brambling	*F.montifringilla*		OB
Greenfinch	*Carduelis chloris*		2
Linnet	*C.cannabina*	Lintie	3
Twite	*C.flavirostris*	Heather Lintie	3
Siskin	*C.spinus*		OB
Redpoll	*C.flammea*		OB
Reed Bunting	*Emberiza schoeniclus*		3

Non-breeding birds

Black-throated Diver	*Gavia arctica*		WP2
Great Northern Diver	*G.immer*	Immer Goose	WP3
White-billed Diver	*G.adamsii*		R
Great Crested Grebe	*Podiceps cristatus*		R

Red-necked Grebe	*P.grisegena*		WP1
Slavonian Grebe	*P.auritus*		WP3
Black-necked Grebe	*P.nigricollis*		R
Black-browed Albatross	*Diomedea melanophris*		R
Cory's Shearwater	*Calonectris diomedea*		P1
Great Shearwater	*Puffinus gravis*		R
Sooty Shearwater	*P.griseus*		P3
Mediterranean Shearwater	*P.yelkouan*		P1
Leach's Petrel	*Oceanodroma leucorhoa*		FB P1
Bittern	*Botaurus stellaris*		R
Little Bittern	*Ixorbrychus minutus*		R
Night Heron	*Nycticorax nycticorax*		R
Squacco Heron	*Ardeola ralloides*		R
Little Egret	*Egretta garzetta*		R
Great White Egret	*Egretta alba*		R
Purple Heron	*Ardea purpurea*		R
Black Stork	*Ciconia nigra*		R
White Stork	*C.ciconia*		R
Glossy Ibis	*Plegadis falcinellus*		R
Spoonbill	*Platalea leucorodia*		R
Bewick's Swan	*Cygnus columbianus*		R
Whooper Swan	*C.cygnus*		FB WP3
Bean Goose	*Anser fabalis*		R
Pink-footed Goose	*A.brachyrhynchus*		P3
White-fronted Goose	*A.albifrons*		WP3
Snow Goose	*A.caerulescens*		R
Canada Goose	*Branta canadensis*		R
Barnacle Goose	*B.leucopsis*	(Horra Goose)	WP4
Brent Goose	*B.bernicla*	(Rood Goose)	P2
Ruddy Shelduck	*Tadorna ferruginea*		R
Mandarin	*Aix galericulata*		R
American Wigeon	*Anas americana*		R
Garganey	*A.querquedula*		P1
Blue-winged Teal	*A.discors*		R
Red-crested Pochard	*Netta rufina*		R
Ring-necked Duck	*Aythya collaris*		R
Ferruginous Duck	*A.nyroca*		R
Scaup	*A.marila*		FB W3
Lesser Scaup	*A.affinis*		R
King Eider	*Somateria spectabilis*		R
Steller's Eider	*Poysticta stelleri*		R
Long-tailed Duck	*Clangula hyemalis*	Calloo	FB W4
Common Scoter	*Melanitta nigra*		FB P1
Surf Scoter	*M.perspicillata*		R
Velvet Scoter	*M.fusca*		W3
Goldeneye	*Bucephala clangula*	Gowdie Duck/Kwink	W3
Smew	*Mergus albellus*		W1
Goosander	*M.merganser*		P1
Honey Buzzard	*Pernis apivorus*		P1
Black Kite	*Milvus migrans*		R
Red Kite	*M.milvus*		R
White-tailed Eagle	*Haliaetus albicilla*		FB R
Marsh Harrier	*Circus aeruginosus*		P1
Pallid Harrier	*C.macrourus*		R
Montagu's Harrier	*C.pygargus*		R
Goshawk	*Accipiter gentilis*		R
Rough-legged Buzzard	*Buteo lagopus*		WP1
Golden Eagle	*Aquila chrysaetos*		FB R
Osprey	*Pandion haliaetus*		P1
Red-footed Falcon	*Falco vespertinus*		R
Hobby	*F.subbuteo*		P1
Gyr Falcon	*F.rusticolus*		R
Ptarmigan	*Lagopus mutus*		FB Ex
Black Grouse	*Tetrao tetrix*		I Ex
Red-legged Partridge	*Alectoris rufa*		I Ex
Spotted Crake	*Porzana porzana*		R
Crane	*Grus grus*		R

Little Bustard	*Tetrax tetrax*		R
Great Bustard	*Otis tarda*		R
Black-winged Stilt	*Himantopus himantopus*		R
Avocet	*Recurvirostra avosetta*		R
Stone Curlew	*Burhinus oedicnemus*		R
Collared Pratincole	*Glareola pratincola*		R
Little Ringed Plover	*Charadrius dubius*		R
Greater Sand Plover	*C.leschenaultii*		R
Dotterel	*C.morinellus*		P1
American Golden Plover	*Pluvialis dominica*		R
Pacific Golden Plover	*P.fulva*		R
Grey Plover	*P.squatarola*		PW3
Sociable Plover	*Chettusia gregaria*		R
Knot	*Calidris canutus*		PW3
Sanderling	*C.alba*		PW3
Semi-palmated Sandpiper	*C.pusilla*		R
Western Sandpiper	*C.mauri*		R
Little Stint	*C.minuta*		P2
Temminck's Stint	*C.temminckii*		R
White-rumped Sandpiper	*C.fuscicollis*		R
Baird's Sandpiper	*C.bairdii*		R
Pectoral Sandpiper	*C.melanotos*		R
Curlew Sandpiper	*C.ferruginea*		P2
Purple Sandpiper	*C.maritima*		W4
Broad-billed Sandpiper	*Limicola falcinellus*		R
Buff-breasted Sandpiper	*Tringites subruficollis*		R
Ruff	*Philomachus pugnax*		P3
Jack Snipe	*Limnocryptes minimus*		PW2
Great Snipe	*Gallinago media*		R
Long-billed Dowitcher	*Limnodromus scolopaceus*		R
Bar-tailed Godwit	*Limosa lapponica*		PW3
Spotted Redshank	*Tringa erythropus*		P1
Marsh Sandpiper	*T.stagnatilis*		R
Greenshank	*T.nebularia*		FB P2
Lesser Yellowlegs	*T.flavipes*		R
Green Sandpiper	*T.ochropus*		P2
Wood Sandpiper	*T.glareola*		P1
Terek Sandpiper	*Xenus cinereus*		R
Spotted Sandpiper	*Actitis macularia*		R
Turnstone	*Arenaria interpres*	Staneputter	PW4
Wilson's Phalarope	*Phalaropus tricolor*		R
Red-necked Phalarope	*P.lobatus*		FB P1
Grey Phalarope	*P.fulicarius*		P1
Pomarine Skua	*Stercorarius pomarinus*		P2
Long-tailed Skua	*S.longicaudus*		P1
Mediterranean Gull	*Larus melanocephalus*		R
Laughing Gull	*L.atricilla*		R
Little Gull	*L.minutus*		P1
Sabine's Gull	*L.sabini*		P1
Ring-billed Gull	*L.delawarensis*		R
Iceland Gull	*L.glaucoides*		PW2
Glaucous Gull	*L.hyperboreus*		PW2
Ross's Gull	*Rhodostethia rosea*		R
Ivory Gull	*Pagophila eburnea*		R
Gull-billed Tern	*Gelochelidon nilotica*		R
Caspian Tern	*Sterna caspia*		R
Roseate Tern	*Sterna dougallii*		R
Bridled Tern	*S.anaethetus*		R
Sooty Tern	*S.fuscata*		R
Black Tern	*Chlidonias niger*		R
White-winged Black Tern	*C.leucopterus*		R
Brunnich's Guillemot	*Uria lomvia*		R
Great Auk	*Pinguinus impennis*		FB Ex
Little Auk	*Alle alle*	Rotchie	PW3
Pallas's Sandgrouse	*Syrrhaptes paradoxus*		R
Stock Dove	*Columba oenas*		R
Turtle Dove	*Streptopelia turtur*		P1

Great Spotted Cuckoo	*Clamator glandarius*	R
Yellow-billed Cuckoo	*Coccyzus americanus*	R
Barn Owl	*Tyto alba*	R
Scops Owl	*Otus scops*	R
Snowy Owl	*Nyctea scandiaca*	R
Tengmalm's Owl	*Aegolius funereus*	R
Nightjar	*Caprimulgus europaeus*	R
Common Nighthawk	*Chordeiles minor*	R
Needle-tailed Swift	*Hirundapus caudacutus*	R
Swift	*Apus apus*	P2
Pallid Swift	*A.pallidus*	R
Alpine Swift	*A.melba*	R
Kingfisher	*Alcedo atthis*	R
Bee-eater	*Merops apiaster*	R
Roller	*Coracias garrulus*	R
Hoopoe	*Upupa epops*	R
Wryneck	*Jynx torquilla*	P1
Green Woodpecker	*Picus viridis*	R
Great Spotted Woodpecker	*Dendrocopos major*	P1
Short-toed Lark	*Calandrella brachydactyla*	R
Woodlark	*Lullula arborea*	R
Shorelark	*Eremophila alpestris*	R
Sand Martin	*Riparia riparia*	P1
Crag Martin	*Ptyonoprogne rupestris*	R
Red-rumped Swallow	*Hirundo daurica*	R
Richard's Pipit	*Anthus novaeseelandiae*	P1
Tawny Pipit	*A.campestris*	R
Olive-backed Pipit	*A.hodgsoni*	R
Tree Pipit	*A.trivialis*	P2
Pechora Pipit	*A.gustavi*	R
Red-throated Pipit	*A.cervinus*	R
Water Pipit	*A.spinoletta*	R
Citrine Wagtail	*Motacilla citreola*	R
Waxwing	*Bombycilla garrulus*	P2
Thrush Nightingale	*Luscinia luscinia*	R
Nightingale	*L.megarhynchos*	R
Bluethroat	*L.svecica*	P1
Black Redstart	*Phoenicurus ochruros*	FB P2
Redstart	*P.phoenicurus*	P3
Pied Wheatear	*Oenanthe pleschanka*	R
Desert Wheatear	*O.deserti*	R
Rock Thrush	*Monticola saxatilis*	R
White's Thrush	*Zoothera dauma*	R
Siberian Thrush	*Z.sibirica*	R
Swainson's Thrush	*Catharus ustulatus*	R
Grey-cheeked Thrush	*C.minimus*	R
Eye-browed Thrush	*Turdus obscurus*	R
Dark-throated Thrush	*T.ruficollis*	R
Fieldfare	*T.pilaris*	FB P4W3
Mistle Thrush	*T.viscivorus*	FB P1
American Robin	*T.migratorius*	R
Pallas's Grasshopper Warbler	*Locustella certhiola*	R
Lanceolated Warbler	*L.lanceolata*	R
Grasshopper Warbler	*L.naevia*	P1
River Warbler	*L.fluviatilis*	R
Paddyfield Warbler	*Acrocephalus agricola*	R
Blyth's Reed Warbler	*A.dumetorum*	R
Reed Warbler	*A.scirpaceus*	P2
Great Reed Warbler	*A.aundinaceus*	R
Booted Warbler	*Hippolais caligata*	R
Icterine Warbler	*H.icterina*	P1
Melodious Warbler	*H.polyglotta*	R
Subalpine Warbler	*Sylvia cantillans*	R
Sardinian Warbler	*S.melanocephala*	R
Barred Warbler	*S.nisoria*	P1
Greenish Warbler	*Phylloscopus trochiloides*	R
Arctic Warbler	*P.borealis*	R

Pallas's Warbler	*P.proregulus*	R
Yellow-browed Warbler	*P.inornatus*	P1
Hume's Leaf Warbler	*P.humei*	R
Radde's Warbler	*P.schwarzi*	R
Dusky Warbler	*P.fuscatus*	R
Western Bonelli's Warbler	*P.bonelli*	R
Wood Warbler	*P.sibilatrix*	P1
Firecrest	*Regulus ignicapillus*	R
Red-breasted Flycatcher	*Ficedula parva*	P1
Collared Flycatcher	*F.albicollis*	R
Pied Flycatcher	*F.hypoleuca*	P2
Bearded Tit	*Panurus biarmicus*	R
Long-tailed Tit	*Aegithalos caudatus*	R
Coal Tit	*Parus ater*	R
Blue Tit	*P.caeruleus*	R
Great Tit	*P.major*	R
Treecreeper	*Certhia familiaris*	R
Golden Oriole	*Oriolus oriolus*	R
Isabelline Shrike	*Lanius isabellinus*	R
Red-backed Shrike	*L.collurio*	P2
Lesser Grey Shrike	*L.minor*	R
Great Grey Shrike	*L.excubitor*	P1
Southern Grey Shrike	*L.meridionalis*	R
Woodchat Shrike	*L.senator*	R
Jay	*Garrulus glandarius*	R
Magpie	*Pica pica*	R
Nutcracker	*Nucifraga caryocatactes*	R
Chough	*Pyrrhocorax pyrrhocorax*	R
Rose-coloured Starling	*Sturnus roseus*	R
Spanish Sparrow	*Passer hispaniolensis*	R
Tree Sparrow	*P.montanus*	FB R
Goldfinch	*Carduelis carduelis*	R
Arctic Redpoll	*C.hornemanni*	R
Two-barred Crossbill	*Loxia leucoptera*	R
Common Crossbill	*L.curvirostra*	P1
Parrot Crossbill	*L.pytyopsittacus*	R
Trumpeter Finch	*Bucanetes githagineus*	R
Common Rosefinch	*Carpodacus erythrinus*	P1
Bullfinch	*Pyrrhula pyrrhula*	PW1
Hawfinch	*Coccothraustes coccothraustes*	P1
Tennessee Warbler	*Vermivora peregrina*	R
Yellow Warbler	*Dendroica petechia*	R
Yellow-rumped Warbler	*D.coronata*	R
White-throated Sparrow	*Zonotrichia albicollis*	R
Lapland Bunting	*Calcarius lapponicus*	P2
Snow Bunting	*Plectrophenax nivalis*	PW3
Pine Bunting	*Emberiza leucocephalus*	R
Yellowhammer	*E.citrinella*	FB P1
Cirl Bunting	*E.cirlus*	R
Ortolan Bunting	*E.hortulana*	R
Cretzschmar's Bunting	*E.caesia*	R
Yellow-browed Bunting	*E.chrysophrys*	R
Rustic Bunting	*E.rustica*	R
Little Bunting	*E.pusilla*	R
Yellow-breasted Bunting	*E.aureola*	R
Black-headed Bunting	*E.melanocephala*	R
Corn Bunting	*Miliaria calandra*	FB R

Bibliography

Adam, P. (1990) *Saltmarsh Ecology*. Cambridge: Cambridge University Press.

Adam, R. G. (1998) Swallows in Orkney 1997. In *Orkney Bird Report for 1997*. Booth, C. J. *et al.* (eds) Kirkwall.

Agassiz, L. (1834) On the fossil fishes of Scotland. Rep. Br. Ass. Advmt Sci, 4th Meeting, Edinburgh, Transactions of Sections 646–9.

Anderson, G. P. (1834) *Guide to the Highlands and Islands of Scotland, including Orkney and Shetland*. London.

Anderson, P. D. (1982) *Robert Stewart, Earl of Orkney, Lord of Shetland 1533–93*. Edinburgh: John Donald.

Andrew, R. H. (1988) Largest and smallest stonefly discoveries. *Bull. Orkney Fld Club* No. 2: 12.

Arthur, G. T. (1950) Orkney's birds. *Bird Notes*, 24: 130–5.

Ashby, E. (1978) *Reconciling Man with the Environment*. London: Oxford University Press.

Ashmole, N. P. (1979) The spider fauna of Shetland and its zoogeographic context. *Proc. R. Soc. Edin.* 78B: 63–122.

Astin, T. R. (1985) The paleogeography of the Middle Devonian Lower Eday Sandstone. *Scot. J. Geol.* 21: 353–75.

Astin, T. R. (1990) The Devonian lacustrine sediments of Orkney, Scotland: implications for climatic cyclicity, basin structure and maturation history. *J. Geol. Soc. Lond.* 147: 147–51.

Astin, T. R. and Rogers, D. A. (1991) 'Subaqueous shrinkage cracks' in the Devonian of Scotland reinterpreted. *J. Sed. Pet*, 61: 850–9.

Atkins, S. M., Jones, A. M. and Simpson, J. A. (1985) The fauna of sandy beaches of Orkney: a review. *Proc. R. Soc. Edin.* 87B: 27–45.

Avery, M. I., Burges, D., Dymond, N. J., Mellor, M. and Ellis, P. M. (1993) The status of Arctic Terns in Orkney and Shetland in 1989. *Seabird*, 15: 17–23.

Baikie, W. B. and Heddle, R. (1848) *Historia Naturalis Orcadensis. Zoology, Part 1*. Edinburgh: Paterson.

Bailey, P. (1971) *Orkney*. Newton Abbot: David and Charles.

Bailey, P. (1995) *Orkney*. Newton Abbott: David and Charles.

Baker, J. R., Jones, A. M., Jones, T. P. and Watson, H. C. (1981) Otter (*Lutra lutra*) mortality and marine oil pollution. *Biol. Cons.* 20: 311–21.

Balfour, E. (1955) Kestrels nesting on the ground in Orkney. *Bird Notes*, 26: 245–53.

Balfour, E. (1962) The nest and eggs of the Hen Harrier in Orkney. *Bird Notes*, 30: 69–73.

Balfour, E. (1967) *Orkney Birds: Status and Guide*. Stromness, Orkney.

Balfour, E. (1968) Breeding birds in Orkney. *Scot. Birds*, 5: 89–104.

Balfour, E. (1970) Iris colour in the Hen Harrier. *Bird Study*, 17: 47.

Balfour, E. (1972) *Orkney Birds. Status and Guide*. Stromness: Senior.

Balfour, E., Anderson, A. and Dunnet, G. M. (1967) Orkney Cormorants – their breeding distribution and dispersal. *Scot. Birds*, 4: 481–93.

Balfour, E. and Cadbury, C. J. (1975) A population study of the Hen Harrier, Circus cyaneus in Orkney. In *The Natural Environment of Orkney*: 122–8. Goodier, R. (ed.) Edinburgh: Nature Conservancy Council.

Balfour, E. and Cadbury, C. J. (1979) Polygyny, spacing and sex ratio among Hen Harriers *Circus cyaneus* in Orkney, Scotland. *Ornis Scand.* 10: 133–41.

Balfour, E. and Macdonald, M. A. (1970) Food and feeding behaviour of the Hen Harriers in Orkney. *Scot. Birds* 6: 157–66.

Balfour-Browne, F. (1949) The aquatic coleoptera of the Orkney islands with some remarks on water beetle faunas of the Scottish islands. *Proc. R. Phys. Soc.* 23: 143–53.

Barclay, R. S. (1965) *The Population of Orkney.* Kirkwall: W. R. Mackintosh.

Barne, J. H., Robson, C. F., Kazanowska, S. S, Doody, J. P, Davidson, N. C. and Buck, A. L. (eds) (1997) *Coasts and Seas of the United Kingdom. Region 2. Orkney.* Peterborough: Joint Nature Conservation Committee.

Barnes, M. P (1998) *The Norn Language of Orkney and Shetland.* Lerwick: Shetland Times

Barnes, R. S. K. (1980) *Coastal Lagoons.* Cambridge: Cambridge University Press.

Barry, G. (1805) *The History of the Orkney Islands.* Edinburgh: Constable.

Baxter, A. N., and Mitchell, J. G. (1984) Camptonite-monchiquite dyke swarms of northern Scotland: age relationships and their implications *Scot. J. Geol.* 20: 297–308

Baxter, J. M. (1982) Population dynamics of *Patella vulgata* in Orkney. *Neth. J. Sea Res.* 16: 96–104.

Baxter, J. M., Jones, A. M. and Simpson, J. A. (1985) A study of long-term changes in some rocky shore communities in Orkney. *Proc. R. Soc. Edin.* 87B: 47–63

Ben, J. (1529) *Descriptio Insularum Orchadearum.* See Appendix VII in Barry, 1805.

Bennett, K. D., Boreham, S., Sharp, M. J. and Switsur, V. R. (1992) Holocene history of environment vegetation and human settlement on Catta Ness, Lunnasting, Shetland. *J. Ecol.* 80: 241–73

Berry, R. J. (1969) Non-metrical variation in two Scottish colonies of the Grey seal. *J. Zool., Lond.* 157: 11–18.

Berry, R. J. (1977) *Inheritance and Natural History.* London: Collins New Naturalist.

Berry, R. J. (1983a) Diversity and differentiation: the importance of island biology for general theory. *Oikos* 41: 523–9.

Berry, R. J. (1983b) Environmental ethics and conservation action. In *The Conservation and Development Programme for the UK,* 407–38. London: Kogan Page.

Berry, R. J. (1985) *The Natural History of Orkney.* London: Collins New Naturalist.

Berry, R. J. (1999) A worldwide ethic for sustainable living. *Ethics, Place and Environment,* 2: 97–107.

Berry, R. J. and Firth, H. (eds) (1986) *The People of Orkney.* Stromness: Orkney Press.

Berry, R. J. and Johnston, J. L. (1980) *The Natural History of Shetland.* London: Collins New Naturalist.

Berry, R. J. and Muir, V. M. L. (1975) Natural history of man in Shetland. *J. Biosoc. Sci.* 7: 319–44.

Berry, R. J. and Rose, F. E. N. (1975) Islands and the evolution of *Microtus arvalis* (Microtinae) *J. Zool., Lond.* 177: 395–409.

Birkhead, T. R. (1984) Distribution of the bridled form of the common guillemot *Uria aalge* in the North Atlantic. *J. Zool., Lond.* 202: 165–76.

Black, G. P. (ed.) (1978) *Orkney: Localities of Geological and Geomorphological Importance.* Newbury: Nature Conservancy Council.

Böker, U. von (1964) Bermerkungen zur Vogelwelt der Orkneyinsel Hoy. *Ornith. Mitt.* 16: 3–12.

Bonner, W. N. (1972) The Grey Seal and Common Seal in European waters. *Oceanogr. Mar. Biol. Ann. Rev.* 10: 461–507.

Bonner, W. N. (1976) *Stocks of Grey Seals and Common Seals in Great Britain.* N.E.R.C. Publications Ser. C, no. 16. London: N.E.R.C.

Bonner, W. N. (1978) Man's impact on seals. *Mamm. Rev.* 8: 3–13.

Bonner, W. N., Vaughan, R. W. and Johnston, J. L. (1973) The status of common seals in Shetland. *Biol. Cons.,* 5: 185–90.

Booth, C. and Booth, J. (1994) *The Mammals of Orkney,* Kirkwall: C. Booth.

Booth, C. and Booth, J. (1998) *Status and Checklist of the Vertebrate Fauna of Orkney,* Kirkwall: C&J Booth.

Booth, C.J. (1995) The status of the Eurasian Jackdaw as a breeding species in Orkney in *Orkney Bird Report 1994.* Booth, C.J., Cuthbert, M. and Meek, E.R. (eds) 63–67. Kirkwall.

Booth, C. J. (1979) A study of ravens in Orkney. *Scot. Birds* 10: 261–7.

Booth, C. J. (1982) *Scot. Birds* 12: 33–8.

Booth, C. J., Cuthbert, Mildred and Reynolds, P. (1984) *The Birds of Orkney.* Stromness: Orkney Press.

Booth, C. J. et al., (1981–1997) *Orkney Bird Reports 1980–1996.* Kirkwall.

Booth, C. J. and Marquiss, M. (1986) The diet of Ravens *Corvus corax* in Orkney. *Bird Study* 33: 190–95.

Bott, M. H. P. and Browitt, C. W. A. (1975) Interpretation of geophysical observations between the Orkney and Shetland Islands. *J. Geol. Soc. Lond.* 131: 353–71.

Bourne, W. R. P. (1983) Birds, fish and offal in the North Sea. *Mar. Poll. Bull.* 14: 294–6.

Boyce, A. J., Holdsworth, V. M. L. and Brothwell, D. R. (1973) Demographic and genetic studies in the Orkney Islands. In *Genetic Variation in Britain:* 109–28. Sunderland, E. and Roberts, D. F. (eds.) London: Taylor and Francis.

Boycott, A. E. (1936) *Neritina fluviatilis* in Orkney. *J. Conchol.* 20: 199–200.

Boyd, J. M. (1963) The Grey Seal (*Halichoerus grypus Fab.*) in the Outer Hebrides in October 1961. *Proc. zool. Soc. Lond.* 141: 635–62.

Bradley, J. D. and Fletcher, D. S. (1979) *A Recorder's Log Book or Label List of British Butterflies and Moths.* London.

Braendegaard, J. (1958) Araneida. *Zoology Iceland,* 3 (54).

Brand, J. (1701) *A Brief Description of Orkney, Zetland, Pightland Firth and Caithness.* Edinburgh: Brown.

Bristowe, W. S. (1931) The spiders of the Orkney and Shetland Islands. *Proc. Zool. Soc., Lond.* for 1931: 951–6.

Britton, R. H. (1974) The freshwater ecology of Shetland. In *The Natural Environment of Shetland*: 119–29. Goodier, R. (ed.), Edinburgh: Nature Conservancy Council.

Brøgger, A. W. (1929) *Ancient Emigrants*. Oxford: Clarendon.

Brothwell, D. (1976) Further evidence of bone chewing by ungulates: the sheep of North Ronaldsay, Orkney. *J. Archaeol. Sc.* 3: 179–82.

Brothwell, D. R., Tills, D. and Muir, V. (1986) Evidence of microevolution in the Orkney islanders. In *The People of Orkney*: 54–88, Berry R. J. and Firth, H. (eds), Stromness: Orkney Press.

Brown, E. S. (1965) Distribution of the ABO and Rhesus (D) blood groups in the north of Scotland. *Heredity*, 20: 289–303.

Brown, G. M. (1969) *An Orkney Tapestry*. London: Gollancz.

Brown, G. M. (1981) *Portrait of Orkney*. London: Hogarth.

Brown, G. M. (1991) *Selected Poems 1954–1988*. London: John Murray.

Brown, J. F. (1975) Potassium-argon evidence for a Permian age for the camptonite dykes in Orkney. *Scot. J. Geol.* 11: 259–62.

Brown, S. G. (1976) Modern whaling in Britain and the north-east Atlantic Ocean. *Mammal Rev.* 6: 25–36.

Buckley, T. E. and Harvie-Brown, J. A. (1891) *A Vertebrate Fauna of the Orkney Islands*. Edinburgh: Douglas.

Bullard, E. R. (1972a) Lagoons and oyces in Orkney. *Bull. Orkney Fld Club* No. 3: 7–8.

Bullard, E. R. (1972b) *Orkney – A Checklist of Vascular Plants and Ferns*. Stromness: Rendall.

Bullard, E. R. (1975) Orkney habitats: an outline ecological framework. In *The Natural Environment of Orkney*: 19–28. Goodier, R. (ed.) Edinburgh: Nature Conservancy Council.

Bullard, E. R. (1995) *Wildflowers in Orkney. A New Checklist*. Kirkwall: E. R. Bullard.

Bullard, E. R. and Goode, D. A. (1975) The vegetation of Orkney. In *The Natural Environment of Orkney*: 31–46. Goodier, R. (ed.) Edinburgh: Nature Conservancy Council.

Bullard, E. R. Shearer, H. D. H., Day, J. D., and Crawford, R. M. M. (1987) Survival and flowering of *Primula scotica* Hook. *J. Ecol* 75: 589–602.

Bullock, I. D. and Gomersall, C. H. (1981) The breeding population of terns in Orkney and Shetland in 1980. *Bird Study* 28: 187–200.

Bunting, M. J. (1996a) The development of heathland in Orkney, Scotland – pollen records from Loch of Knithcen (Rousay) and Loch of Torness, Hoy. *Holocene*, 6: 193–212.

Bunting, M. J. (1996b) Holocene vegetation and environment of Orkney in *The Quaternary of Orkney*: 20–9. Hall, A. M. (ed.). Cambridge: Quaternary Research Association.

Burkill, H. M. (1968) James Sinclair, 1913–1968: an obituary and appreciation. *Garden Bull., Singapore*, no. 23.

Burnett, J. H. (ed.) (1964) *The Vegetation of Scotland*. Edinburgh: Oliver and Boyd.

Cadbury, C. J. (1980) The status and habitats of the Corncrake in Britain, 1978–79. *Bird Study* 27: 203–18.

Calder, A. (1952) Orkney's changing agriculture. *Scot. Agriculture*, 37–41.

Capper, D. P. (1937) *The Vikings of Britain*. London: Allen and Unwin.

Carlquist, S. (1974) *Island Biology*. New York and London: Columbia University Press.

Chapman, H. M. and Crawford, R. M. M. (1981) Growth and regeneration in Britain's most northerly natural woodland. *Trans. Bot. Soc. Edin.* 43: 327–35.

Charleson, M. M. (ed.) (1905) *Orcadian Papers*. Kirkwall.

Charter, E. (1995) *Farming with Wildlife in Mind, A Handbook for Farmers in Orkney*. Kirkwall: Orkney Farming and Wildlife Advisory Group.

Childe, V. G. (1931) *Skara Brae. A Pictish Village in Orkney*. London: Kegan Paul.

Childe, V. G. and Clarke, D. V. (1983) *Skara Brae*. Edinburgh: HMSO.

Clouston, J. S. (1927) *The Orkney Parishes*. Kirkwall.

Clouston, J. S. (1932) *A History of Orkney*. Kirkwall: W. R. Mackintosh.

Cluness, A. T. (1951) *The Shetland Isles*. London: Hale.

Cluness, A. T. (ed.) (1967) *The Shetland Book*. Lerwick: Zetland Education Committee.

Coleman, V. and Wheeler, R. (1980) *Living on an Island*. Findhorn, Moray: Thule.

Comfort, A. (1937) Land shells of the West Mainland. *Orcadian*, 13 May 1937.

Consultative Committee (1963) *Grey Seals and Fisheries*. London: HMSO.

Cooper, A. (1997) Plant species coexistence in cliff habitats, *J Biogeog.* 24: 483-494.

Corbet, G. B. (1961) Origin of the British insular races of small mammals and of the 'Lusitanian' fauna. *Nature, Lond.* 191: 1037–40.

Corbet, G. B. (1979) Report on rodent remains. In *Excavations in Orkney*: 135–7. Renfrew, C. (ed.) London: Society of Antiquities.

Corbet, G. B. and Harris, S. (1991) *The Handbook of British Mammals*, 3rd edn. Oxford: Blackwell Scientific.

Corse, C. J. and Adam, R. G. (1997) Orkney Rookery survey 1996. *Orkney Bird Report 1996*. Kirkwall.

Coughtrey, P. J. (ed.) (1983) *Ecological Aspects of Radionuclide Release*. Oxford: Blackwell.

Cowan, L. and Sinclair, M. (1998) *Orkney by Bike*. Finstown, Orkney: Information Plus.

Coward, M. P., Enfield, M. A. and Fischer, M. W. (1989) Devonian basins of Northern Scotland: extension and inversion related to late Caledonian-Variscan tectonics. In *Inversion Tectonics*: 275–307. Cooper, M. A. and Williams, G. D. London: Geological Soc. Spec. Pubn.

Cowie, J. R. (1871) *Shetland and its Inhabitants*. Aberdeen: Lewis, Smith.

Cramp, S., Bourne, W. R. P. and Saunders, D. (1974) *Seabirds of Britain and Ireland*. London: Collins.

Crampton, C. B. (1911) *The Vegetation of Caithness, considered in relation to the geology*. Cambridge: Committee for the Survey and Study of British Vegetation.

Crawford, B. E. (ed) (1995) *Northern Isles Connections*. Kirkwall: Orkney Press.

Crawford, R. M. M. (1997a) Habitat fragility as an aid to long-term survival in arctic vegetation. In *Ecology of Arctic Environments*: 113–36. Woodin, S. J. and Marquiss, M. (eds) Oxford: Blackwell Scientific.

Crawford, R. M. M. (1997b) Oceanicity and the ecological disadvantages of warm winters. *Bot.J. Scot.* 49: 205–21.

Crawford, R. M. M and Palin, M. A. (1981) Root respiration and temperature limits to the north-south distribution of four perennial maritime species. *Flora* 171: 338–54.

Crichton, W. T. (1866) *A Naturalist's Rambles to the Orcades*. London.

Cunningham, P., Dix, T. and Snow, P. (1995) *Bird Watching in the Outer Hebrides*. Oban.

Cursiter, J. W. (1894) *List of Books and Pamphlets relating to Orkney and Shetland*. Kirkwall: Peace.

Cuthbert, O. D. (1995) *The Life and Letters of an Orkney Naturalist*. Kirkwall: Orkney Press.

Cuthbert, O. D., Brostoff, J., Wraith, D. G. and Brighton, W. D. (1979). *Clin. Allergy*: 9: 229–36.

Cuthbert, O. D., Jeffrey, I. G., McNeill, H. and Topping, M. D. (1983) Barn allergy among Scottish farmers. *Clin. Allergy,* 13.

Darling, F. F. and Boyd, J. M. (1964) *The Highlands and Islands*. London: Collins New Naturalist.

Davidson, D. A and Carter, S. P (1997) Soils and their evolution. In *Scotland: Environment and Archaeology, 8000 BC-AD1000*: 45–62. Edwards, K. J. and Ralston, I. B. M. (eds) Chichester: Wiley.

Davidson, D. A. (1979) The Orcadian environment and cairn location. In *Excavations in Orkney*: 7–20. Renfrew, C. (ed.) London: Society of Antiquities.

Davidson, D. A., Jones, R. L. and Renfrew, C. (1976) Palaeoenvironmental reconstruction and evaluation: a case study from Orkney. *Trans. Inst. Brit. Geog.* 1: 346–61.

Davies, I. M. (1985) Marine pollution in Orkney. *Proc. R. Soc. Edin.* 87B: 105–112.

Davis, J. E. and Anderson, S. S. (1976) Effects of oil pollution on breeding Grey Seals. *Mar. Pollution Bull.* 7: 115–18.`

De Cock, L. (1956) The Pilot Whale stranding on the Orkney Island of Westray, 1955. *Scot. Nat.* 68: 63–70.

Dennis, R. W. G. (1972) Fungi of the Northern Isles. *Kew Bull.* 26: 427–32.

Dennis, R. and Shreeve, T. (1996) *Butterflies on British and Irish Offshore Islands*. Wallingford: Gem.

Dickson, C. A. and Dickson, J. H. (1975) Macroscopic plant remains from the Stones of Stenness, Orkney. *Proc. Soc. Ant. Scot.* 107: 40–3.

Dickson, N. (1990) *An Island Shore. The Life and Work of Robert Rendall*. Kirkwall: Orkney Press

Donaldson, G. (1966) *Northwards by Sea*. Edinburgh: Grant.

Douglas, C. K. M. (1952) Synoptic aspects of the storm over N. Scotland on Jan. 15, 1952. *Meteor. Mag.* 81: 104–06.

Downes, J. A. (1988) The post-glacial colonization of the North Atlantic islands. *Mem. Can. Ent. Soc.* 144: 55–92.

Dry, F. T. and Robertson, J. S. (1982) *Soil and Land Capability for Agriculture. Orkney and Shetland*. Aberdeen: Macaulay Institute.

Dry, F. T. (ed.) (1985) *The Soils of Orkney*. Aberdeen: Macaulay Institute.

Duck, C. D. (1997) Seals. In *Coasts and Seas of the United Kingdom. Region 2. Orkney*: 116–19. Barne, J. H. *et al.* (eds) Peterborough: JNCC.

Duffey, E. (1955) Notes on the natural history of Eynhallow. *Scot. Nat.* 67: 40–51.

Dunn, M. D. (1973) Notes on the flora of Loch Harray and Loch Stenness. *Trans. Proc. Bot. Soc. Edin.* 32: 368–72.

Dunn, R. (1837) *The Ornithologist's Guide to the Islands of Orkney and Shetland*. Hull.

Dunnet, G. M. (1992) A forty-three year study of the Fulmars on Eynhallow, Orkney. *Scottish Birds*, 16: 155–159.

Dunnet, G. M., Ollason, J. and Anderson, A. (1978) The estimation of survival rate in the Fulmar, *Fulmarus glacialis. J. anim. Ecol.* 47: 507–20.

Ellis, A. E. (1951) Census of the distribution of British non-marine Mollusca (7th edition). *J. Conchol.* 23: 171–244.

Ellison, G. (1906) *The Orkney Vole. Microtus orcadensis* (Millais). Kirkwall: Mackintosh.

Enfield, M.A. and Coward, W.P. (1987) Structure of the West Orkney Basin, northern Scotland. *J. Geol. Soc. Lond.* 144: 871–83.

Ennos, R. A., Cowie, N.R., Legg, C. J and Sydes, C. (1997) Which measures of genetic variation are relevant in plant conservation? In *The Role of Genetics in Conserving Small Populations:* 73–79. Tew, T. E., Crawford, J., Spencer, J. W., Stevens, D. P., Usher, M. B. and Warren, J. (eds) Peterborough: Joint Nature Conservation Committee.

Evans, A. H. and Buckley, T. E. (1899) *A Vertebrate Fauna of the Shetland Islands.* Edinburgh: Douglas.

Evans, P. G. H. (1976a) An analysis of sightings of Cetacea in British waters. *Mammal Rev.* 6: 5–14.

Evans, P. G. H. (1976b) *Guide to Identification of Cetaceans in British Waters.* Reading: Mammal Society.

Evans, P. G. H. (1980) Cetaceans in British waters. *Mamm. Rev.* 10: 1–52.

Evans, P. G. H. (1997) Whales, dolphins, and porpoises. In *Coasts and Seas of the United Kingdom. Region 2. Orkney:* 120–3. Barne, J. M. *et al.* (eds) Peterborough: JNCC.

Fannin, N. G. T. (1969) Stromatolites from the Middle Old Red Sandstone of western Orkney. *Geol. Mag.* 106: 77–88.

Fenton, A. (1978) *The Northern Isles: Orkney and Shetland.* Edinburgh: John Donald.

Firth, H. (ed) (1995) *In from the Cuithes. An Orkney Anthology.* Kirkwall: Orkney Press.

Flett, J. S. (1897) On the discovery in Orkney of the John o' Groats horizon of the Old Red Sandstone. *Proc. R. Phys. Soc. Edin.* 13: 225–57.

Flett, J. S. (1898) The Old Red Sandstone of the Orkneys. *Trans. R. Soc. Edin.* 39: 383–424.

Flett, J. S. (1920) The submarine contours around the Orkneys. *Trans. Edin. Geol. Soc.* 11: 42–9.

Flinn, D. (1969a) A geological interpretation of the aeromagnetic maps of the continental shelf around Orkney and Shetland. *Geol. J.* 6: 279–92.

Flinn, D. (1969b) On the development of coastal profiles in the north of Scotland, Orkney and Shetland. *Scot. J. Geol.* 5: 393–9.

Flinn, D. (1973) The topography of the sea floor around Orkney and Shetland and in the northern North Sea. *Q. J. Geol. Soc. Lond.* 129: 39–59.

Flinn, D. (1974) The coastline of Shetland. In *Natural Environment of Shetland:* 13–23. Goodier, R. (ed.) Edinburgh: Nature Conservancy Council.

Flinn, D. (1978) The most recent glaciation of the Orkney-Shetland Channel and adjacent areas. *Scot. J. Geol.* 14: 109–23.

Flinn, D. (1981) A note on the glacial and late glacial history of Caithness. *Geol. J.* 16: 175–9.

Flint, S. (1979) *Let the Seals Live!* Sandwick, Shetland: Thule.

Ford, E. B. (1955) *Moths.* London: Collins New Naturalist.

Forrest, J. E. (1938) Notes concerning some animals recently obtained from three German warships recently salvaged at Scapa Flow, Orkney. *Scot. Nat.* No. 229: 3–8.

Forsythe, D. (1982) *Urban-Rural Migration, Change and Conflict in an Orkney Island Community.* North Sea Oil Panel Occasional Paper No. 14. London: Social Science Research Council.

Foster, A. P. and Parsons, M. S. (1997) Land and freshwater invertebrates. In *Coasts and Seas of the United Kingdom. Region 2. Orkney:* 79–82. Barne, J. H. *et al.* (eds) Peterborough: JNCC.

Gallagher, M. J., Michie, U. McL., Smith, R. T. and Haynes, L. (1971) New evidence of uranium mineralization in Scotland. *Trans. Inst. Min. Met.* 80B: 150–7.

Geikie, A. (1877) The glacial geology of Orkney and Shetland. *Nature, Lond.* 16: 414–16.

Glover, B. J. and Abbott, R. J. A. (1995) Low genetic diversity in the Scottish endemic *Primula scotica* Hook. *New Phytol.* 129: 147–53.

Godfrey, R. (1906) Land shells in Orkney. *Ann. Scot. Hist.* for 1906: 55.

Godfrey, R. (1906) Notes on the Orkney Vole. *Ann. Scot. Nat. Hist.* for 1906: 195–8.

Goodier, R. and Ball, D. F. (1975) Ward Hill, Orkney: patterned features and their origin. In *The Natural Environment of Orkney:* 47–56. Goodier, R. (ed.) Edinburgh: Nature Conservancy Council.

Goodier, R. (ed.) (1974) *Natural Environment of Shetland.* Edinburgh: Nature Conservancy Council.

Goodier, R. (ed.) (1975) *The Natural Environment of Orkney.* Edinburgh: Nature Conservancy Council.

Goudie, G. (1904) *The Celtic and Scandinavian Antiquities of Shetland.* Edinburgh and London: Blackwood.

Green, J. and Green, R. (1980) *Otter Survey of Scotland 1977–1979.* London: Vincent Wildlife Trust.

Grimshaw, P. H. (1905) Diptera Scotica IV. Orkney and Shetland. *Ann. Scot. Nat. Hist.,* for 1905, 22–35.

Groundwater, W. (1974) *Birds and Mammals of Orkney.* Kirkwall: Kirkwall Press.

Groves, J. and Bullock-Webster, G. R. (1920) *The British Charophyta 1. Nitelleae.* London: Ray Society.

Groves, J. and Bullock-Webster, G. R. (1924) *The British Charophyta 2. Chareae.* London: Ray Society.

Gunn, J. (ed.) (1909) *The Orkney Book.* London and Edinburgh: Nelson.

Hall, A. M. (ed) (1996) *The Quaternary of Orkney: Field Guide.* Cambridge: Quaternary Research Association.

Halliday, A. N., McAlpine, A. and Mitchell, J. G. (1977) The age of the Hoy Lavas, Orkney. *Scot. J. Geol* 13: 43–52.

Hammond, P. S., Hall, A. J., and Prime, J. H. (1994) The diet of grey seals around Orkney and other island and mainland sites in north-eastern Scotland. *J. Appl. Ecol.* 31: 340–50.

Hansom, J. D. and Evans, J. D. A, (1995) The Old Man of Hoy. *Scot. Geogr. Mag.* 111: 172–4.

Hardin, G. (1964) The tragedy of the commons. *Science, N.Y.,* 162: 1243–8.

Harvey, R. G., Suter, D. and Tills, D. (1986) Relationships of the Orcadians: the view from Faroe. In *The People of Orkney*: 107–17. Berry, R. J. and Firth, H. (eds). Stromness: Orkney Press.

Harwood, J. and Prime, J. H. (1978) Some factors affecting the size of British Grey Seal populations. *J. Appl. Ecol.* 15: 401–11.

Harwood, J. (1978) The effect of management policies on the stability and resilience of British Grey Seal populations. *J. Appl. Ecol.* 15: 413–21.

Haswell-Smith, H. (1996) *The Scottish Islands*. Edinburgh: Canongate.

Heddle, M. F. (1878) *The County Geognosy and Mineralogy of Scotland, Orkney and Shetland*. Truro.

Hedges, J. (1975) Excavation of two Orcadian burnt mounds at Liddle and Beaquoy. *Proc. Soc. Ant. Scot.* 106: 39–98.

Hedges, J. W. (1982) An archaeodemographical perspective on Isbister. *Scot. Archaeol. Rev.* 1: 5–20.

Hedges, J. W. (1984) *Tomb of the Eagles*. London: John Murray.

Hedges, J. W. (1986) From the first inhabitants to the Viking settlement. In *People of Orkney*: 20–53. Berry, R. J. and Firth, H. (eds) Stromness: Orkney Press.

Henshall, A. S. (1963) *The Chambered Tombs of Scotland*. Edinburgh.

Heppleston, P. B. (1972) Life history and population fluctuations of *Lymnaea truncata*, the snail vector of fascioliasis. *J. Appl. Ecol.* 9: 229–42.

Heppleston, P. B. (1981) The Curlew in Orkney. In *Orkney Bird Report 1980*. Booth, C. J. *et al.* (eds) Kirkwall.

Heppleston, P. B. (1983a) How salty are Orkney's lochs? *Bull. Orkney Fld Club* No. 1: 5–6.

Heppleston, P. B. (1983b) Observations on some macro-invertebrates in Orkney freshwaters. *Bull. Orkney Fld Club* No. 1: 11–14.

Heppleston, P. B. (1983c) *Gammarus pulex* in Orkney, Scotland. *Crustaceana* 46: 20.

Heppleston, P. B. (1983d) The use of Orkney farmland in winter by wading birds. *Orkney Bird Report for 1982*: 52–7.

Hewer, H. R. (1964) The determination of age, sexual maturity, longevity and a life-table in the Grey Seal (*Halichoerus grypus*) *Proc. Zool. Soc. Lond.* 142: 593–624.

Hewer, H. R. (1974) *British Seals*. London: Collins New Naturalist.

Hewson, R. (1948) Some observations on the Orkney Vole, *Microtus o. orcadensis*. *Northw. Nat.* 23: 7–10.

Hiby, L., Duck, C., Thompson, D., Hall, A. and Harwood, J. (1996) Seal stocks in Great Britain. *NERC News* January 1996: 20–2.

Hillier, S. J., and Marshall, J. E. A. (1992) Organic maturation, thermal history and hydrocarbon generation in the Orcadian basin, Scotland *J. Geol. Soc. Lond.* 149: 491–502.

Hillyard, P. D. (1977) The spiders of Orkney. *Bull. Orkney Fld Club* No. 1: 7–8.

Hinton, M. A. C. (1913) Note on the voles of the *orcadensis* group. *Ann. Mag. Nat. Hist.* (8), 12: 452–62.

Hope-Jones, P. (1979) Roosting behaviour of long-tailed ducks in relation to possible oil pollution. *Wildfowl* 30: 155–8.

Hoppe, G. (1965) Submarine peat in the Shetland Islands. *Geogr. Annlr* 47A: 195–203.

House, M. R. and Gale, A. S. (1995) Orbital forcing timescales and cyclostratigraphy. London: *Geol. Soc. Spec. Pubn.* no. 85.

Hudson, R. (1965) The spread of the Collared Dove in Britain and Ireland. *British Birds*, 58: 105–39.

Huxtable, J., Hedges, J. W., Renfrew, C. and Aitken, M. J. (1976) Dating a settlement pattern by thermo-luminescence: the burnt mounds of Orkney. *Archaeometry*, 18: 4–11.

Innes, G., Kidd, C. and Ross, H. S. (1968) Mental subnormality in north-east Scotland. *Brit. J. Psychiat.* 114: 35–41.

Institute of Geological Sciences (1978) *Regional Geochemical Atlas: Orkney*. London: Institute of Geological Sciences.

Jakobsen, J. (1897) *The Dialect and Place Names of Shetland*. Lerwick: Manson.

Jakobsen, J. (1901) Shetlandsøernes stednavne. *Abøger for nordisk oldkyndighed og historie*, 2nd ser 16: 55–258.

Jameson, R. (1813) *Mineralogical Travels through the Hebrides, Orkney and Shetland Islands and Mainland of Scotland*. 2 vols, Edinburgh.

Jarvik, E. (1948) On the morphology and taxonomy of the Middle Devonian osteolepid fishes of Scotland. *K. Svenska vidensk Akad.* (3), 15: 1–301.

Jensen, A. D. (ed.) (1928–72) *The Zoology of the Faroes*. Copenhagen: Høst.

Johnstone, J.L. (1998) *A Naturalist's Shetland*. London: Poyser.

Jones, A. M. (1975) The marine environment of Orkney. In *The Natural Environment of Orkney*: 85–94. Goodier, R. (ed.), Edinburgh: Nature Conservancy Council.

Jones, K. H. and Kennard, A. S. (1919) Notes on the non-marine Mollusca observed in Easter Ross and the Orkney and Shetland Islands. *Proc. Malac. Soc. Lond.* 13: 146–52.

Keatinge, T. H. and Dickson, J. H. (1979) Mid-Flandrian changes in vegetation on Mainland Orkney. *New Phytol.* 82: 585–612.

Kellock, E. and Maitland, P. S. (1969) Ephemoptera and Plecoptera from Orkney. *Entomologist*, 102: 235–44.

Kellock, E. (1969) Alkaline basic igneous rocks in the Orkneys. *Scot. J. Geol.* 5: 140–52.

Kruuk, H. and Hewson, R. (1978) Spacing and foraging of otters (*Lutra lutra* L.) in a marine habitat. *J. Zool., Lond.* 195: 205–12.

Kruuk, H. (1995) *Wild Otters: Predation and Populations.* Oxford: Oxford University Press.

Lack, D. (1942) The breeding birds of Orkney. *Ibis* 85: 461–84.

Lack, D. (1943) The breeding birds of Orkney. *Ibis* 86: 1–27.

Lack, D. (1969) The numbers of bird species on islands. *Bird Study* 16: 193–209.

Lack, D. (1976) *Island Biology.* Oxford: Blackwell.

Laing, L. (1974) *Orkney and Shetland. An archaeological guide.* Newton Abbot: David and Charles.

Laing, S. (1877) Glacial geology of Orkney and Shetland. *Nature, Lond.* 16: 418–19.

Laurence, B.R. (1997) Diptera in the Northern Isles of Britain. *Ent. Monthly Mag.* 133: 225–32.

Lea, D. and Bourne, W. R. P. (1975) The birds of Orkney. *Brit. Birds* 68: 261–82.

Lea, D. and Bourne, W. R. P. (1975) The birds of Orkney. In *The Natural Environment of Orkney:* 98–121. Goodier, R. (ed.) Edinburgh: Nature Conservancy Council.

Lea, D. (1976) Obituary: Eddie Balfour. *Scot. Birds* 9: 69–71.

Leask, A. (1928) Shell sand deposits in Orkney. *J. Orkney Agric. Discuss. Soc.* 3: 57–8.

Linklater, E. (1965) *Orkney and Shetland.* London: Hale.

Linklater, M. (1981) Uranium: a questionable commodity. *Orkney Heritage,* 1: 7–21.

Lloyd, C., Tasker, M. L. and Partridge, K. (1991) *The Status of Seabirds in Britain and Ireland.* London: Poyser.

Locket, G. H., Millidge, A. F. and Merrett, P. (1974) *British Spiders, volume III.* London: Ray Society.

Lockley, R. M. (1966) *Grey Seal, Common Seal.* London: Deutsch.

Lorimer, R. I. (1975) Lepidoptera in Orkney. In *The Natural Environment of Orkney:* 57–79. Goodier, R. (ed.), Edinburgh: Nature Conservancy Council.

Lorimer, R. I. (1983) *The Lepidoptera of the Orkney Islands.* Faringdon: Classey.

Lorimer, R. I. (1998) *Unfinished Business.* Faringdon: Hedera.

Love, J. (1982) Harvie-Brown: a profile. *Scot. Birds,* 12: 49–53.

Low, G. (1813) *Fauna Orcadensis.* Edinburgh.

Low, G. (1879) *A Tour through Orkney and Shetland.* Kirkwall.

Lyle, L. (1929) Marine algae of some German warships in Scapa Flow and of the neighbouring shores. *J. Linn. Soc. (Bot.)* 48: 231–57.

Mabey, R. (1980) *The Common Ground.* London: Hutchinson.

Macan, T. T. (1961) A key to the nymphs of the British species of Ephemeroptera. *Sci. Publ. Freshw. Biol. Ass.* 20: 1–64.

MacArthur, R. H. and Wilson, E. O. (1963) An equilibrium theory of insular zoogeography. *Evolution* 17: 373–87.

MacArthur, R. H. and Wilson, E. O. (1967) *The Theory of Island Biogeography.* Princeton: Princeton University Press.

McConnell, B. (1985) Seals in Orkney. *Proc. R. Soc. Edin.* 87B: 195–204.

MacDiarmid, H. (1939) *The Islands of Scotland.* London: Batsford.

Macdonald, A. (1967) Trial plantations established by the Forestry Commission on the Island of Hoy, Orkney. *J. R. Scot. For. Soc.* 21: 163–72.

McMillan, N. F. (1960) *Hygromia hispida* L. on Hoy, Orkney. *J. Conchol.* 24: 395–7.

McMillan, N. F. (1966) Kennard's record of fossil *Helix nemoralis* L. in Orkney. *J. Conchol.* 26: 135–6.

McMillan, N. F. (1966) *Margaritifera margaritifera* L. in hard water in Scotland. *J. Conchol.* 26: 69.

McMillan, N. F. (1968) Obituary of Robert Rendall. *J. Conchol.* 26: 273–4.

McMillan, N. F. (1971) Large *Cardium edule* L. and *Mytilus edulis* L. *J. Conchol.* 26: 253.

McQuillin, R. (1968) Geophysical surveys in the Orkney Islands. *Geophys. Paper No. 4, Inst. Geol. Sci.* 1–18.

McVean, D. N. and Ratcliffe, D. A. (1962) *Plant Communities of the Scottish Highlands.* London: HMSO.

Maitland, P. S. and Kellock, E. (1971) The freshwater leeches (Hirudinea) of Orkney. *Glasg. Nat.* 18: 558–64.

Maitland, P. S. (1979) *Synoptic Limnology: the analysis of British freshwater ecosystems.* Cambridge: Institute of Terrestrial Ecology.

Major, C. I. (1905) The affinities of the Orkney Vole (*Microtus orcadensis* Millais). *Ann. Mag. nat. Hist.* (1) 15: 323–4.

Marler, P. (1952) Variations in the song of the Chaffinch, *Fringilla coelebs. Ibis* 94: 958–72.

Marshall, J. E. A., Brown, J.F. and Hindmarsh, S. (1985) Hydrocarbon source rock potential of the Devonian rocks of the Orcadian Basin. *Scot. J. Geol.* 21: 301–20.

Marshall, J. E. A., Rodgers, D. A. and Whiteley, M. J. (1996) Devonian marine incursions into the Orcadian Basin, Scotland. *J. Geol. Soc. Lond.,* 153: 451–66.

Marwick, E. (1975) *The Folklore of Orkney and Shetland.* London: Batsford.

Marwick, H. (1923) Celtic place-names in Orkney. *Proc. Soc. Ant. Scot.* 57: 251–65.

Marwick, H. (1930) An Orkney Jacobite farmer. *J. Orkney Agric. Discussion Soc.* 5: 1–12.

Marwick, H. (1951) *Orkney.* London: Hale.

Mason, J., Newton, A. W., McKay, D. W. and Kinnear, J. A. M. (1985) Fisheries in the Orkney area. *Proc. R. Soc. Edin.* 87B: 65–81.

Mather, A. S., Ritchie, W. and Smith, J. S. (1974) *Beaches of Orkney.* Aberdeen: Dept. Geography.

Mather, A. S., Ritchie, W. and Smith, J. S. (1975) An introduction to the morphology of the Orkney coastline. In *The Natural Environment of Orkney:* 10–18. Goodier, R. (ed.) Edinburgh: Nature Conservancy Council.

Matthews, L. H. (1952) *British Mammals.* London: Collins New Naturalist.

Matthey, R. (1953) Les chromosomes des Muridae. *Rev. Suisse Zool.* 60: 225–83.

Mayr, E. (1954) Change of genetic environment and evolution. In *Evolution as a Process:* 157–80. Huxley, J., Hardy, A. C. and Ford, E. B. (eds) London: Allen and Unwin.

Meade–Briggs, A. R. and Page, R. J. C. (1967) Ectoparasites from hares collected throughout the United Kingdom, January–March 1964. *Entomol. Mon. Mag.* 103: 26–34.

Meek, E. (1995) *Islands of Birds.* Lerwick: RSPB.

Meek, E. R. (1993a) The status of the Pintail in the Orkney Islands. *Scot. Birds,* 17: 14–19.

Meek, E. R. (1993b) Population fluctuations and mortality of Mute Swans on an Orkney loch system in relation to a Canadian Pondweed growth cycle. *Scot. Birds,* 17: 85–93.

Meek, E. R., Rebecca, G. W., Ribbands, J. B. and Fairclough, K. (1998) Orkney Hen Harriers: a major population decline in the absence of persecution. *Scot. Birds,* 19: 290–9.

Meek, E. R., Sim, I. M. W., and Ribbands, J. B. (1994) Breeding skuas in Orkney: the results of the 1992 census. *Seabird* 8: 21–3.

Meinertzhagen, R. (1939) A note on the birds of Hoy, Orkney. *Ibis,* 14th ser. 3: 258–64.

Michie, V. McL. and Cooper, D. C. (1979) Uranium in the Old Red Sandstone of Orkney. *Rep. Inst. Geol. Sci.* No. 78: 16.

Miles, R. S. and Westoll, T. S. (1963) Two new genera of coccosteid Athrodira from the Middle Old Red Sandstone of Scotland and their stratigraphical distribution. *Trans. R. Soc. Edin.* 66: 179–210.

Millais, J. G. (1904) On a new British vole from the Orkney Islands. *Zoologist,* ser 4, 8: 241–6.

Millais, J. G. (1905) *Mammals of Great Britain and Ireland.* London: Longmans.

Miller, G. S. (1908) Eighteen new European voles. *Ann. Mag. Nat. Hist.* (8) 1: 194–206.

Miller, H. (1849) *Footprints of the Creator.* Edinburgh: Nimmo.

Miller, R. (1976) *Orkney.* London: Batsford.

Miller, R. and Luther-Davies, S. (1969) *Eday and Hoy. A Development Study.* Glasgow: Dept. Geography.

Moar, N. T. (1969) Two pollen diagrams from the Mainland. Orkney Islands. *New Phytol.* 68: 201–08.

Møller, F. H. (1945) *Fungi of the Faeröes Part II.* Copenhagen.

Møller, F. H. (1958) *Fungi of the Faeröes Part II.* Copenhagen.

Mooney, J. (1931) Notes on agricultural progress in Orkney. *J. Orkney Agric. Discussion Soc.* 6: 40–9.

Muir, R. O. and Ridgway, J. M. (1975) Sulphide mineralisation of the continental Devonian sediments of Orkney (Scotland). *Mineral Deposita (Berlin),* 10: 205–15.

Murchison, R. I. (1859) On the succession of the older rocks in the northernmost counties of Scotland: with some observations on the Orkney and Shetland Islands. *Q. J. Geol. Soc. Lond.* 15: 353–418.

Murray, E., Dalkin, M. D., Fortune, F.. and Begg, K. (1999) Marine Nature Conservation Review. Sector 2: The Orkney Isles. Area Summaries. Peterborough: Joint Nature Conservation Committee.

Murray, J. and Pullar, L. (1908) *Bathymetric Survey of the Freshwater Lochs of Scotland: the Lochs of Orkney.* Edinburgh.

Mykura, W. (1975) The geological basis of the Orkney environment. In *The Natural Environment of Orkney:* 1–9. Goodier, R. (ed.). Edinburgh: Nature Conservancy Council.

Mykura, W. (1976) *British Regional Geology.* Orkney and Shetland. Edinburgh: Institute of Geological Sciences.

Mykura, W. (1991) Old Red Sandstone. In *Geology of Scotland:* 297–346. Craig, G.Y. (ed.). London: Geological Society.

Nature Conservancy Council (1984) *Nature Conservation in Great Britain.* London: Nature Conservancy Council.

Neill, P. (1806) *A Tour through some of the Islands of Orkney and Shetland.* Edinburgh.

Nicol, E. A. T. (1938) The brackish-water lochs of Orkney. *Proc. R. Soc. Edin.* 58: 181–91.

Nicolson, J. R. (1972) *Shetland.* Newton Abbot: David and Charles.

O'Dell, A. C. (1939) *The Land Utilisation Survey of Britain. Part 4. Orkney.* London: Geographical Publications.

Oldham, C. (1928) *Paludestrina jenkinsi* in Orkney and Caithness. *J. Conchol.* 18: 272.

Oldham, C. (1932) Notes on some Scottish and Shetland Pisidia. *J. Conchol.* 19: 271–8.

Ollason, J. and Dunnet, G. M. (1983) Modelling annual changes in numbers of breeding Fulmars, *Fulmarus glacialis,* at a colony in Orkney. *J. Anim. Ecol.* 52: 185–98.

Omand, D. (ed.) (1972) *The Caithness Book.* Inverness: Highland Printers.

Omand, D. (ed.) (1982) *The Sutherland Book.* Golspie: Northern Times.

Omond, J. (1925) *How to Know the Orkney Birds*. Kirkwall.

Orkney Islands Council (1994) *Orkney Structure Plan*. Kirkwall.

Parnell, J. (1983a) Ancient duricrusts and related rocks in perspective: a contribution from the Old Red Sandstone. *Spec. Publ. geol. Soc. Lond*. No. 12.

Parnell, J. (1983b) The distribution of hydrocarbon minerals in the Orcadian Basin. *Scot. J. Geol*. 19: 205–13.

Peach, B. N. and Horne, J. (1880) The glaciation of the Orkney Islands. *Q. J. Geol. Soc. Lond*. 36: 648–63.

Peach, B. N. and Horne, J. (1883) The geology of the Orkneys. In *Orkneys and Shetland*: 180–94. Tudor, J. R. (ed.) London: Stanford.

Peglar, S. (1979) A radiocarbon-dated pollen diagram from Lock of Winlass. *New Phytol*. 82: 254–63.

Pennie, I. D. (1964) Scottish ornithologists. I. Sir Robert Sibbald 1641–1722. *Scot. Birds*, 3: 159–66.

Picozzi, N. (1980) Food, growth, survival and sex ratio of nestling Hen Harriers *Circus cyaneus* in Orkney. *Ornis Scand*. 11: 1–11.

Picozzi, N. (1981) Common gull predation of Winter Moth larvae. *Bird Study*, 28: 68–9.

Picozzi, N. (1981) Weight, wing-length and iris colour of Hen Harriers in Orkney. *Bird Study*, 28: 159–61.

Picozzi, N. (1983a) Growth and sex of nestling Merlins in Orkney. *Ibis*, 125: 377–82.

Picozzi, N. (1983b) Two hens, but a single nest: an unusual case of polygyny by Hen Harriers in Orkney. *Brit. Birds*, 76: 123–8.

Picozzi, N. (1984) Breeding biology of polygynous Hen Harriers in Orkney. *Ornis Scand*, 15: 1–10.

Picozzi, N. and Cuthbert, M. F. (1982) Observations and food of Hen Harriers at a winter roost in Orkney. *Scot. Birds*, 12: 73–80.

Plant, J. A. and Dunsire, A. (1974) *The Climate of Orkney*. Edinburgh: Meteorological Office.

Plowright, C. M. S., Plowright, R. C. and Williams, P. H. (1997) Replacement of *Bombus muscorum* by *Bombus pascorum* in northern Britain? *Can. Ent*. 129: 985–90.

Poppius, B. R. (1905) Contributions to the knowledge of the Coleopteran fauna of the Shetland and Orkney Islands. *Ofr. Finska Vet. Soc. Forh*. 47: 1–13.

Prentice, H. C. and Prentice, I. C. (1975) The hill vegetation of North Hoy, Orkney. *New Phytol*. 75: 313–67.

Racey, P. A. (1977) A vagrant noctule from Orkney. *J. Zool., Lond*. 183: 555–6.

Ralegh Radford, C. A. (1983) Birsay and the spread of Christianity to the North. *Orkney Heritage* 2: 13–35.

Rasmussen, R. (1952) *Føroya Flora*. Torshavn: Thomsen.

Ratcliffe, D. A. (1984) The Peregrine breeding population of the United Kingdom in 1981. *Bird Study* 31: 1–18.

Reinert, A. (1971) Højere dyr på land. *Danmarks Natur*. 10: 537–8.

Rendall, R. (1948) Wallace's list of Orkney mollusca. *J. Conchol*. 23: 17–19.

Rendall, R. (1956) Mollusca orcadensia. *Proc. R. Soc. Edin*. 66B: 131–201.

Rendall, R. (1960) *Orkney Shore*. Kirkwall: Kirkwall Press.

Renfrew, C. (1979) *Investigations in Orkney*. London: Society of Antiquaries.

Renfrew, C. (1979) The Orcadian monuments and society. In *Excavations in Orkney*: 199–223. Renfrew, C. (ed.) London: Society of Antiquaries of London.

Renfrew, C. (ed.) (1985) *The Prehistory of Orkney*. Edinburgh: Edinburgh University Press.

Renfrew, C., Harkness, D. D. and Switsur, R. (1976) Quanterness, radio-carbon and the Orkney cairns. *Antiquity* 50: 194–204.

Reynolds, P. and Booth, C. J. (unpublished) Cetaceans in Orkney waters, 17th century to 1982.

Reynolds, P. and Booth, C. J. (1987) Orkney Cormorants – an aerial census of the breeding population. *Scottish Birds* 14: 131–7.

Richardson, J. B. (1965) Middle Old Red Sandstone spore assemblages from the Orcadian basin, North-east Scotland. *Palaeontology* 7: 559–605.

Ritchie, A. and Ritchie, G. (1978) *The Ancient Monuments of Orkney*. Edinburgh: HMSO.

Ritchie, A. (1983) Birsay around AD 800. *Orkney Heritage* 2: 56–66.

Ritchie, A. (1993) *Viking Scotland* London: Batsford.

Ritchie, A. (1996) *Exploring Scotland's Heritage. Orkney* Edinburgh: Stationary Office

Ritchie, G. and Ritchie, A. (1974) Excavation of a barrow at Queenafjold, Twatt, Orkney. *Proc. Soc. Ant. Scot*. 105: 33.

Ritchie, J. C. (1954) *Primula scotica* Hook. *J. Ecol*. 42: 623–8.

Ritchie, J. N. G. (1978) The Stones of Stenness, Orkney. *Proc. Soc. Ant. Scot*. 107: 1.

Ritchie, W. (1979) Machair development and chronology in the Uists and adjacent islands. *Proc. R. Soc. Edin*. 77B: 107–22.

Roberts, D. F. (1986) Genetic affinities of the Orkney islanders. In *The People of Orkney*: 89–106. Berry, R. J. and Firth, H. (eds). Stromness: Orkney Press.

Roberts, D. F., Papiha, S. S. and Poskanzer, D. C. (1979) Polymorphisms and multiple sclerosis in Orkney. *J. Epidem. comm. Hlth*, 33: 236–42.

Roberts, D. F., Roberts, M. J. and Cowie, J. A. (1979) Inbreeding levels in Orkney islanders. *J. Biosoc. Sci*. 11: 391–5.

Roberts, D. F., Roberts, M. J. and Poskanzer, D. C. (1979) Genetic analysis of multiple sclerosis in Orkney. *J. Epidem. Comm. Hlth*, 33: 229–35.

Robertson, D. J. (1934) *Notes from a Bird Sanctuary*. Kirkwall: Orcadian.

Robertson, J. D. M. (ed) (1991) *An Orkney Anthology. The Selected Works of Ernest Walter Marwick*. Edinburgh: Scottish Academic Press.

Robinson, H. W. (1934) First nesting of Leach's Fork-tailed Petrel in Orkney. *Scot. Nat.* for 1930: 93.

Rodgers, D. A., and Astin, T. R. (1991) Ephemeral lakes, mud pellet dunes and wind blown sand and silt: reinterpretation of Devonian lacustrine cycles in north Scotland. *Spec. publ. int. Assoc. Sediments*, 13: 199–221.

Rose, F. E. N. (1975) A note on the Orkney Vole. In *The Natural Environment of Orkney*: 29–30. Goodier, R. (ed.) Edinburgh: Nature Conservancy Council.

Rosie, J. H. (1976) Some notes on the macrolepidoptera of Caithness. *Ent. Gaz.* 27: 13–26.

Ryder, M. L. (1983) *Sheep and Man*. London: Duckworth.

Ryder, M. L., Land, R. B. and Ditchburn, R. (1974) Coat colour inheritance in Soay, Orkney and Shetland Sheep. *J. Zool., Lond.* 173: 477–85.

Sadler, J. P. (1993) Records of modern and fossil Coleoptera from the Orkney Islands. *Ent. Monthly Mag.* 129: 201–4.

Sadler, J. P. and Buckland, P. C. (1998) The biogeography of the Coleoptera of the Orkney Isles of Britain. *Bol. Mus. Mun. Funchal*, suppl. no. 5: 363–98.

Safriel, U. N., Volis, S. and Kark, S. (1994) Core and peripheral populations and global climate change. *Israel J. Plant Sci.* 42: 331–45.

Saxon, J. (3rd edn, 1991) *The Fossil Fishes of the North of Scotland*. Thurso: Humphries.

Saxton, W. I. and Hopwood, A. T. (1919) On a Scandinavian erratic from the Orkneys. *Geol. Mag.* 56: 273–4.

Scarth, G. (1911) The grassland of Orkney: an oecological analysis. *Trans. Bot. Soc. Edin.* 24: 143–63.

Scharf, W. C. and Balfour, E. (1970) Growth and development of nestling Hen Harriers. *Ibis*, 113: 323–9.

Schei, L. K. and Moberg, G. (1985) *The Orkney Story*. London: Batsford.

Schei, L. K. and Moberg, G. (1988) *The Shetland Story*. London: Batsford.

Schei, L. K. and Moberg, G. (1991) *The Faroe Islands*. London: John Murray.

Schrank, G. (1995) *An Orkney Estate. Improvements at Graemeshall 1827–1888*. East Linton: Tuckwell.

Scriven, P. (1992) Robertsonian translocations introduced into an island population of mice. *J. Zool., Lond.* 227: 493–503.

Scriven, P. and Brooker, P. C (1990) Caithness revisited: Robertsonian chromosome polymorphisms in Caithness house mice. *Heredity* 64: 25–7.

Sea Mammal Research Unit (1984) *Interactions between Grey Seals and UK Fisheries*. Cambridge: Natural Environmental Research Council.

Searle, J. B. (1991) A hybrid zone comprising staggered chromosomal clines in the house mouse (*Mus musculus domesticus*). *Proc. R. Soc. Lond. B.*, 246: 47–52.

Senior, W. H. and Swan, W. B. (1972) *Survey of Agriculture in Caithness, Orkney and Shetland*. Special Report No. 8. Inverness: Highland Development Board.

Shaw, F. J. (1980) *The Northern and Western Islands of Scotland*. Edinburgh: John Donald.

Shearer, J., Groundwater, W. and Mackay, J. D. (1966) *The New Orkney Book*. London: Nelson.

Sheldrick, M. C. (1976) Trends in the strandings of Cetacea on the British coasts. *Mammal Rev.* 6: 15–23.

Shetelig, H. (1940) *Viking Antiquities in Great Britain and Ireland*. Oslo: Aschehoug.

Shirreff, J. A. (1814) *A General View of the Agriculture of the Orkney Islands*. Edinburgh.

Sibbald, R. (1711) *The Description of the Isles of Orkney and Zetland*. Edinburgh.

Sinclair, J. (1950) The marine algae of Stronsay. *Notes from R. Bot. Garden* 20: 160–79.

Skene, A. (1984) Marine Mollusca recording. *Bull. Orkney Fld Club* No. 2: 17–19.

Slater, P. J. B. and Ince, S. A. (1979) Cultural evolution in Chaffinch song. *Behaviour* 71: 146–66.

Small, A. (1968) The historical geography of the Norse Viking colonization of the Scottish Highlands. *Norsk geogr. Tidsskr*, 22: 1–16.

Smith, D. E., De la Vega, A. C., and Dawson, S. (1996) Relative sea-level changes in Orkney. In *The Quaternary of Orkney*: 11–29. Hall, A. M. (ed) Cambridge: Quarternary Research Association.

Smith, E. A. (1966) A review of the world's Grey Seal population. *J. Zool., Lond.* 150: 463–89.

Smith, K. and Smith, V. (1983) *A Bibliography of the Entomology of the Smaller British Offshore Islands*. Faringdon: Classey.

South, R. (1888) Distribution of lepidoptera in the Outer Hebrides, Orkney, and Shetland. *Entomologist*. 21: 28–30, 98–9.

Spence, D. H. N. (1974) Sub-arctic debris and scrub vegetation in Shetland. In *The Natural Environment of Shetland*: 73–88. Goodier, R. (ed.) Edinburgh: Nature Conservancy Council.

Spence, D. H. N. (1979) *Shetland's Living Landscape: a Study in Island Plant Ecology*. Lerwick: Thuleprint.

Spence, M. (1914) *Flora Orcadensis*. Stromness: Spence.

Spence, P. F. (1981) An eye-witness account of the division of the Birsay Commons. *Orkney Heritage* 1: 92–8.

Steavenson, A. G. (1928) The geology of Stronsay Parish, Orkney. *Proc. Orkney Nat. Hist. Soc.* 1–19.

Steers, J. A. (1953) *The Sea Coast.* London: Collins New Naturalist.

Summers, C. F. (1978) Trends in the size of British Grey Seal populations. *J. Appl. Ecol.* 15: 395–400.

Summers, C. F., Bonner, W. N. and Van Haaften, J. (1978) Changes in the seal populations of the North Sea. *Rapp. P.-v. Réun. Couns. Int. Explor. Mer.* 172: 278–85.

Surtees, M. J. (1976) The spiders of Hoy. *Bull. Orkney Fld Club* No. 2: 11–12.

Sutcliffe, D. W. (1974) On *Gammarus* from freshwaters in the islands of Orkney and Shetland. *Crustaceana* 27: 109–11.

Sutherland, D. (1966) *Against the Wind.* London: Heinemann.

Sutherland, D. G. (1991) The glaciation of the Shetland and Orkney Islands. In *Glacial Deposits in Great Britain and Ireland*: 121–7. Ehlers, J., Gibbard, P. L. and Rose, J. (eds). Rotterdam: Balkema.

Sutherland, D. G., and Gordon, J. E. (1993) The Orkney Islands. In *The Quaternary of Scotland*: 71-82. Gordon, J. E. and Sutherland, D. G. (eds) London: Chapman and Hall.

Swan, M. J. S (1997) Amphibians and reptiles in *Coasts and Seas of the United Kingdom. Region 2. Orkney* .114–15. Barne, J. H. *et al.* (eds) Peterborough: JNCC.

Tait, C. (1997) *The Orkney Guide Book,* 2nd edn. Kirkwall: Tait.

Tait, J. B. (1937) The surface water drift in the northern and middle areas of the North Sea and in the Faroe-Shetland Channel. *Sci. Invest. Fish. Scot. for 1937,* No. 1.

Tait, W. S. (1936) Farming in a bygone day. *J. Orkney Agric. Discussion Soc.* 11: 13–18.

Tay and Orkney Ringing Groups (1984) The Shorebirds of the Orkney Islands. Perth: Tay Ringing Group.

Thomas, F. W. L. (1884) What is a pennyland? *Proc. Soc. Ant. Scot.* 18: 253–85.

Thomson, G. (1980) *The Other Orkney Book.* Edinburgh: Northabout.

Thomson, M. (1997) The ecology and hydrology of the brackish Loch Stenness, Orkney. Unpublished B.Sc thesis.

Thomson, W. P. L. (1981) *The Little General and the Rousay Crofters.* Edinburgh: John Donald.

Thomson, W. P. L. (1983) *Kelp-Making in Orkney.* Stromness: the Orkney Press.

Thomson, W. P. L. (1986) Settlement and identity. In *The People of Orkney*: 209–24. Berry, R. J. and Firth, H. (eds), Stromness: Orkney Press.

Thomson, W. P. L. (1987) *History of Orkney.* Edinburgh: Mercat.

Thorpe, K. (1998) Marine Conservation Review Sectors 1 and 2: Lagoons in Shetland and Orkney. Area Summaries. Peterborough: Joint Nature Conservation Committee.

Tickell, W. L. N. (1970) The exploitation and conservation of the Common Seal (*Phoca vitulina*) in Shetland. *Biol. Conservation* 2: 179–84.

Tomison, J. (1904) Sule Skerry, Orkney and its bird life. *Ann. Scot. Nat. Hist. for 1904:* 16–98.

Tomlin, J. R. le B. (1937) Orkney land and freshwater shells. *J. Conchol.* 20: 341.

Traill, G. W. (1890) The marine algae of the Orkney Islands. *Trans. Proc. Bot. Soc. Edin.* 18: 302–42.

Traill, G. W. (1892) Supplementary notes on the marine algae of the Orkney Islands. *Trans. Proc. Bot. Soc. Edin.* 19: 544–6.

Traill, G. W. (1895) Supplementary notes (number 2) on the marine algae of the Orkney Islands. *Trans. Proc. Bot. Soc. Edin.,* 20: 341–5.

Traill, J. W. H. (1869) Notes on the Lepidoptera of Orkney. *Entomologist* 4: 197–200.

Traill, J. W. H. (1888) The lepidoptera of the Outer Hebrides, Orkney and Shetland. *Scot. Nat.* 8: 298–304.

Traill, J. W. H. (1889) The Peronosporeae of Orkney. *Scot. Nat.* 10: 30–2.

Traill, J. W. H. (1890) Revision of the Uredineae and the Ustilagineae of Scotland. *Scot. Nat.* 10: 302–27.

Traill, T. S. (1806) Observations chiefly mineralogical on the Shetland Islands made in the course of a tour through these islands in 1803. *Nicholson's J.* 15: 353–67.

Traill, T. S. (1830) Orkney Islands. In *Brewster's Edinburgh Encyclopaedia.* Edinburgh.

Traill, W. (1868) On submarine forests and other remains of indigenous wood in Orkney. *Trans. Bot. Soc. Edin.* 9: 146.

Trowbridge, R. and Heppleston, P. B. (unpublished MS) Lochs Harray and Stenness, Orkney: their salinity and associated invertebrate fauna in 1936 and 1978.

Tudor, J. R. (1883) *The Orkneys and Shetland: their past and present state.* London: Stanford.

Tulloch, R. and Hunter, F. (1972) *Guide to Shetland Birds.* Lerwick: Shetland Times.

Tulloch, R. J. (1978) *A Guide to Shetland Mammals.* Lerwick: Shetland Times.

Turner, D. T. L. (1965) A contribution to the ecology and taxonomy of Microtus arvalis on the island of Westray, Orkney. *Proc. Zool. Soc., Lond.* 144: 143–50.

Turtle, C. E. (1997) Land mammals. In *Coasts and Seas of the United Kingdom Region 2. Orkney.* 114–15. Barne, J. H. *et al.* (eds) Peterborough: Joint Nature Conservation Committee.

Upton, B. G. J., Mitchell, R. H., Long, A. and Aspen, P. (1992) Primitive melanephelinite dykes from Orkney Islands, Scotland. *Geol. Mag.* 129: 319–24.

Vaughan, R. W. (1969) Grey Seal numbers in Orkney. *Bull. Mamm. Soc. Br. Is.* 32: 11–15.

Vaughan, R. W. (1975) Seals in Orkney. In *Natural Environment of Orkney*: 95–7. Goodier, R. (ed.) Edinburgh: Nature Conservancy Council.

Vaughan, R. W. (1977) A review of the status of the Common Seal, *Phoca vitulina*, in Scotland. I.C.E.S. Marine Mammals Committee 18: 1–5.

Venables, L. S. V. and Venables, U. M. (1955) *Birds and Mammals of Shetland*. Edinburgh and London: Oliver and Boyd.

Wainwright, F. T. (ed.) (1955) *The Problem of the Picts*. Edinburgh and London: Nelson.

Wainwright, F. T. (ed.) (1962) *The Northern Isles*. Edinburgh and London: Nelson.

Walker, F. T. (1950) Sublittoral seaweed survey of the Orkney Islands. *J. Ecol.* 38: 139–45.

Wallace, J. (1700) *An Account of the Islands of Orkney*. London: Tonson.

Wanless, S., French, D. D., Harris, M. P. and Langslow, D. R. (1982) Detection of annual changes in the number of cliff-nesting seabirds in Orkney 1976–1980. *J. Anim. Ecol.* 51, 785–95.

Waterston, J. (1903) Mollusca observed at Stromness, Orkney. *Ann. Scot. Nat. Hist.* for 1903: 52–3.

Watson, A. D. (1977) *The Hen Harrier*. Berkhamsted: Poyser.

Watson, D. M. S. (1932) On three new species of fish from the Old Red Sandstone of Orkney and Shetland. *Mem. Geol. Surv. Summ. Prog.* for 1931, part 2: 157–66.

Watson, H. (1978) *Coastal Otters in Shetland*. Privately printed.

Watts, A. B. (1971) Geophysical investigations on the continental shelf and slope north of Scotland. *Scot. J. Geol.* 7: 189–218.

Welsh, M. (1994) *Walks in Orkney*. Kendal: Westmoreland Gazette.

West, J. F. (1972) *Faroe: the Emergence of a Nation*. London: Hurst.

West, W. and West, G. S. (1905) Freshwater algae from the Orkneys and Shetlands. *Trans. Bot. Soc. Edin.* 23: 3–41.

White, F. B. (1882) The Lepidoptera of Orkney, Shetland and the Outer Hebrides. *Scot. Nat.* 2: 289–91, 337–44.

Whittaker, R. J. (1998) *Island Biogeography*. Oxford: Oxford University Press.

Whittle, A., Keith-Lucas, M., Miles, A., Noddle, B., Rees, S. and Romans, J. (1986) *Scord of Brouster. An early agricultural settlement on Shetland*. Oxford: Oxford Committee for Archaeology.

Wickham-Jones, C. (1998) *Orkney. An Historical Guide*. Edinburgh: Birlinn.

Wiener, G., Suttle, N. F., Field, A. C., Herbert, J. G. D. and Williams, J. A. (1978) Breed differences in copper metabolism in sheep. *J. Agric. Sci., Camb.* 91: 433–41.

Wilkinson, M. (1975) The marine algae of Orkney. *Brit. Phycol. J.*

Williamson, K. (1948) *The Atlantic Islands*. London: Collins.

Williamson, K. (1965) *Fair Isle and its Birds*. Edinburgh and London: Oliver and Boyd.

Williamson, M. H. (1981) *Island Populations*. Oxford: University Press.

Willis, D. P. (1983) *Moorland and Shore. Their place in the human geography of old Orkney*. O'Dell Memorial Monogr. No. 14. Aberdeen: Dept. Geography.

Wilson, G. V., and Knox, J. (1936) The geology of the Orkney and Shetland Islands. *Proc. Geol. Ass.* 47: 270–82.

Wilson, G. V., Edwards, W., Knox, J., Jones, R. C. B. and Stephens, J. V. (1935) *The Geology of the Orkneys. Mem. Geol. Surv. GB*. Edinburgh: HMSO.

Wilson, M. (1934) The distribution of the *Uredineae* in Scotland. *Trans. Bot. Soc. Edin.* 31: 345–49.

Winchworth, R. (1920) Giant race of *Cardium edule*. *J. Conchol.* 26: 569.

Withrington, D. J. and Grant, I. R. (eds) (1978) *The Statistical Account of Scotland 1791–1799. Vol. XIX. Orkney and Shetland*. Wakefield: E.P. Publishing.

Wood, D. (1997a) An estimate of the numbers of Storm Petrels breeding on Auskerry, Orkney. *Seabird*, 19: 22–30.

Wood, D. (1997b) An estimate of the numbers of storm petrels *Hydrobates pelagicus* breeding on Auskerry, Orkney. *Seabird* 19: 40-46.

Wood, R. D. and Imahori, K. (1965) *A Revision of the Characeae*. Weinheim: J. Cramer.

Wright Smith, W. and Fletcher, H. R. (1942) Genus *Primula*: section Farinosae. *Trans. R. Soc. Edin.* 61: 1–69.

Wylie, J. (1987) *The Faroe Islands, Interpretations of History*. Lexington: Kentucky University Press.

Young, D. (1985) Agriculture. In *The Soils of Orkney*. Dry, F. T. (ed.) Aberdeen: Macaulay Institute.

Zimmermann, K. (1959) Über eine Kreuzung von Unterarten der Feldmans *Microtus arvalis*. *Zool. Jb. (Syst.)* 87: 1–12.

Index

The ferry St Ola in Hoy Sound off St John's Head.
Photo: Richard Welsby

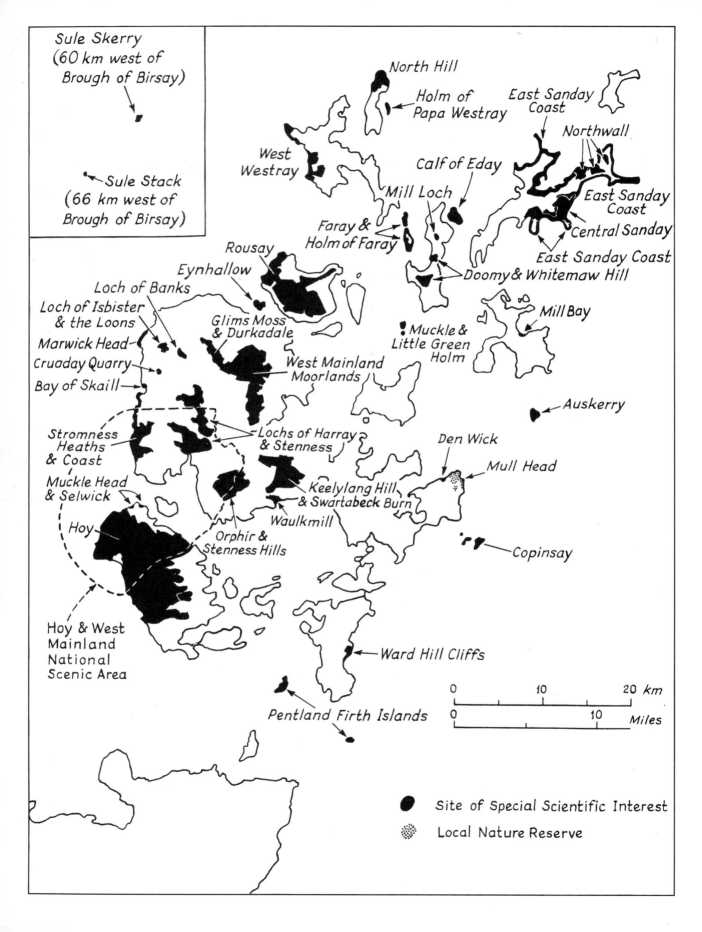

Sule Skerry
(60 km west of
Brough of Birsay)

Sule Stack
(66 km west of
Brough of Birsay)

North Hill

Holm of
Papa Westray

East Sanday
Coast

Northwall

West
Westray

Calf of Eday

Mill Loch

East Sanday
Coast

Faray &
Holm of Faray

Central Sanday

East Sanday Coast

Rousay

Doomy & Whitemaw Hill

Eynhallow

Loch of Banks

Glims Moss
& Durkadale

Mill Bay

Loch of Isbister
& the Loons

Muckle &
Little Green
Holm

Marwick Head

West Mainland
Moorlands

Cruaday Quarry

Bay of Skaill

Auskerry

Stromness
Heaths
& Coast

Lochs of Harray
& Stenness

Den Wick

Mull Head

Muckle Head
& Selwick

Keelylang Hill
& Swartabeck Burn

Hoy

Waulkmill

Orphir &
Stenness Hills

Copinsay

Hoy & West
Mainland
National
Scenic Area

Ward Hill Cliffs

Pentland Firth Islands

| 0 | | 10 | | 20 km |

| 0 | | | 10 | Miles |

Site of Special Scientific Interest

Local Nature Reserve